Mathematics
—— LEVEL 5 ——

JEAN HOLDERNESS

CAUSEWAY PRESS

Published by Causeway Press Ltd
PO Box 13, Ormskirk, Lancs L39 5HP

First published 1990

British Library Cataloguing in Publication Data
Holderness, Jean
  Mathematics.
  Level 5.
  1. Mathematics
  I. Title
  510

  ISBN 0-946183-61-9

Other titles by Jean Holderness published by
Causeway Press:
GCSE Maths: Higher Level
GCSE Maths: Intermediate Level
GCSE Maths: Foundation Level
Pure Maths in Practice

Typesetting and printing by
The Alden Press Oxford

Preface

This book has been written for pupils in the first year of secondary school, when they will be beginning Key Stage 3 of the National Curriculum.

It is based on covering the programme of study for level 5, but also includes some of the earlier work so as to consolidate it, since the pupils may have come from several different classes or different schools, and the work previously covered may have varied a great deal.

The teacher can decide how best to use the book with a particular class. (There are some notes for teachers on page *x*.) For more able pupils, the book could be used as the basis for the 1st year's work, and for others there is sufficient material included for it to be used for more than a year.

I have had much help and encouragement from my family and friends while I have been planning and writing this book. I would like to thank them all, but especially those who have helped with the production of the book, Sue and Andrew, John, my brother Jim, and the staff at Alden Press. From Causeway Press I have had much help and advice from Fred, Dave and Will, and especially from Mike, and I give them all my grateful thanks.

Jean Holderness

To Christopher

Acknowledgements

Artwork, page design and cover Susan and Andrew Allen

Photography Jim Holderness and Andrew Allen

Programme of Study: Level 5 pages *xii–xiii*,
from *Mathematics in the National Curriculum*,
reproduced with the permission of the Controller
of Her Majesty's Stationery Office

Computer work The assistance of John Rawlinson
is gratefully acknowledged

Copyright photographs
Audience Planners pp. 158 (bottom right), 191
British Railways Board p. 166 (bottom)
Bruce Coleman Ltd p. 158 (bottom left)
Ed Buziak pp. 159 (top), 167 (left)
Hulton–Deutsch Collection p. 220
Liverpool Daily Post and Echo pp. 149 (bottom), 179 (bottom)
Picturesport Associates pp. 77 (bottom), 159 (bottom left), 196 (bottom),
                197 (bottom), 245 (bottom right), 303 (bottom), 344
Sally and Richard Greenhill pp. 40 (top), 66, 122, 244, 303 (top),
                311 (bottom left)
Topham Picture Source pp. 17 (bottom), 41 (bottom), 54 (bottom), 197 (top),
                205 (top), 276
United States Information Service p. 159 (right)

Contents

Topics for Activities (included in the miscellaneous sections)

Activities using a computer

To the teacher

This book has been planned for use in the 1st year of secondary school. To link with the National Curriculum it contains all the topics mentioned in the Programme of Study and Attainment Targets for level 5.

If the pupils were being assessed at 11, such a book as this could assume all the previous level's work had been covered, but that will not be the case for a few years yet. So, for the topics needed for level 5, the appropriate introductory work has also been included. For example, the chapter on angles begins with basic ideas, so that the level 5 topics such as measurement of angles can be fitted into place. For completeness also, a chapter on 'Money and Time' is included, although not mentioned in level 5, because these topics are relevant to many real-life activities which might be used. Since some activities are open-ended, some ideas will necessarily merge with later levels, so a few topics, such as parallelograms, have been given a brief introduction in this book.

The book is organised as follows:- For each chapter there is an introductory section called 'Thinking About . . .' You could use these sections, or parts of them, for class discussion, for group work or for individual work. They could take a brief few minutes or several lessons. You might find that by extending the ideas there you are covering the work of the chapter quite adequately and very little follow-up work will be needed.

The main part of the chapter consists of bookwork and worked examples, followed by straightforward exercises. There should be no need for most pupils to have to work through the whole of any of these exercises. They are there in case practice is needed, and to give the pupils confidence in using the mathematical techniques. It is useful to have the bookwork available for reference. If the teacher has planned a good lesson then it may be unnecessary to use the bookwork at all, but children are not always present in every lesson, and the absentees need some text to help them later.

The last exercise of each chapter is more varied, giving ideas for applications and activities of various lengths. It has not been suggested which ones should be done as group work or as a whole class activity, because the class organisation is best decided by the class teacher.

The book has 24 chapters, giving roughly 8 for each term if the book is to be used for a year. After every 8 chapters there is a miscellaneous section with aural questions, revision questions and more suggestions for activities. There are puzzle questions fitted in at the ends of chapters where there is space. These are in no particular order and are there to give further interest.

The chapters are arranged in an order which interlinks Arithmetic, Geometry, Algebra, Statistics and Probability, so that there is a variety of maths in each part of the book. This allows time for assimilation of a topic before it is taken further. However, there is no reason why you should not plan your work in a different way. For example, Chapter 2 on angles could be immediately followed by Chapter 12 on triangles, the experimental probability of chapter 13 could be followed by the theoretical probability of chapter 20, and so on, especially if the discoveries of the class lead on naturally to it.

I have started the book with a short section on tables because I think that these are very important. Those who know the basic number facts will take a more confident part in aural work and discussion, will do written work quickly and accurately, and will find Maths more enjoyable. This will have a cumulative effect on their progress in future years.

I think that applications or activities which are related to everyday life are very useful, and many have been included in the book. However, the best topics are those which apply directly to the interests of the class, to topics currently being studied in other subjects, to what is happening in your school or neighbourhood, or to what is currently in the news. So it is hoped that the teacher will think of the mathematical connections and introduce them.

I have also avoided use of statistics such as road accidents or deaths. They have their place but must be introduced by a teacher who knows the class. If a young child comes from a family with a recent bereavement such a lesson can be very upsetting. Similarly, I have avoided introducing social issues in the questions. A teacher can decide whether it is appropriate with a particular class at a particular time to include discussion of such matters as health topics, sex discrimination, government spending, etc.

There are problems I have encountered when writing the book which I should mention here:

Protractors. On circular protractors the outside row of figures may go clockwise or anti-clockwise so check with the class so that they are clear which figures to use.

Calculators. There are so many variations. I have used 8 figures as that is what my calculator shows, but some may show less figures. One calculator shows 8− instead of the usual −8. Mine has the key y^x but another has the key labelled x^y. To mention all these variations in the text would be too confusing, and the problems are best resolved by the teacher, with the particular calculator being used.

Computers. I hope that if you have got computers you will have the software to go with them, and you will make good use of them. In this book I have just given a few examples of programs the pupils might write and use, together with some very introductory work on using a database.

Answers. To produce a book without answers as well as an edition with answers would increase the costs. (This is the publisher's problem, not mine.) I have tried to compromise by giving the answers to the straightforward questions, but not always giving answers to the activities questions, where it is important that the pupils make their own discoveries. The puzzle answers are not given, either. I have arranged for the answers to begin on a right-hand page, so that if you do not want the class to have them, they can be cut out of the book.

Level 5   Programme of Study

To achieve level 5 within the attainment targets pupils should be:

Using and applying mathematics

- selecting the materials and the mathematics to use for a task; checking there is sufficient information; working methodically and reviewing progress.
- interpreting mathematical information presented in oral, written or visual form.
- making and testing simple statements.

Number

- using index notation to express powers of whole numbers.
- using unitary ratios.
- understanding and using non-calculator methods by which a 3-digit number is multiplied by a 2-digit number and a 3-digit number is divided by a 2-digit number.
- calculating fractions and percentages of quantities.
- multiplying and dividing mentally single-digit multiples of powers of 10.
- using negative numbers in context.
- using 'trial and improvement' methods and refining.
- approximating, using significant figures or decimal places.

Algebra

- understanding and using terms such as 'prime', 'square', 'cube', 'square root', 'cube root', 'multiple' and 'factor'.
- generating sequences.
- recognising patterns in numbers through spatial arrangements.
- understanding and using simple formulae or equations expressed in symbolic form.
- expressing simple functions symbolically.
- understanding and using coordinates in all four quadrants.

Measures

- understanding the notion of scale in maps and drawings.
- using Imperial units still in daily use and knowing their rough metric equivalents.
- converting one metric unit to another.
- measuring and drawing angles to the nearest degree.

Shape and space	● understanding congruence of simple shapes.
	● using properties associated with intersecting and parallel lines and triangles and knowing associated language.
	● identifying the symmetries of various shapes.
	● using networks to solve problems.
	● specifying location by means of coordinates in four quadrants.
Handling data	● designing and using an observation sheet to collect data; collating and analysing results.
	● collecting and grouping continuous data and creating frequency tables.
	● inserting and interrogating data in a computer database and drawing conclusions.
	● constructing and interpreting pie charts from a collection of data with a few variables.
	● constructing and interpreting conversion graphs.
	● constructing and interpreting frequency diagrams and choosing class intervals for a continuous variable.
	● distinguishing between estimates of probabilities based on statistical evidence and those based on assumptions of symmetry.
	● knowing that if each of n events is assumed to be equally likely, the probability of one occurring is $1/n$.
	● knowing that different outcomes may result from repeating an experiment.

1 Thinking about numbers

Everyday numbers

You may be having Maths as the 1st lesson of the day or it may be the 7th. How many Maths lessons do you have each week ? How long do they last ?

Now, already we have used **numbers**. Think of all other situations when you have used or been aware of numbers today. Make a list. Have you needed to **calculate** with these numbers ?

Kinds of numbers

When we first talk about numbers we usually mean 1, 2, 3, ..., that is, the positive whole numbers. But there are other kinds of numbers. For instance, there is the number 0. List all the other kinds of numbers you know about, and give examples of situations where they are used.

Describe the different uses of numbers shown here.

Patterns in numbers

In the first chapter we are using the positive whole numbers. We want to look for patterns in numbers so here is one to begin with. Copy it down and complete it.

$9 - 1 = 8$	$\frac{1}{2}$ of 8 is 4	$4 \times 4 = 16$	$(9 \times 1) + 16 = 25$
$8 - 2 = 6$	$\frac{1}{2}$ of 6 is 3	$3 \times 3 = 9$	$(8 \times 2) + 9 = 25$
$7 - 3 = 4$	$\frac{1}{2}$ of 4 is 2	. . .	
. . .			

You can try a similar pattern starting with $19 - 1$, then $18 - 2$.
See if you can discover a number pattern.

On the 12th day of Christmas my true love sent to me

12 drummers drumming	6 geese a-laying
11 pipers piping	5 gold rings
10 lords a-leaping	4 colly birds
9 ladies dancing	3 French hens
8 maids a-milking	2 turtle doves
7 swans a-swimming	And a partridge in a pear tree.

Over the 12 days, how many gifts altogether ?

An example of a triangular number

A number game

Have you played 'buzz' ? Try this with some of your friends. You call out numbers in turn, 1, 2, 3, etc., but whoever's turn it is when you get to 7, any multiple of 7, or any number containing a figure 7, such as 17, says 'buzz' instead of that number. Then the counting continues with the next number. Anyone going wrong is 'out'. When you get too good at that game, you change it to 'fizz-buzz', where you say 'fizz' for the 5's as well. For certain numbers, such as 35, you would say 'fizz-buzz'. Of what use to you are number games ? What other number games do you know ?

Numbers at work

Name some situations where these people would need to count or use whole numbers and explain how they would use them.

A teacher	A football referee
A nurse	A darts player
A shepherd	A shopkeeper

Think of some other people who would use counting or whole numbers in their jobs or their leisure activities and explain how they would use them.

1 Numbers

Tables

You should be able to work out simple number calculations in your head. Although you can use a calculator when necessary, it is a waste of valuable time to use it for simple questions like 8 + 6, 9 × 7, how many 4's in 24, what is twice 32.

First you must check that you know your multiplication tables up to 12 × 12.
If you are not sure of all of them, begin by copying this chart onto squared paper.

	2	3	4	5	6	7	8	9	10	11	12
2	4										
3	6										
4	8										
5											
6											
7											
8											
9											
10											
11											
12											

Fill in the results of multiplication so that the first column is the 2 times table and the numbers in the first few squares are 4, 6, 8, . . . from 2 × 2, 2 × 3, 2 × 4, . . . (or 2 × 2, 3 × 2, 4 × 2, . . . if you prefer to think of them that way).
When you have filled in all the squares and made sure they are correct, then you must learn all the results you do not already know.

Can you discover some number patterns in the chart ?
Look at the units figures in each column.
Look at the arrangement of the odd numbers.
Look at the diagonal lines of the table.
What is the sum of the digits (figures) in each result in the 9's column ? Are there similar patterns in other columns ?

Make another similar chart and choose spaces at random to fill in, until you can work out the results in any order.
Then test yourself by doing the questions in the next exercise.
If you still need to improve then do give yourself further practice, because it is very important **to you** that you know your tables at this stage. It will make such a difference to your chances of understanding and enjoying future work.

Exercise 1.1

1. Do these multiplication questions as quickly as you can. Work downwards in columns, and write down the answers only.

8 × 1	9 × 6	7 × 7	12 × 6	9 × 0
5 × 6	3 × 2	8 × 9	1 × 4	6 × 7
2 × 7	8 × 0	0 × 5	3 × 3	12 × 11
8 × 6	7 × 4	2 × 1	9 × 1	10 × 10
5 × 5	3 × 8	9 × 9	9 × 7	1 × 11
0 × 1	5 × 9	3 × 11	5 × 2	4 × 6
6 × 2	12 × 8	7 × 12	10 × 11	8 × 8
11 × 8	4 × 5	4 × 4	4 × 3	7 × 5
12 × 4	11 × 7	3 × 6	7 × 8	10 × 7
10 × 3	10 × 2	12 × 12	5 × 12	6 × 6

2. Write down the answers to these division questions, doing them as quickly as you can. Work downwards in columns.

55 ÷ 5	72 ÷ 6	15 ÷ 3	81 ÷ 9	0 ÷ 5
72 ÷ 8	30 ÷ 5	49 ÷ 7	42 ÷ 6	27 ÷ 3
35 ÷ 7	77 ÷ 7	45 ÷ 9	96 ÷ 8	132 ÷ 12
36 ÷ 3	60 ÷ 12	32 ÷ 8	56 ÷ 7	60 ÷ 10
9 ÷ 1	48 ÷ 8	144 ÷ 12	33 ÷ 11	36 ÷ 4

3. Write down the answers to these questions, doing them as quickly as you can.
   1. What is 8 more than 6 ?
   2. What is 12 doubled ?
   3. What must be added to 7 to make 20 ?
   4. How many times does 6 go into 54 ?
   5. What is 11 multiplied by itself ?
   6. What is half of 46 ?
   7. What number multiplied by itself makes 49 ?
   8. What is left when 15 is taken from 19 ?
   9. What is three-quarters of 24 ?
   10. What is 12 less than 30 ?

4. What is the answer, and the remainder, when the first number is divided by the second one?

1	28 ÷ 5	3	57 ÷ 11	5	100 ÷ 12
2	18 ÷ 7	4	32 ÷ 4		

5. What must be added to:

1	5 × 11, to make 60,	3	9 × 7, to make 70,	5	12 × 3, to make 40 ?
2	6 × 4, to make 30,	4	8 × 6, to make 50,		

Numbers

Even and odd numbers

An **even number** is a number which divides exactly by 2. The units figure is 2, 4, 6, 8 or 0.

An **odd number** is a number which does not divide exactly by 2. The units figure is 1, 3, 5, 7 or 9.

Numbers which divide by 5

A number divides exactly by 5 if its unit figure is 5 or 0.

Numbers which divide by 3

There is a useful way to tell if a number divides exactly by 3.
Add up the digits (figures) in the number. If the answer is more than 9 then add up the digits of that answer, and repeat this until you get a 1-figure number. If this number is 3, 6 or 9, which all divide by 3, then the original number divides by 3.
e.g. 879. Add up 8 + 7 + 9 = 24. Add up 2 + 4 = 6. Since this number is 6, which divides by 3, the original number 879 divides by 3.
If the 1-figure number is 9 then the original number will divide by 9.
e.g. 4653. Add up 4 + 6 + 5 + 3 = 18. Add up 1 + 8 = 9. Since this number is 9, 4653 will divide by 9.

Multiples

The multiples of 3 are numbers which 3 divides exactly into, including 3 itself.
The first four multiples of 3 are 3, 6, 9, 12.
Some other multiples of 3 are 33, 72, 300, 1005.
Some multiples of 5 are 5, 60, 100, 205, 455.
Some multiples of 7 are 7, 14, 21, 70, 147, 1001.

Factors

Factors of 24 are numbers which divide exactly into 24.
$$24 = 1 \times 24$$
$$= 2 \times 12$$
$$= 3 \times 8$$
$$= 4 \times 6$$
The factors of 24 are 1, 2, 3, 4, 6, 8, 12, 24.
Every number has a factor 1. Every number has itself as a factor.
The factors of 70 are 1, 2, 5, 7, 10, 14, 35, 70.

Prime numbers

A number which has no factors, except 1 and itself, is called a **prime number**. The first few prime numbers are 2, 3, 5, 7, 11, 13, 17, 19, . . .

To find whether a number is a prime number

Check that it has no factors (except itself and 1) by dividing by the first few prime numbers 2, 3, 5, 7, 11, . . .

Examples

Is 39 a prime number ?

Does 39 divide exactly by 2 ?
No, because it is not an even number.
Does 39 divide exactly by 3 ?
Yes. 39 ÷ 3 = 13.
So 39 has a factor 3 (and a factor 13) and so it is not a prime number.

Is 67 a prime number ?
Does 67 divide exactly by 2 ?   No.
Does 67 divide exactly by 3 ?   No.
Does 67 divide exactly by 5 ?   No, because it does not have a units figure of 5 or 0.
Does 67 divide exactly by 7 ?   No.
There is no need to check that it divides by 11 or any greater prime number (see below).
67 has no factors (except itself and 1).
So 67 is a prime number.

Where to stop:

Divide by the prime numbers in order, first 2, then 3, then 5, . . .
Since 5 × 5 = 25,   25 is the smallest number which needs to be checked to see if it divides by 5.
Since 7 × 7 = 49,   49 is the smallest number which needs to be checked to see if it divides by 7.
Since 11 × 11 = 121,   121 is the smallest number which needs to be checked to see if it divides by 11.
A similar rule works if you are checking larger numbers.

Index notation

2×2 can be written as 2^2, (read as 2 squared).

$2 \times 2 \times 2$ can be written as 2^3, (read as 2 cubed, or 2 to the power 3).

$2 \times 2 \times 2 \times 2$ can be written as 2^4, (read as 2 to the 4th, or 2 to the 4th power, or 2 to the power 4).

$2 \times 2 \times 2 \times 2 \times 2$ can be written as 2^5, (read as 2 to the 5th, or 2 to the 5th power, or 2 to the power 5).

Similarly,

$7 \times 7 \times 7 = 7^3$

$10 \times 10 \times 10 \times 10 \times 10 \times 10 = 10^6$.

Working out the values

$2^5 = 2 \times 2 \times 2 \times 2 \times 2 \ (= 4 \times 2 \times 2 \times 2 = 8 \times 2 \times 2 = 16 \times 2)$
$\quad = 32$

$3^3 = 3 \times 3 \times 3 \ (= 9 \times 3)$
$\quad = 27$

$4^2 = 4 \times 4$
$\quad = 16$

$10^6 = 10 \times 10 \times 10 \times 10 \times 10 \times 10$
$\quad\ \ = 1\,000\,000$ (one million)

Squares of numbers

The square of number 7 is 7^2 which equals $7 \times 7 = 49$

The square of 12 is 12^2 which equals $12 \times 12 = 144$

The square of 1 is 1^2 which equals $1 \times 1 = 1$

Square numbers are $1^2, 2^2, 3^2, 4^2, 5^2, \ldots$ which worked out are 1, 4, 9, 16, 25, ...

Square roots

The square of 8 is 64, and the square root of 64 is 8.
The square of 11 is 121, and the square root of 121 is 11.
The square root of 400 is 20, since $20^2 = 400$.
The square root of 25 is 5, since $5^2 = 25$.
The square root of 1 is 1, since $1^2 = 1$.

The sign for square root is $\sqrt{}$, so $\sqrt{9} = 3$.

Cubes of numbers

The cube of number 5 is 5^3 which equals $5 \times 5 \times 5 = 125$.

The cube of 10 is 10^3 which equals $10 \times 10 \times 10 = 1000$

The cube of 1 is 1^3 which equals $1 \times 1 \times 1 = 1$

Cube numbers are 1^3, 2^3, 3^3, 4^3, 5^3, . . . which worked out are 1, 8, 27, 64, 125, . . .

Cube roots

The cube of 6 is 216, and the cube root of 216 is 6.
The cube of 10 is 1000, and the cube root of 1000 is 10.
The cube root of 64 is 4, since $4^3 = 64$.
The cube root of 8 is 2, since $2^3 = 8$.
The cube root of 1 is 1, since $1^3 = 1$.

The sign for cube root is $\sqrt[3]{}$, so $\sqrt[3]{27} = 3$.

Sequences of numbers

Many patterns involve numbers which follow a definite sequence. Here are some examples.

Whole numbers   1, 2, 3, 4, . . .

Odd numbers   1, 3, 5, 7, . . .

Even numbers   2, 4, 6, 8, . . .

Multiples of 5   5, 10, 15, 20, . . .

Square numbers 1, 4, 9, 16, . . .

Cube numbers 1, 8, 27, 64, . . .

Triangular numbers 1, 3, 6, 10, 15, . . .

Powers of 2 2, 4, 8, 16, 32, . . .

Square numbers can be represented by dots in the form of squares.

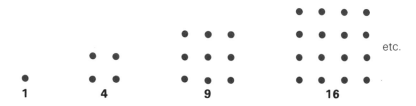

Triangular numbers can be represented by dots in the form of triangles.

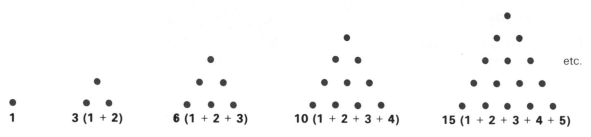

Exercise 1.2

1. From these numbers 102, 213, 415, 528, 677, 717, 725, 828, 1000
    1 Which numbers are odd ?
    2 Which numbers divide by 5 ?
    3 Which numbers divide by 3 ?

2. From these numbers 30, 32, 34, 35, 39, 42, 44, 45, 48, 49
    1 Which are multiples of 3 ?
    2 Which are multiples of 5 ?
    3 Which are multiples of 7 ?

3.   List all the factors of

        1   12   **2**   30   **3**   40

4.   Write down all the numbers from 2 to 30, inclusive.
Except for number 2, cross out all the numbers which divide by 2.
Except for number 3, cross out all the numbers which divide by 3.
Except for number 5, cross out all the numbers which divide by 5.
The remaining numbers are prime numbers. Write them down in a neat list.

5.   Find a number which is a factor of both these numbers. If you can find more
than one, give the highest one.

      1   77, 88   **5**   28, 16   **8**   48, 40
      2   27, 45   **6**   24, 12   **9**   14, 22
      3   45, 35   **7**   9, 27   **10**   63, 49
      4   30, 50

6.   Find a number which is less than 50 and is a multiple of both these numbers. If you
can find more than one, give the lowest one.

      1   3, 7   **5**   10, 15   **8**   2, 3
      2   12, 9   **6**   11, 33   **9**   14, 4
      3   5, 7   **7**   9, 6   **10**   8, 10
      4   8, 6

7.   Find whether these numbers divide exactly by 2, 3, 5, 7 and then say which are
prime numbers:

      71,   72,   73,   75,   77,   79,   81,   85,   88,   91.

8.   **1**   Find the values of 2^3, 3^2, 5^3, 7^2, 10^4.

      2   Write in index notation $5 \times 5 \times 5 \times 5$, $2 \times 2 \times 2 \times 2 \times 2 \times 2 \times 2$, 11×11.

9.   **1**   Write down the squares of these numbers:- 8, 12, 7, 1, 9.
      2   Write down the square roots of 36, 4, 121, 25, 100.
      3   Write down the cubes of these numbers:- 4, 1, 10.

10.   From the numbers 20, 23, 25, 27, 31, 36, write down:
      1   the prime numbers,
      2   the square numbers,
      3   the numbers which are multiples of 3,
      4   a cube number,
      5   two numbers with a difference of 8.

11. Copy and complete this number pattern.

$9 \times 1 = 21 - 12 = 9 \times (2 - 1)$
$9 \times 2 = 31 - 13 = 9 \times (3 - 1)$

$9 \times 8 = 91 - 19 = 9 \times (9 - 1)$

12. Continue these sequences for three more terms each.

1	3, 6, 9, 12, . . .	**6**	100, 94, 88, 82, 76 . . .
2	64, 56, 48, 40, . . .	**7**	100, 99, 97, 94, 90, . . .
3	1, 3, 9, 27, . . .	**8**	5, 10, 20, 40, 80, . . .
4	1, 2, 5, 10, 17, . . .	**9**	16384, 4096, 1024, 256, 64, . . .
5	1, 8, 27, 64, . . .	**10**	2, 5, 11, 20, 32, . . .

Exercise 1.3 Applications and Activities

1. **1** How many more 4's than 6's are there in 48 ?
   2 How many more 9's than 12's are there in 72 ?
   3 How many more 3's than 4's are there in 36 ?
   4 How many more 10's than 12's are there in 60 ?
   5 How many more 4's than 10's are there in 20 ?

2. **1** I think of a number, multiply it by itself and add 8. The result is 44. What was the original number ?
   2 I think of a number, divide it by 3 and add 12. The result is 20. What was the number ?
   3 I think of a number, subtract 5 and then divide by 4. The result is 9. What was the number ?
   4 I think of a number, add 3 and then multiply by 5. The result is 100. What was the number ?
   5 I think of a number, divide by 4 and then subtract 10. The result is 20. What was the number ?

3. **1** Start from 1 and keep adding 6's until you reach a number greater than 50. What number is this ?
   2 Start from 100 and keep subtracting 9's until you reach a number less than 10. What number is this ?
   3 Start from 3 and keep doubling the number until you reach a number greater than 100. What number is this ?

> **4** Start from 240 and keep halving the number until you reach a number less than 20. What number is this ?
>
> **5** Start from 1458 and keep dividing by 3 until you reach a number less than 10. What number is this ?

4. Represent some number patterns by drawings, and make some discoveries about them.

Here are two ideas using drawings on isometric paper.

Hexagonal numbers

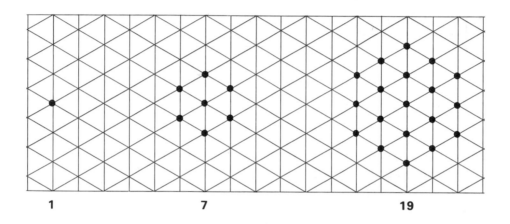

1   7   19

Cube numbers

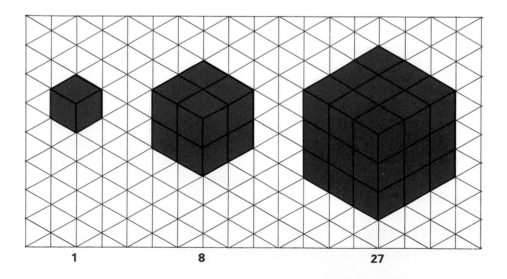

1   8   27

5.   **Number chains**

These change a number into another number by a certain rule. Then the new number is changed, and the process is repeated.

e.g. **Rule**: For 2-figure numbers, multiply the 10's digit by 3 and add to the units digit. Stop the chain when you get to a single figure.

So 29 → 2 × 3 + 9 = 15 → 1 × 3 + 5 = 8.

54 → 5 × 3 + 4 = 19 → 1 × 3 + 9 = 12 → 1 × 3 + 2 = 5.

To investigate this chain, make a grid of 2-figure numbers.

10	11	12	13	14	15	16	17	18	19
20	21	22	.	.	.				
30	31	.	.	.					
.									
.									
.									

With a felt-tip or crayon, circle round each number which leads to a single figure of 8. In other colours, circle numbers which lead to each of the other single figure numbers. See what discoveries you can make. Could you adapt the rule for 3-figure numbers ?

Make other number chains using different rules and investigate them.

6.   **The Sieve of Eratosthenes**

Write down the numbers 2 to 50 inclusive. Draw a circle round 2 and then cross out every other number which divides by 2. The 1st number not circled or crossed out is 3. Draw a circle round 3 and then cross out every other number which divides by 3. The next number not crossed out or circled is 5. Draw a circle round 5 and then cross out every other number which divides by 5. The next number not crossed out is 7. Draw a circle round 7 and then cross out every other number which divides by 7. Now draw a circle round all the remaining numbers which are not crossed out. The circled numbers are the prime numbers. Write them down in a list.

Why was it sufficient to stop at 7 ? If we had made a list up to 125 what other number would need to be crossed out ?

This method can be used to find the prime numbers up to any large number. It is useful to set the numbers down on squared paper in neat columns and then a pattern can be seen as you cross out the numbers.

Set out in columns of 10,

1	2	3	4	5	6	7	8	9	10
11	12	13	14	15	16	17	18	19	20
21	22	.	.	.					

or try other columns, especially columns of 6.

1	2	3	4	5	6
7	8	9	10	11	12
13	14	15	16	17	18
19	20	.	.	.	

1 is a special number, so mark it in a different way. It is not counted as a prime number although it has no factors other than itself.

This method is known as 'The Sieve of Eratosthenes'. See if you can find out anything about Eratosthenes who lived a long time ago.

7.   Make a list showing numbers and all their factors, and see what discoveries you can make. (Perhaps you might choose to begin with numbers up to 50.)

Number	Factors	Number of factors	Sum of factors, excluding the number itself
1	1	1	–
2	1, 2	2	1
3	1, 3	2	1
4	1, 2, 4	3	3
5	1, 5	2	1
6	1, 2, 3, 6	4	6
.			
.			
.			

Here are some questions to consider, but you may think of others.

1   What is special about numbers with just two factors ?

2   What is special about numbers with an odd number of factors ?

3   What do you notice about the sum of factors of the numbers which are powers of 2, i.e. 2, 4, 8, 16, . . . ?

4   If the sum of the factors, excluding the number itself, is equal to the number, then the number is called a perfect number. So 6 is a perfect number. What is the next smallest perfect number ?

8.   This diagram shows a number grid with 10 columns, and a cross shown on it. We
      can describe this cross as 'centred at 32'. The cross can be centred at other numbers
      on the grid.
      You can make some discoveries about the numbers in the cross.

1	2	3	4	5	6	7	8	9	10
11	12	13	14	15	16	17	18	19	20
21	22	23	24	25	26	27	28	29	30
31	32	33	34	35	36	37	38	39	40
41	42	43	44	45	46	47	48	49	50
51	52	53	54	55	56	57	58	59	60
61	62	63	64	65	66	67	68	69	70
71	72	73	74	75	76	77	78	79	80
81	82	83	84	85	86	87	88	89	90
91	92	93	94	95	96	97	98	99	100

      Here are some ideas to think about:
      Which numbers can the cross not be centred at ?
      Is there any connection between the sum of the numbers in the cross, and the
      centre number ?
      Is there any connection between the product of the top and bottom numbers in
      the cross, or of the two side numbers, and the centre number ?

      You can extend this investigation by making a new grid with a different number
      of columns.
      You can also investigate different shapes on the grid, such as

                          or

9.   From the numbers 11, 12, 13, 14, 15, 16, 17, 18, 19, 20, write down
      1   the even numbers,
      2   a square number,
      3   the numbers which are multiples of 5,
      4   the prime numbers,
      5   the numbers which are factors of 60.

10.   Copy and complete this number pattern.

$1 \times 9 + 1 = 1 \times 8 + 2 = 1 \times 7 + 3 = 1 \times 6 + 4 = 1 \times 5 + 5 = 1 \times 4 + 6 = 1 \times 3 + 7 = 1 \times 2 + 8 = 10$

$2 \times 9 + 2 = 2 \times 8 + 4 = 2 \times 7 + 6 = 2 \times 6 + 8 = \qquad\qquad\qquad\qquad = 20$

$3 \times 9 + 3 = 3 \times 8 + 6 = 3 \times 7 + 9 = \qquad\qquad\qquad\qquad\qquad\quad = 30$

. . .

Finish with the line beginning $10 \times 9 + 10$

PUZZLES

1. If it takes 3 minutes to boil 2 eggs, how long will it take to boil 4 eggs ?

2. Four forms had two representatives each, and had to send one representative to each of three meetings.
    At the 1st meeting, Adam (from 1P), Bimal (from 1Q), Carole (from 1R) and Davina (from 1S) attended.
    At the second meeting, Edward, Bimal, Francis and Davina were present.
    At the third meeting, Adam, Edward, Bimal and Gillian were present.
    (Heidi could not attend any of the meetings as she was ill.)
    Find the names of the second representatives from each form.

3. The sketch map shows the road round the village green, with five houses built round it.
    Mrs Baker often walks across the green to see Mrs Cook, and Mr Cook sometime walks across to see Mr Eaton. The Eaton children mostly play with their neighbours, the Dyer boys, but they travel to school with the Archer children.
    Who are the neighbours of the Bakers ?

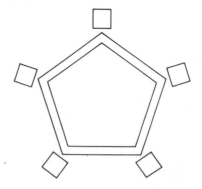

4. The scrap-metal dealer decided to make a set of weights from scrap metal, to use for weighing up to 40 kg. His assistant told him that he needed weights of 1, 2, 4, 8, 16 and 32 kg.
    'No, that will take 63 kg of metal and I can do it with less, by making weights of 1, 3, 9 and 27 kg. That way I only have to make 4 weights and only use 40 kg of metal altogether.'
    Show how the dealer can use his weights on his balance scales to weigh any whole number of kilograms from 1 kg to 40 kg.

2 Thinking about angles

Angles and their measurement

What is an angle ?
Look for different-sized angles in objects seen in daily life.
What kind of angle do we see most often ?

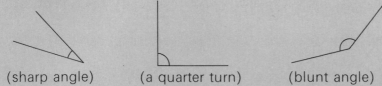

(sharp angle)   (a quarter turn)   (blunt angle)

What are the proper names given to these sorts of angles ? Look up the meanings of the words in a dictionary and you will see why these names were chosen.

What do we call an angle making a complete turn ?
What smaller units do we use to measure angles ?
What instrument do we use to measure angles ? There are also instruments used to measure complete turns, especially in machines. What are these called ?
We do not split a complete turn into 100 (or 10) smaller units because we are not using a metric system for angle measurement. How many units do we split it into ?
The units were established in Ancient Babylon. Where is Babylon ? Why was such a number of units chosen for a complete turn ?

What is a reflex angle ?

What other facts do you know, concerning angles ?

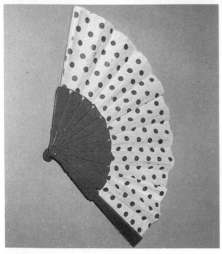

How big is the angle of the fan?

What size is the (hidden) angle at the centre in each sector?

Why are these lines, dividing the swimming lanes, parallel?

Why are railway lines parallel?
Why do they not look parallel?

Angles and turning

Give some examples of things which **turn**.
Open your desk lid, the classroom door, or your textbook, to make various angles with its closed position. Guess the sizes of the angles turned through.
Estimate the sizes of the angles involved when you turn on a tap, screw in a screw, turn a key to unlock a door, turn a handle to open a door, open a door to enter a room, dial the number 1 on a telephone with a dial, or put your arm out to signal for a bus to stop. You can think of other examples for yourself.

Looking at angles

Which of these angles is the bigger one ?

Parallel lines

What is meant by **parallel** lines ?
Why are railway lines parallel ?
Look about you in the room. What examples of parallel lines can you see ?
Give examples of parallel lines which we see in daily life.

2 | Angles

An angle measures the amount of turning or the change of direction between two lines.

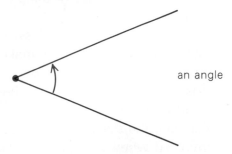

an angle

1 complete turn is called a revolution.
It is divided into 360° (360 degrees).

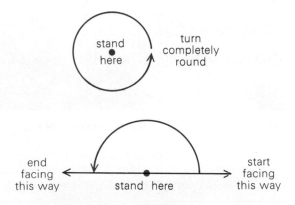

stand here

turn completely round

1 half-turn is 180°

end facing this way

stand here

start facing this way

Right-angle

1 quarter-turn is 90°. This is also called a **right angle**.

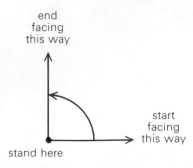

end facing this way

start facing this way

stand here

The sign for a right angle is a mark in the corner of the angle making a small square.

Acute angle

An angle less than 90° is called an **acute** angle.

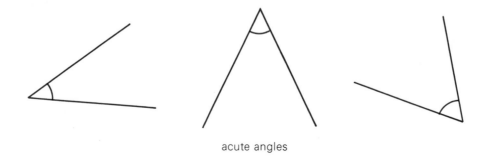

acute angles

Obtuse angle

An angle between 90° and 180° is called an **obtuse** angle.

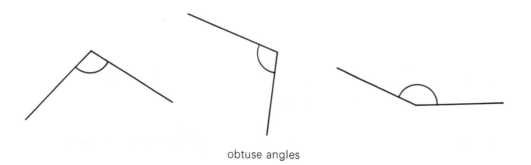

obtuse angles

Reflex angle

An angle between 180° and 360° is called a **reflex** angle.

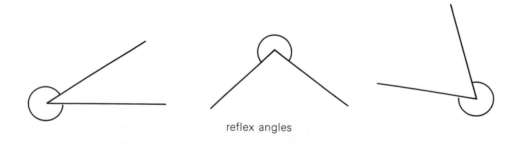

reflex angles

Naming of angles

In this chapter, we are going to identify angles by labelling them with small letters, (not capital letters, which we will use to label points).

This angle is *b*.

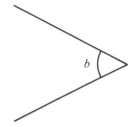

Use of a Protractor

1 To measure an angle

(1)   Put the centre point of the protractor on the point of the angle.
(2)   Put the 0° line of the protractor on one of the lines of the angle.
(3)   Count round from 0° to read the size of the angle.
       If the 0° you are using is on the **outside** set of figures, use those figures, counting past 10°, 20°, 30°, etc.
       If the 0° you are using is on the **inside** set of figures, then you will use those figures.
       (Not all circular protractors are marked in the same way so yours may not be numbered like the one shown below.)

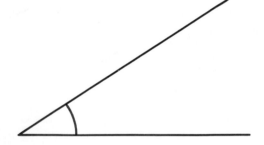

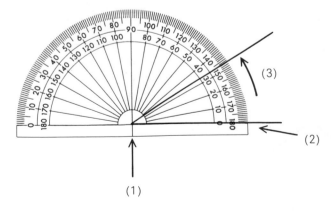

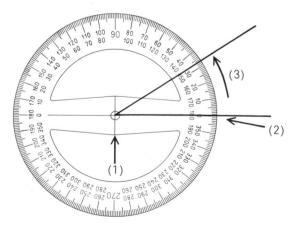

This is an angle of 33°.

Use the other 0° line if it is more convenient.

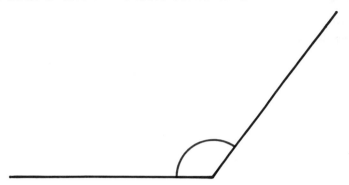

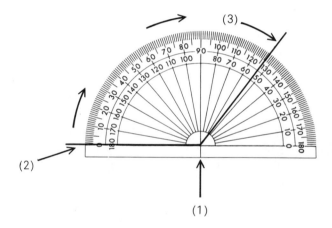

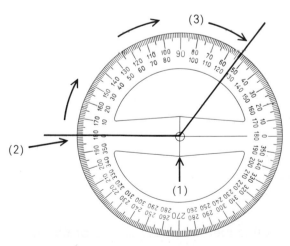

This is an angle of 127°.

2 **To draw an angle**

Mark a point *P* on a line *PQ*, as shown.
At point *P*, using the line *PQ*, make an angle of 28°.

(1)   Put the centre point of the protractor on the point *P*.
(2)   Put the 0° line of the protractor on the line *PQ*.
(3)   Count round from 0° to 28°. Put a dot at 28°.
       (Decide from where 0° is, whether you are using the inside or the outside set
       of figures.)

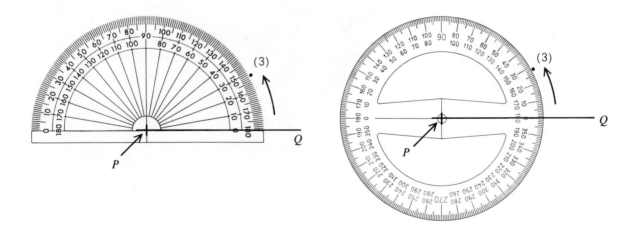

(4)   When you have removed the protractor, join the dot to point *P*.

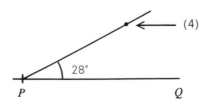

Using this method, draw angles of 65°, 82°, 108° and 144°.

Mark a point *P* on a line *PR*, as shown.
At point *P*, using the line *PR*, make an angle of 105°.

(1)   Put the centre point of the protractor on the point *P*.
(2)   Put the 0° line of the protractor on the line *PR*.
(3)   Count round from 0° to 105°. Put a dot at 105°.

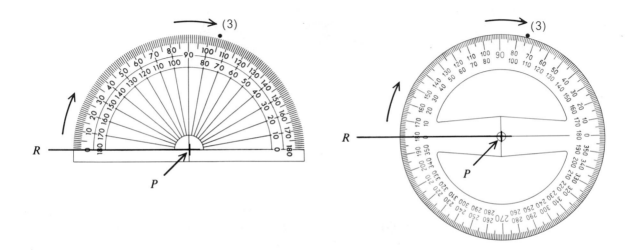

(4)   When you have removed the protractor, join the dot to point *P*.

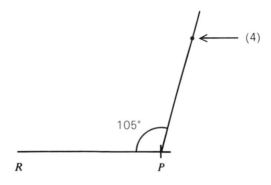

Using this method, draw angles of 25°, 72°, 126° and 157°.

Exercise 2.1

1. Say whether these angles are acute, obtuse or reflex angles.

1   **2**    **3**   **4**

5   **6**   **7**

8   **9**   **10**

2. Start with a line and a point **P**. Using the 0° mark on the left side of your protractor, draw these angles at the point **P**, using a separate diagram for each one.

    1   20°   **2**   75°   **3**   108°   **4**   90°   **5**   152°

3. Start with a line and a point **Q**. Using the 0° mark on the right side of your protractor, draw these angles at the point **Q**, using a separate diagram for each one.

    1   100°   **2**   67°   **3**   45°   **4**   143°   **5**   85°

4.   Copy these figures with the angles drawn accurately.

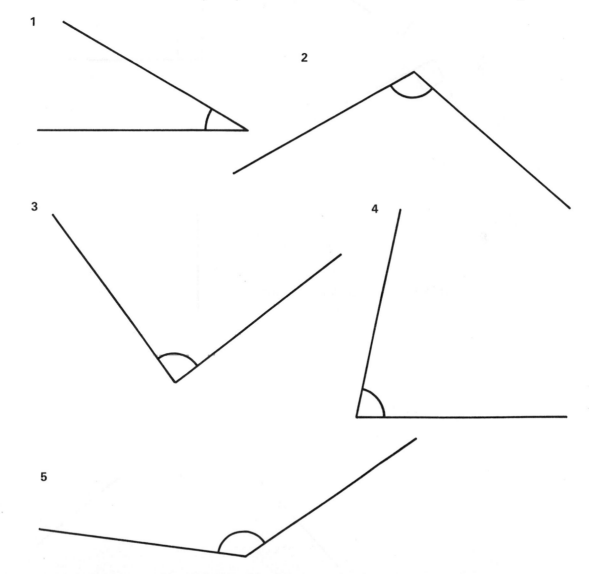

1   53°

2   116°

3   161°

4   35°

5.   First, look at these angles and say whether they are acute angles, right angles or obtuse angles.
      Then measure them with your protractor and write down their sizes in degrees.

1

2

3

4

5

6.   Lines which are at right angles to each other are called **perpendicular lines.**
     Check with your protractor that these lines are perpendicular lines.

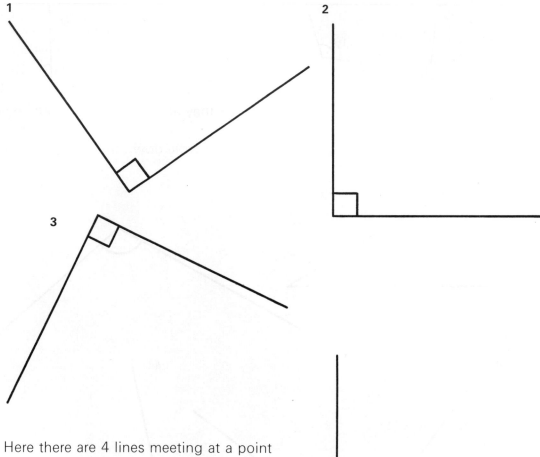

7.   Here there are 4 lines meeting at a point
     making 4 angles *a*, *b*, *c* and *d*.
     Can you decide what the **sum** of the 4
     angles will equal ?
     Measure the angles *a*, *b*, *c* and *d* with
     your protractor.
     Find *a* + *b* + *c* + *d* and see whether
     your previous decision was correct. (It
     may not agree exactly due to having to
     measure to the nearest degree.)

8.   Can you decide what the sum of the
      5 angles *p*, *q*, *r*, *s*, *t* will equal ?
      Measure the angles and find
      p + *q* + *r* + *s* + *t*.
      Was your decision correct ?
      Angles in a diagram like this are
      called **angles at a point**.

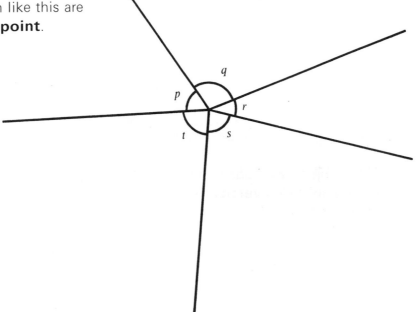

9.   These angles are called
      **adjacent angles on a straight
      line**.
      (Adjacent means 'next to each
      other'.)
      Can you decide what the sum of
      the angles *a* and *b* will equal ?
      Measure your angles and find
      a + *b*.
      Was your decision correct ?

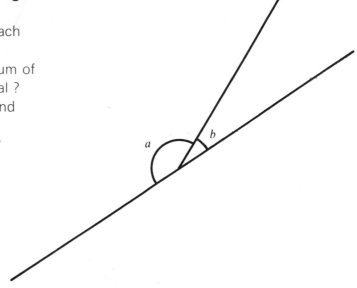

10.   Repeat question 9 using angles
      c and *d*.

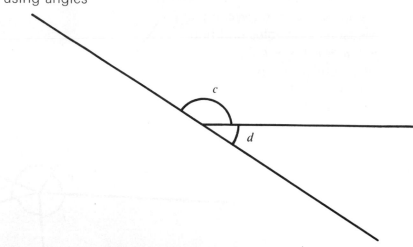

11.   These angles are made by two straight lines crossing each other.
      g and *j* are called **vertically opposite angles**, so are *h* and *k*.
      (Here, vertically means having the same vertex, that is, they are at the same point.
      It does not mean that any of the lines are vertical.)
      Can you decide anything about the sizes of *g* and *j*, or of *h* and *k* ?
      Measure the angles to see if your decision is correct.

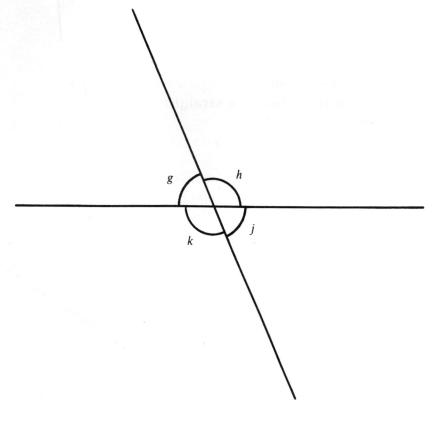

12.   Repeat question 11 using vertically
       opposite angles *p* and *r*, and *q* and *s*.

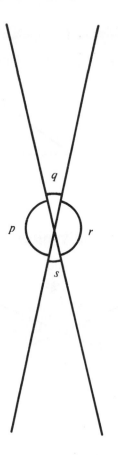

Calculations with angles

Angles at a point

These add up to 360°

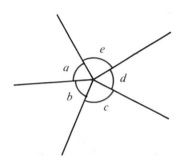

$a + b + c + d + e = \mathbf{360°}$

Adjacent angles (on a straight line)

These add up to 180°

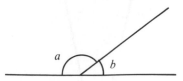

$a + b = \mathbf{180°}$

Vertically opposite angles

These are equal

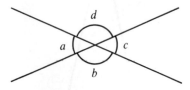

$a = c$
$b = d$

Examples

1   Calculate the size of angle a.

$a + 133° + 154° = 360°$ (angles at a point)
$a = 73°$

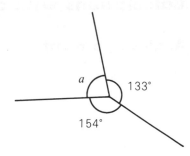

2   Calculate the sizes of angles b, c, d.

$b + 135° = 180°$ (adjacent angles)
$b = 45°$
$c = 45°$ (vertically opposite to b)
$d = 135°$ (vertically opposite to 135°)

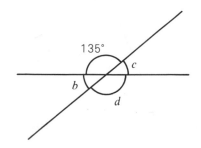

Exercise 2.2

In question 1 to 6, find the sizes of the angles marked with small letters, by calculation. The angles are not drawn accurately.

1.

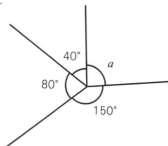

2.

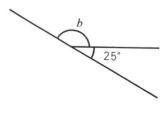

3.

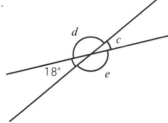

4.

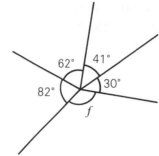

5.

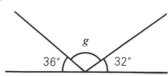

6.

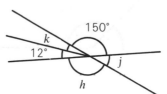

7.   The 5 angles in this figure are equal. Find their size.

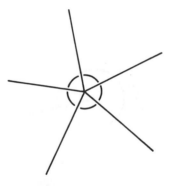

8.   The angles k and m are equal. Find their size.

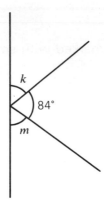

In these diagrams measure angle a with your protractor and use your answer to calculate the size of angle b.

9.

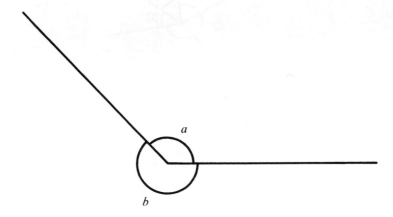

10.

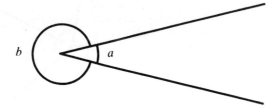

Parallel lines

Parallel lines are lines with the same direction. They remain the same distance apart, so never meet each other.
The sign for parallel lines is similar arrows on the lines.

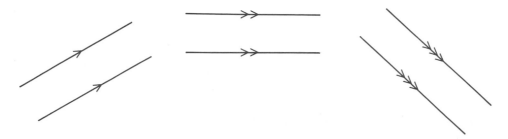

To draw parallel lines with a set-square

Example

Draw a line through C, parallel to AB.

Place the longest side of the set-square on
AB so that, if possible, the set-square is
placed over C.
Place a ruler along one of the other sides of
the set-square.

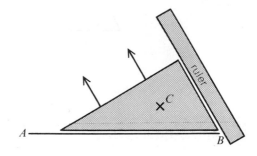

Keeping the ruler fixed, slide the set-square
along the ruler until its longest side passes
through C. Draw a line along this edge.

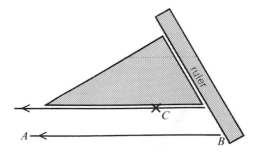

Practise drawing different parallel lines until you are sure that you can draw them
correctly.

Calculations with angles and parallel lines

Corresponding angles

These are equal

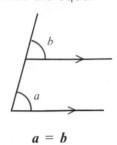

$$a = b$$

Alternate angles

These are equal

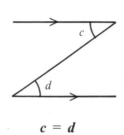

$$c = d$$

Interior angles

These add up to 180°

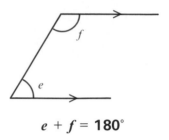

$$e + f = \mathbf{180°}$$

Example

Calculate the size of angles a, b, c.

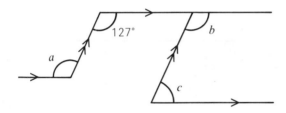

$a = 127°$ (alternate angles)
$b = 127°$ (corresponding angles)
$c = 180° - 127°$ (interior angle to b)
  $= 53°$

Exercise 2.3

1. These parallel lines have been drawn accurately. Measure the marked angles and
    check that the corresponding angles are equal, the alternate angles are equal, and
    the interior angles add up to 180°

1

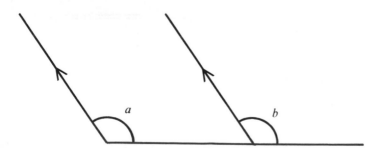

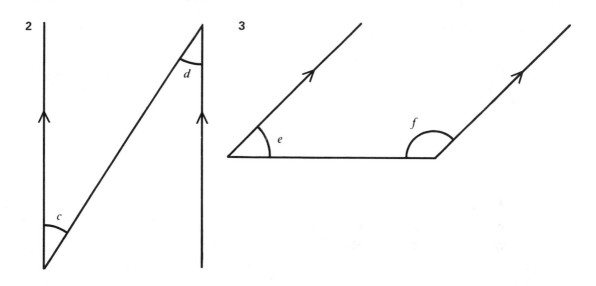

2. **Practice in drawing parallel lines**

1   Draw two lines AB and AE making an obtuse angle at A.
Mark the point C about halfway along AE.
Use your ruler and set-square to draw a line through C parallel to AB.

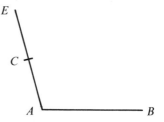

Measure the angles a and c to check that your lines are really parallel.

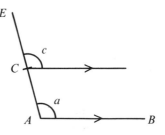

2   Draw two lines AB and BC making an acute angle at B. Mark the point C clearly.
Use your ruler and set-square to draw a line through C parallel to AB.

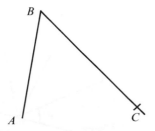   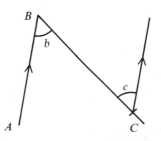

Measure the angles b and c to check that your lines are really parallel.

3.   Calculate the sizes of the marked angles.

1

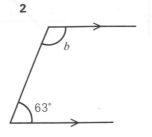

2

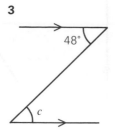

3

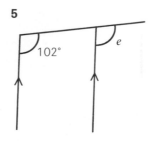

4

5

6

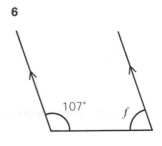

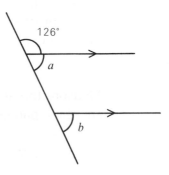

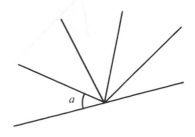

4.   Calculate the size of angle *a* and use your answer to
     calculate the size of angle *b*.

Exercise 2.4   Applications and Activities

1.   **1**   If all the angles in the diagram are equal, find
           the size of angle *a*.

     2   If *a* = 80° and the other angles are all equal,
           find their size.

In questions 2 to 8, calculate the sizes of the marked angles.

2.
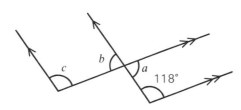

3.
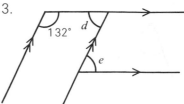

4.
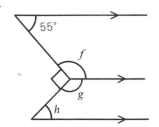

5.
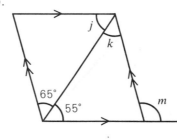

6.
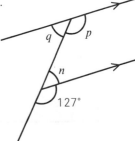

7.
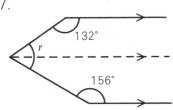

8.
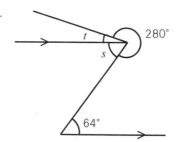

9. **Clocks**

1   How long does the hour hand take to make
    a complete revolution?

2   Through how many degrees does the hour
    hand turn in 1 hour ?

3   Through how many degrees does the hour
    hand turn between 2 pm and 6.30 pm ?

4   What is the size of the obtuse angle between
    the hands of a clock at 4 pm ?

5   What is the size of the acute angle between
    the hands of a clock at 4.30 pm ?

6   Through how many degrees does the minute hand of a clock turn in
    1 minute ?

7   How many minutes does it take for the minute hand to turn through 150° ?

8   Through how many degrees has the minute hand turned between 8.53 pm and
    9.18 pm ?

10. **Triangles**

1 Measure the angles of these triangles.

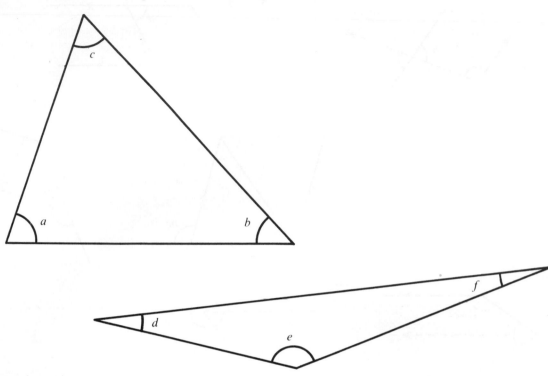

Find the sum of the three angles in each triangle.
Can you deduce anything about the sum ? If so, check your result by
drawing other different-shaped triangles.

2 Draw a triangle on paper and cut it out.
Colour the 3 angles and mark the corner of
each, then tear them off. Arrange them
together with points and edges touching.
Which diagram shows the result ? What does
this demonstrate ?

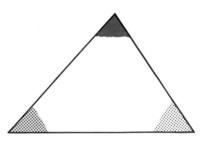

A   B   C

      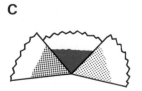

3   Draw a triangle on paper and cut it
out.
Colour the 3 angles on both sides of
the paper.
Find the mid-points of 2 sides and
make a crease joining them.
Fold along the crease so that it looks
like this.

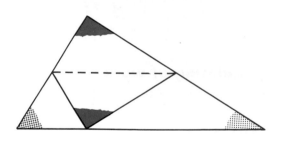

Make 2 more creases at right angles to
the first one.
Fold along them.

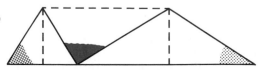

Where are the 3 angles of the original
triangle ?
What does this demonstrate ?

4   In this diagram the angles of the triangle
are *a*, *b*, *c*.

A line parallel to **AB** is drawn through
point *C*.
What is the sum of the angles *d* + *c* + *e*,
and why ?
Which angle is equal to *d*, and why ?
Which angle is equal to *e*, and why ?
What does this show about the sum of
the angles of the triangle, *a* + *b* + *c* ?

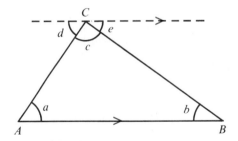

PUZZLE

5.   'Andrew has joined the navy,' said Beverley.
'No, he's in the RAF,' said Carol.
'Beverley is right,' said Dawn.
'I only know that he's not gone into the army,' said Elaine.
'You're all wrong,' said Fiona.
If only one of these statements was true, and all the others false, which one of the three
services had Andrew joined ?

3 Thinking about calculating

Calculating at work

Have you needed to do any calculating today ? If so, for what purpose ?

We use calculations continually, with money, time, lengths, weights, as well as with numbers. Think of situations where these people need to calculate, probably without using a calculator:

A teacher planning a school trip

A householder going shopping for food

The driver of a bus, who also has to collect the fares

A farmer who keeps a herd of cows for milking

You can probably think of more than one kind of calculation in each case.

A Chinese abacus, which is an ancient calculating instrument, still in use nowadays.
Did you ever use a similar counting frame ?

Calculating instruments

The pictures show calculating instruments. You are lucky in having one of the latest models, unknown 30 years ago. Calculators save a lot of time, so you can spend the time saved on doing more interesting Mathematics. However, there are times when you will not have your calculator available, or when the calculation is so simple that you can do it more quickly in your head. You will improve your efficiency with practice, and, as you can see, you will need to be able to calculate in many situations in your life.

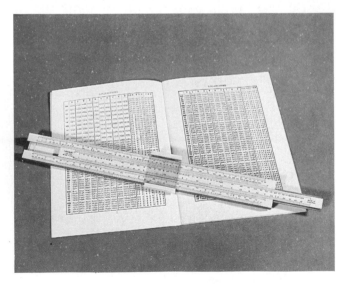

Engineers may still use slide rules. Logarithm tables were used in schools, for calculating, until very recently.

An old adding machine

Name some of the uses of present-day computers.

One of the first computers, in Moscow in 1955. Notice how huge it was. It could perform about 7500 arithmetical operations per second.

3 Calculation

Some multiplication and division without using a calculator

Multiplying whole numbers by 10

$$7 \times 10 = 70$$
$$87 \times 10 = 870$$
$$987 \times 10 = 9870$$
$$980 \times 10 = 9800$$
$$900 \times 10 = 9000$$

The figures 7 units, 8 tens and 9 hundreds have all become ten times bigger by moving up one place to become 7 tens, 8 hundreds and 9 thousands. 0's are used to fill the empty spaces.

Multiplying whole numbers by 100 or 1000

To multiply by 100 is simply the same as multiplying by 10 and then by 10 again, so the numbers move up two places.
To multiply by 1000 is the same as multiplying by 10, by 10 again and then by 10 again, so the numbers move up three places.

$$8 \times 100 = 800$$
$$78 \times 100 = 7800$$
$$678 \times 100 = 67\,800$$
$$5670 \times 100 = 567\,000$$
$$5000 \times 100 = 500\,000$$

$$23 \times 1000 = 23\,000$$
$$123 \times 1000 = 123\,000$$
$$4020 \times 1000 = 4\,020\,000$$

Multiplying whole numbers by 20, 30, 40, . . . , 200, 300, 400, . . . , 2000, 3000, 4000, . . .

$$
\begin{aligned}
70 \times 500 &= 7 \times 10 \times 5 \times 100 \\
&= 7 \times 5 \times 10 \times 100 \\
&= 35 \times 1000 \\
&= 35\,000
\end{aligned}
$$

$$
\begin{aligned}
800 \times 20 &= 8 \times 2 \times 1000 \\
&= 16\,000
\end{aligned}
$$

$$
\begin{aligned}
5000 \times 20 &= 5 \times 2 \times 10\,000 \\
&= 100\,000
\end{aligned}
$$

$$
\begin{aligned}
9000 \times 3000 &= 9 \times 3 \times 1\,000\,000 \\
&= 27\,000\,000
\end{aligned}
$$

Dividing whole numbers by 10, 100 or 1000

$$9000 \div 10 = 900$$
$$6800 \div 10 = 680$$
$$6850 \div 10 = 685$$

The figures have all become ten times smaller by moving down one place. 0's no longer needed disappear.

$$
\begin{array}{ll}
9300 \div 100 &= 93 \quad \text{(Moving down 2 places)} \\
800 \div 100 &= 8 \\
30\,000 \div 1000 &= 30 \quad \text{(Moving down 3 places)} \\
34\,000 \div 1000 &= 34 \\
534\,000 \div 1000 &= 534
\end{array}
$$

Dividing whole numbers by 20, 30, 40, . . . , 200, 300, 400, . . . , 2000, 3000, 4000, . . .

$$6000 \div 30 = \frac{600\cancel{0}}{3\cancel{0}} = \frac{600}{3} = 200$$

The 0's are crossed out because we are dividing both numbers by 10. (This can be called **cancelling**.)

What we are really doing is
$$6000 \div 30 = (6000 \div 10) \div 3 = 600 \div 3 = 200$$

$$800 \div 400 = \frac{8\cancel{0}\cancel{0}}{4\cancel{0}\cancel{0}} = \frac{8}{4} = 2$$

(We have divided both numbers by 10, and then by 10 again.)

$$30\,000 \div 5000 = \frac{30\,\cancel{0}\cancel{0}\cancel{0}}{5\cancel{0}\cancel{0}\cancel{0}} = \frac{30}{5} = 6$$

$$7200 \div 60 = \frac{720\cancel{0}}{6\cancel{0}} = \frac{720}{6} = 120$$

$$3500 \div 700 = \frac{35\cancel{0}\cancel{0}}{7\cancel{0}\cancel{0}} = \frac{35}{7} = 5$$

You can still use this method without writing anything down, if you have to do it in your head.

e.g. $40\,000 \div 800$ equals $400 \div 8$ which is 50, (mentally dividing by 100 first).

Numbers to the nearest ten

e.g. For numbers between 50 and 60.
Any number less than 55 is given as 50, to the nearest ten.
Any number from 55 upwards is given as 60, to the nearest ten.
(Actually, 55 is exactly halfway between 50 and 60 but it is usual to round it **up** to 60.)

So, if the units figure is 5 or more, correct **up** to the next ten.

Examples

64 = 60, to the nearest ten.
78 = 80, to the nearest ten.
85 is halfway between 80 and 90, but it is usual to give it as 90, to the nearest ten.

Numbers to the nearest hundred

e.g. For numbers between 200 and 300.
Any number less than 250 is given as 200, to the nearest hundred.
Any number from 250 upwards is given as 300, to the nearest hundred.
You will notice that it does not matter what the units figure is, it is the tens figure you must look at.

So, if the tens figure is 5 or more, correct up to the next 100.

Examples

264 = 300, to the nearest hundred, since the 10's figure is 6.
246 = 200, to the nearest hundred, since the 10's figure is 4.

Numbers to the nearest thousand

e.g. For numbers between 7000 and 8000.
Any number less than 7500 is given as 7000, to the nearest thousand.
Any number from 7500 upwards is given as 8000, to the nearest thousand.

Here you must look at the hundreds figure. If this is 5 or more, correct up to the next 1000.

Examples

9264 =   9000, to the nearest thousand, since the 100's figure is 2.
5721 =   6000, to the nearest thousand, since the 100's figure is 7.
9721 = 10 000, to the nearest thousand. Here, 9 has been corrected up to 10.

Use of a calculator

What a wonderful little machine this is ! Maybe you have a fairly simple one, which will do addition, subtraction, multiplication and division, and probably square root as well, or maybe you have a scientific one which seems quite complicated.

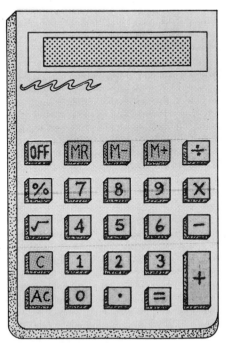

Simple calculator

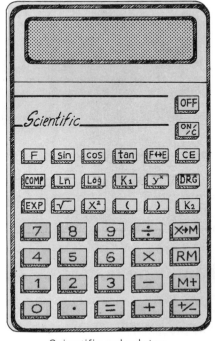

Scientific calculator

Make sure your calculator is working properly, and get to know how to use it for different operations. Not all calculators work in the same way.

It is advisable to start every new calculation by pressing the $\boxed{C}$ key (for CLEAR), but you may find that on your calculator this is unnecessary if you have just pressed the $\boxed{=}$ key.

Read the instruction booklet of your own calculator and try the examples shown there. You may find that there are quicker ways than you normally use to do some calculations.

Checking calculator answers

It is easy to get a wrong answer from a calculator by pressing the wrong keys, so look at the answer and see if it seems right.

You could also do the calculation twice, possibly entering the figures in reverse order, to see if you get the same result.

You could check the units figure

5816 + 1957
The unit figures are 6 and 7.
6 + 7 = 13, so the units figure in the answer is 3.
(The answer is 7773.)

16 × 57
6 × 7 = 42 so the units figure in the answer is 2.
(The answer is 912.)

5816 − 1957
You cannot use 6 − 7 so use 16 − 7 = 9 and the units figure in the answer is 9.
(The answer is 3859.)

(You cannot do a similar check for division.)

You could check by doing the reverse operation

To check 5816 − 1957 = 3859, do the calculation 3859 + 1957 and you will get 5816.

To check 5816 ÷ 2 = 2908, do the calculation 2908 × 2 and you will get 5816.

To find the square of a number

To find 13^2.

You can press 13 $\boxed{\times}$ 13 $\boxed{=}$ (and you will get 169).
Try pressing 13 $\boxed{\times}$ $\boxed{=}$ (and if you get 169, this works on your calculator and is quicker).

If there is a key $\boxed{x^2}$, press 13 $\boxed{x^2}$

To find the square root of a number, use the $\boxed{\sqrt{}}$ key

To find the square root of 169, press 169 $\boxed{\sqrt{}}$ (and you will get 13).
If you find the square root of a number on your calculator and the result is not an exact whole number then the original number is not a square number.

To find the cube of a number

To find 7^3.

You can press 7 $\boxed{\times}$ 7 $\boxed{\times}$ 7 $\boxed{=}$ and you will get 343.
Try pressing 7 $\boxed{\times}$ $\boxed{=}$ $\boxed{=}$ (and if you get 343, this works on your calculator and is quicker).

If there is a key $\boxed{y^x}$, then here **y** = 7 and **x** = 3. Press 7 $\boxed{y^x}$ 3 $\boxed{=}$.

To find the remainder in a division sum

e.g. 79 ÷ 19.

Press 79 $\boxed{\div}$ 19 $\boxed{=}$ getting 4.157 . . . So 19 divided into 79 goes 4 times.
Now find out what 4 × 19 equals.
4 × 19 = 76 and 79 − 76 = 3, so the remainder is 3.

Mixed questions and brackets

If someone says to you '6 plus 4 multiplied by 5', what would be your answer ?
It depends on whether they mean
    6 + 4 worked out, then multiplied by 5;
or
    6 plus the answer to 4 multiplied by 5.

In a written question it can be made absolutely clear by using brackets. The part in brackets must be worked out first.

$(6 + 4) \times 5 = 10 \times 5 = 50$
$6 + (4 \times 5) = 6 + 20 = 26$
$8 \times (10 - 6) = 8 \times 4 = 32$
$30 \div (3 + 2) = 30 \div 5 = 6$
$(15 + 40) \div 5 = 55 \div 5 = 11$

If the question was written without brackets, then we would have to have a rule to use. Our rule is that:
1 brackets must be worked out first,
2 multiplication and division are worked out next,
3 addition and subtraction are worked out last.

So 6 + 4 × 5 means the same as 6 + (4 × 5), since if there are no brackets, multiplication must be done before addition.

8 × 10 − 6 = (8 × 10) − 6 = 80 − 6 = 74
30 ÷ 3 + 2 = (30 ÷ 3) + 2 = 10 + 2 = 12
15 + 40 ÷ 5 = 15 + (40 ÷ 5) = 15 + 8 = 23

A fraction line is also a bracket.

$\dfrac{30}{3 + 2}$ means 30 ÷ (3 + 2) = 30 ÷ 5 = 6

$\dfrac{15 + 40}{5}$ means (15 + 40) ÷ 5 = 55 ÷ 5 = 11

Be careful when you use your calculator for mixed operations

There are different methods for the two types of calculator. Enter 6 ⊞ 4 ⊠ 5 ⊟ and you will get either of the answers 26 or 50. If you get the answer 26, read the first set of instructions. It is probably a scientific calculator. If you get the answer 50, read the instructions for a simpler calculator.

Scientific calculators, or those giving the answer 26.

It will treat 6 ⊞ 4 ⊠ 5 ⊟ as 6 + (4 × 5) and give the answer 26.
Try 15 ⊞ 40 ⊟ 5 ⊟ and it will treat it as 15 + (40 ÷ 5) and give the answer 23. In other words, it keeps to the rules and does multiplication and division as if they were in brackets, and there is no need to use brackets round them.
But, if you really intend it to do (6 + 4) × 5 or (15 + 40) ÷ 5, you must either use brackets, which you will find on your calculator, **or** work out the answer to the bracket by pressing ⊟ before carrying on.
So press 〔(6 ⊞ 4)〕 ⊠ 5 ⊟   or   6 ⊞ 4 ⊟ ⊠ 5 ⊟
and   〔(15 ⊞ 40)〕 ⊟ 5 ⊟   or   15 ⊞ 40 ⊟ ⊟ 5 ⊟

Simpler calculators, or those giving the answer 50.

It is reading all the operations in the order in which you enter them.
So for 6 ⊞ 4 ⊠ 5 ⊟ it will do it as if it was (6 + 4) × 5 and give the answer 50, and for 15 ⊞ 40 ⊟ 5 ⊟ it will read it as (15 + 40) ÷ 5 and give the answer 11.
But, if you really want to do 6 + (4 × 5) then either turn it round to do (4 × 5) + 6 which it will do properly, or press 6 and put it into the memory, then work out 4 × 5 and add this to the memory. Then press ⌈RM⌉ (recall memory) for the complete answer. This is 6 ⌈M+⌉ 4 ⊠ 5 ⊟ ⌈M+⌉ ⌈RM⌉ and you will get the answer 26.
Now cancel the memory before you forget !

Exercise 3.1

Work out the answers to questions 1 and 2 without using a calculator.

1.   **1** 47×10 **5** 700×3000 **8** 60×5000
     2 840×100 **6** 9000×50 **9** 7000×40
     3 601×1000 **7** 200×800 **10** 80×300
     4 40×20

2.   **1** $5000 \div 10$ **5** $800 \div 200$ **8** $6000 \div 50$
     2 $700 \div 100$ **6** $90\,000 \div 30$ **9** $20\,000 \div 400$
     3 $90\,000 \div 1000$ **7** $4000 \div 200$ **10** $7000 \div 20$
     4 $6000 \div 100$

3.   Write these numbers to the nearest ten.

     59   503   129   1043   286   94   1427   581   97   206

4.   Write these numbers to the nearest hundred.

     1258   2481   20 997   506   1058   1038   3105   9091   449   786

5.   Write these numbers to the nearest thousand.

     4273   14 691   2723   27 857   2634   55 881   9108   81 164
     3935   10 487

6.   Use your calculator to find
     1 the squares of 25, 52, 106, 111,
     2 the square roots of 676, 961, 2025, 7744,
     3 the cubes of 11 and 53.

7.   Say what the units figure will be in each of these calculations. Then do the
     questions on your calculator, checking that the units figures are correct.
     1 $132 + 250 + 379$ **4** 685×52
     2 $2103 - 519$ **5** $775 - 696 + 317$
     3 324×89

8.   Use your calculator to find the numbers represented by $\square$ in these statements.
     Then repeat each calculation in its normal order to check your answer.

     1 $\square + 225 = 1030$ **6** $850 - \square = 490$
     2 $\square \times 17 = 221$ **7** $124 \times \square = 1364$
     3 $\square - 53 = 127$ **8** $1368 \div \square = 152$
     4 $\square \div 24 = 15$ **9** $2 \times (\square + 54) = 166$
     5 $1967 + \square = 1990$ **10** $(51 \times \square) - 93 = 264$

9.   Find the answers to these calculations without using your calculator.
     Then repeat the questions using your calculator, making sure that you get the
     same results.

     1   (5 × 3) − 2   **5**   36 ÷ (5 + 4)   **8**   18 − (12 ÷ 6)
     2   (8 − 2) × 4   **6**   (36 ÷ 4) + 5   **9**   (9 × 8) − (7 × 6)
     3   17 − (3 × 4)   **7**   (23 + 7) ÷ 6   **10**   12 + (3 × 5) − 2
     4   12 × (5 − 2)

10. Do these division questions using your calculator. Find the answer and the
     remainder, if any.
     1   300 ÷ 9   **4**   610 ÷ 45
     2   8164 ÷ 17   **5**   708 ÷ 12
     3   1800 ÷ 28

11. Copy and complete this number pattern to the line which includes +0.

         0 × 9 + 8 = 8
         9 × 9 + 7 = 88
        98 × 9 + 6 =
       987 × 9 + 5 =
        . . .

12. Copy and complete this table.
     (It would be useful to memorise these results.)

     1   Is there any pattern in the unit figures
             in the squares column ?
     2   Is there any pattern in the unit figures
             in the cubes column ?

number	square	cube
1	1	1
2	4	8
3	9	
.		
.		
.		
10		

Exercise 3.2   Applications and Activities

You should not need to use a calculator in questions 1 to 10. In the other questions,
only use a calculator when you cannot manage the calculations without one.

1.   The distance by sea from Liverpool to New York is three thousand
     and ninety-one miles. Write this distance in figures.

2. A carton holds 30 tins.
    1 How many tins are there in 20 cartons ?
    2 How many cartons must be used to pack 480 tins ?

3. The number of insects in a colony doubles each week. If there were 100 insects there at first, how many would there be after 6 weeks ?

4. There were 800 children in a school and 40 teachers. What is the average number of children per teacher ?

5. Write down any number less than 10, add 2 to it and square the result. Then add 5 and multiply by 10. Take 100 away. Divide by 2, add 5 and divide by the number you started with. Subtract 20 and double the result. Divide by 10 and subtract the number you started with. What is your answer ?

6. A typist agrees to type 480 pages in 17 days. In the first four days she does 50 pages each day. Then she is ill and does none for the next three days. How many pages will she have to do, on average, each day to finish the work on time ?

7. Instead of writing down $(10 + 6) \times (3 + 7)$, Stephen wrote down $(10 \times 6) + (3 \times 7)$ by mistake.
    1 What is the answer to the correct question ?
    2 What is the answer to the question Stephen wrote down ?

8. Araf and Habib worked on two machines. Araf produced 40 components each hour, Habib produced 50 per hour. They worked for 8 hours each day. How many extra components had Habib produced after 30 working days ?

9. The attendances at five mid-week football matches were:
    1987   4306   5275   6758   11 833
    Give these attendances
    1 correct to the nearest hundred,
    2 correct to the nearest thousand.

10. Find the values of
    1 $(6 \times 5) + 8$ **5** $6 \times 5 \times 8$ **8** $\sqrt{(6^2 + 8^2)}$
    2 $6 \times (5 + 8)$ **6** $(8 + 6) \div (8 - 6)$ **9** $8^2 - 5^2$
    3 $6 + (5 \times 8)$ **7** $6^2 + 8^2$ **10** $(8 - 5)^2$
    4 $(6 + 5) \times 8$

11. Using your calculator, find which is larger, $\sqrt{576} + \sqrt{49}$ or $\sqrt{(576 + 49)}$, and by how much.

12. The table shows the dinners ordered for the 1st year forms at a school, for a week in September.

	1A	1B	1C	1D	Total
Mon	30	28	22		103
Tues	29	28	18	24	
Wed	28		21	26	99
Thur	28	25			
Fri		26	22		101
Total for week	141		105	123	

Copy the table and fill in the missing figures, including the total number of dinners ordered for the week by all the 1st year forms.

1   On which day were least dinners ordered ?

2   If the dinners cost 80 p each, what was the total cost of all the dinners for the week ?

13. A school has these numbers of pupils in its 5 year-groups:
176,   192,   189,   198,   211.
Write down these numbers to the nearest ten.
Find the sum of the 5 numbers in your answers.
This sum was used as an estimate for the total number of pupils in the school.
Is it a reasonable estimate ?

14. Multiply the sum of 65 and 25 by their difference. Then find the value of $65^2 - 25^2$. What do you notice ? Try this for other pairs of numbers.

15. **Making number patterns with your calculator**

Press 2 $\boxed{\times}$ $\boxed{=}$ $\boxed{=}$ $\boxed{=}$ . . . and see what you get.
(On some calculators you may have to press
2 $\boxed{\times}$ $\boxed{\times}$ $\boxed{=}$ $\boxed{=}$ $\boxed{=}$ . . .)

Try 7 $\boxed{+}$ $\boxed{=}$ $\boxed{=}$ $\boxed{=}$ . . . (or 7 $\boxed{+}$ $\boxed{+}$ $\boxed{=}$ $\boxed{=}$ $\boxed{=}$ . . .)
Try 1 $\boxed{+}$ 7 $\boxed{=}$ $\boxed{=}$ $\boxed{=}$ . . . (or 7 $\boxed{+}$ $\boxed{+}$ 1 $\boxed{=}$ $\boxed{=}$ $\boxed{=}$ . . .)
Try 100 $\boxed{-}$ 6 $\boxed{=}$ $\boxed{=}$ $\boxed{=}$ . . . (or 6 $\boxed{-}$ $\boxed{-}$ 100 $\boxed{=}$ $\boxed{=}$ $\boxed{=}$ . . .)

Simple calculator

16. **Magic Squares**

Rearrange these numbers so that each row, each
column and each diagonal add up to 15.
(Leave 5 in the centre and put 4 in a corner.)

1	2	3
4	5	6
7	8	9

Copy and complete this magic square which
uses numbers 1 to 16.
All rows, columns and the main diagonals add
up to 34.

			12
3	16		
15	4	14	

17. Copy and complete this number pattern to the row which begins 1×9^2.

$$9 \times 1^2 + 1^3 = 10 = 1^2 \times 10$$
$$8 \times 2^2 + 2^3 = 40 = 2^2 \times 10$$
$$7 \times 3^2 + 3^3 = \ldots$$
$$\ldots$$

18. Can you discover a number pattern involving the squares of numbers from
50 to 59 ?

number	square
50	25⎪00
51	26⎪01
. . .	

You could then investigate the squares of numbers from 41 to 49.

PUZZLE

6. If it were possible to take a sheet of paper, a tenth of a millimetre thick, and double it over
on itself fifty times, how thick would the resulting wad of paper be ? Approximately 10 cm,
10 m, 1 km, 100 km or 100 000 000 km ?

4 Thinking about decimals

Decimals today

In these days of calculators and computers, decimals are used more and more. They are used in cases where we want accurate figures, rather than approximate ones.

Look in a newspaper and cut out examples of decimals being used. Have you used decimals yourself recently, possibly in lessons in other subjects such as science or technology? If so, for what purposes were they used?

Name some people who will use decimals in their work, and say for what purposes they are used.

The car has gone 5570 miles altogether, but the lower reading shows that since that scale was re-set to zero, it has travelled 134.2 miles.

USA runner Sydney Maree setting the 1500 m world record in 3 min 31.23 sec at Cologne, in 1983. Why is the time measured so accurately?

This car radio is set to get Radio 1, on the 98.9 MHz wavelength.

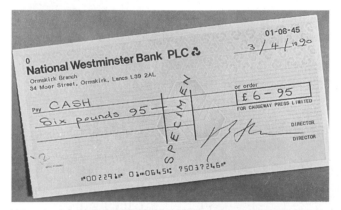

What is the amount shown on this cheque?
Why is a dash written instead of a decimal point?

A radio requires 6 volts. How many of these batteries are needed?

A decimal problem

Mr Briden was planning to put fencing along the end of his garden.
He measured the length, which was 18 m.
He decided to have 5 posts, so he needed 4 spaces in-between them, with wire stretched across.

How far apart would the posts be?
(Assume that he measures to the centre of each post then it does not matter how wide they are.)
What calculation would he do on his calculator?
What is the answer?
I got 4.5. What does .5 mean?
So the distance between the posts was 4.5 m. This seemed rather a large gap so Mr Briden decided to have 9 posts. He did the calculation again and got 2.25.
What does .2 mean? What does .25 mean?
How long are the spaces between the posts, in metres?
How long are the spaces between the posts, in centimetres?
When he went to buy the posts he could only get 8 of them. So to calculate how far apart to put them he did 18 ÷ 7.
The answer was 2.5714285.
What does .5 mean? How many cm is 0.5 m?
What does .57 mean? How many cm is 0.57 m?
What does .571 mean? How many cm is 0.571 m?
Is it any use to know that the answer was 2.5714285?
How far apart will he put his posts?

4 Decimals

Decimals are fractions which have denominators of 10, or of powers of 10 such as 100, 1000, 10 000, . . .
The decimal point is used to separate the whole number part from the decimal part of a number.

e.g. **1**   **251.37**

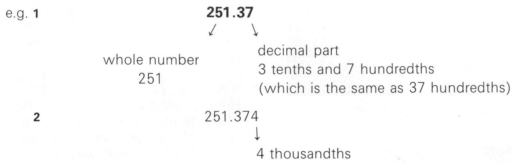

whole number
251

decimal part
3 tenths and 7 hundredths
(which is the same as 37 hundredths)

2   251.374

4 thousandths

This number is read as two hundred and fifty-one point three seven four.

If there is no whole number part it is usual to write a 0 before the point. Write 0.3 rather than .3 because the 0 helps to draw attention to the decimal point. This number can be read as point three. On your calculator it is sufficient to press .3

In the number 1.26, the 2 represents 2 tenths and the 6 represents 6 hundredths.
6 hundredths are smaller than 1 tenth.
Here are units, represented by squares, divided into tenths and hundredths.

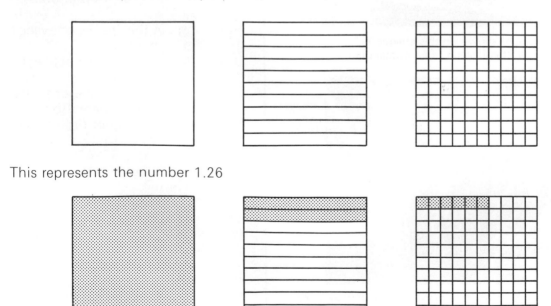

This represents the number 1.26

Multiplying by 10, 100, 1000, . . .

You can already multiply whole numbers by 10.

e.g. $3 \times 10 = 30$
         $53 \times 10 = 530$
        $600 \times 10 = 6000$

The figures 3 units, 5 tens, 6 hundreds have all become ten bigger by moving up one place to become 3 tens, 5 hundreds, 6 thousands. 0's are used to fill in the empty spaces.

The same thing happens with decimals.

$0.2 \times 10 = 2$
$0.24 \times 10 = 2.4$
$0.007 \times 10 = 0.07$
$3.007 \times 10 = 30.07$

The figures 2 tenths, 4 hundredths, 7 thousandths, have all become ten bigger by moving up one place to become 2 units, 4 tenths, 7 hundredths. The 0's which were filling up empty spaces have disappeared if they are no longer needed.

To multiply by 100 is simply the same as multiplying by 10, and then by 10 again. To multiply by 1000 is the same as multiplying by 10, by 10 again and by 10 again. Here are the rules:
To multiply by 10, 100, 1000, . . . , the numbers grow larger, so the figures move upwards (to the left) 1, 2, 3, . . . places, assuming that the decimal point is fixed. Add 0's to fill any empty places between the figures and the decimal point.

Examples

$1.2 \times 10 = 12$
$0.76 \times 10 = 7.6$
$0.2 \times 100 = 20$
$1.84 \times 100 = 184$
$0.003 \times 100 = 0.3$
$0.61 \times 1000 = 610$

Dividing by 10, 100, 1000, . . .

The numbers become smaller, so the figures move downwards (to the right) 1, 2, 3, . . . places, assuming that the decimal point is fixed. Add 0's to fill any empty places between the decimal point and the figures.

Examples

```
6       ÷ 10    = 0.6
7.17    ÷ 100   = 0.0717
83.05   ÷ 1000  = 0.08305
0.2     ÷ 10    = 0.02
350     ÷ 100   = 3.5
```

Adding, subtracting, and multiplying and dividing by small whole numbers

You can do these questions without using your calculator.
Just keep the figures in their correct positions relative to the decimal point.

Examples

1 12.3 + 3.85

```
   12.3
+  3.85
 ──────
  16.15
```

2 14.5 − 1.83

```
  14.50
−  1.83
 ──────
  12.67
```

3 27.5 × 3

```
   27.5
×     3
 ──────
   82.5
```

4 216.81 ÷ 9

```
9)216.81
 ────────
   24.09
```

Sometimes the division is not exact and it will be necessary to stop after a suitable number of decimal places. The method for this is similar to that used to correct numbers to the nearest 10, 100, etc.
Look at the figure to the right of the last figure you need. If this extra figure is 5 or more, add 1 to the final figure of your answer.

Example

Find the value of 29 ÷ 7, correct to 3 decimal places.

Since we want 3 decimal places, find the figures in the first 4 decimal places, that is one more place than we need.

```
7)29.0000
 ─────────
  4.1428
```

Since the figure in the 4th decimal place (8) is 5 or more, the figure in the 3rd decimal place must be corrected up from 2 to 3.
29 ÷ 7 = 4.143, correct to 3 decimal places.

If you had used your calculator the answer given would be 4.142857143
Since you want the answer to 3 decimal places you look at the figure in the 4th decimal place, which is 8, as we had before. The answer to 3 decimal places is 4.143. You do not need to consider the rest of the figures on the calculator (57143).

Here are some other examples of numbers corrected up:

3.2976   = 3.298 to 3 decimal places
0.8692   = 0.869 to 3 decimal places
0.0827   = 0.083 to 3 decimal places
0.00426 = 0.004 to 3 decimal places

0.849   = 0.85 to 2 decimal places
3.297   = 3.30 to 2 decimal places
1.0347   = 1.03 to 2 decimal places

0.849   = 0.8   to 1 decimal place
3.297   = 3.3   to 1 decimal place
1.0347   = 1.0   to 1 decimal place
1.0747   = 1.1   to 1 decimal place

Use your calculator to do multiplication and division by decimal numbers.

e.g.   38.7   × 7.9   = 305.73   (If you need this answer correct to
                                    1 decimal place, it is 305.7)
         0.009 × 1.2   = 0.0108
         0.048 ÷ 1.6   = 0.03
         270   ÷ 0.12 = 2250

If a division question does not work out exactly, you will have to decide how many decimal places to leave in the answer. Usually 1, 2 or 3 will be sufficient.
e.g.   128 ÷ 0.63 = 203.1746032

If you want the answer correct to the nearest whole number it is 203, if to 1 decimal place it is 203.2, to 2 decimal places it is 203.17 or to 3 decimal places it is 203.175

         2.13 ÷ 5.62 = 0.379003559
To 2 decimal places this is 0.38, to 3 decimal places it is 0.379

Significant figures

Instead of deciding to give an answer correct to a certain number of decimal places, we sometimes decide to give it correct to a certain number of figures.

Significant figures are the figures of the number not counting any 0's which are just filling in spaces at the beginning or end of the number.

Correct to 3 significant figures means that you should write down the first three figures of the number, checking the 4th figure to see if the 3rd figure must be corrected up.

Here are some examples of numbers corrected to **3 significant figures**.

587.9   = 588   7 is corrected up to 8 because the 4th figure (9) is 5 or more.

4.962   = 4.96   6 is not corrected up because the 4th figure (2) is not 5 or more.

9487   = 9490   We have had to add a 0 to fill the space in the units place.

265 204 = 265 000   We have had to use 3 0's to fill in the gaps in the hundreds, tens and units places.

0.04217 = 0.0422   The 0 after the decimal point is simply filling in a place. It is not counted as a significant figure. The 0 in front of the decimal point is not counted, either. (It just draws attention to the point.)

5.04217 = 5.04   0's in the middle of numbers **are** counted as significant figures.

Here are some numbers corrected to **2 significant figures**.

585.9   = 590

4.96   = 5.0   The 9 is corrected up, so 4.9 goes up to 5.0. Here it is useful to write the 0 to show that we are writing correct to 2 significant figures.

9487   = 9500

265 204 = 270 000

0.04217 = 0.042

5.04217 = 5.0

5.05217 = 5.1

Reading numbers on scales

Example

Decide between which two whole numbers the reading lies. This one lies between 4 and 5 so starts 4.

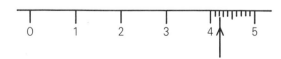

Here is an enlargement of the part of the scale between 4 and 5.
Decide between which two tenths the reading lies. This one lies between 2 and 3 so it is 4.2.
If you have to answer correct to 1 decimal place decide whether it is nearer 2 or 3. This one is nearer 3 so give the answer as 4.3.

If you have to estimate the answer to 2 decimal places, imagine an enlargement of the part of the scale between 4.2 and 4.3. The reading is nearer 4.3 than 4.2 so it is bigger than 4.25. It is approximately 4.27.

Exercise 4.1

Try to do questions 1 to 8 without using your calculator, then use your calculator to check your answers.

1. **1** 0.9 × 10
    2 8.02 × 10
    3 34.12 × 10
    4 0.061 × 10
    5 0.45 × 10

2. **1** 3.79 × 100
    2 0.15 × 100
    3 1.25 × 1000
    4 0.0036 × 1000
    5 0.07 × 1000

3. 1   14.92 ÷ 10
    2   47.6 ÷ 10
    3   2.08 ÷ 10
    4   0.3 ÷ 10
    5   0.04 ÷ 10

6. 1   4.07 − 1.99
    2   9.67 − 8.6
    3   8.3 − 1.09
    4   2 − 0.37
    5   3.5 − 0.02

4. 1   29.5 ÷ 100
    2   7.6 ÷ 100
    3   0.5 ÷ 100
    4   35.8 ÷ 1000
    5   19 ÷ 1000

7. 1   8.02 × 7
    2   1.5 × 8
    3   0.72 × 4
    4   6.02 × 5
    5   0.03 × 6

5. 1   1.12 + 2.8 + 3.25
    2   0.9 + 8.02 + 6.98
    3   6.49 + 1.26 + 0.47
    4   0.04 + 0.82 + 0.17
    5   23.93 + 0.03 + 8.07

8. 1   9.42 ÷ 3
    2   9.6 ÷ 5
    3   5.04 ÷ 8
    4   0.6 ÷ 4
    5   0.056 ÷ 7

9. On graph paper, you can represent numbers in this way:

1 unit

 strips are tenths

 small squares are hundredths

Represent these numbers.
    1   1.58   2   2.02   3   1.46   4   3.33   5   1.99

10. Write these numbers correct to 1 decimal place.
    1   5.31   2   5.493   3   0.39   4   1.08   5   2.062

11. Write these numbers correct to 2 decimal places.
    1   3.578   2   5.806   3   0.704   4   6.589   5   0.008

12. Write these numbers correct to 2 significant figures.
    1   36.9   5   0.304   8   0.288
    2   24.1   6   0.296   9   0.0506
    3   4.78   7   0.591   10 0.734
    4   4.52

13. Write these numbers correct to 3 significant figures.
    1   0.04506   5   716 360   8   0.03029
    2   4.2678   6   320.6   9   6.046
    3   18.051   7   49 620   10 5.904
    4   9267

14.   Use your calculator to work out the answers to these questions.
       1   13.06 × 26.1   **4**   16.2 × 0.07
       2   463 × 0.17   **5**   0.049 × 3.4
       3   0.0625 × 1.74

15.   Use your calculator to work out the answers to these questions. Give them correct
       to 2 decimal places.
       1   0.46 ÷ 2.9   **4**   26.7 ÷ 9.3
       2   0.11 ÷ 0.015   **5**   362 ÷ 5.4
       3   5.4 ÷ 0.73

16.   Read the numbers marked at A, B, C, D, E correct to 1 decimal place.

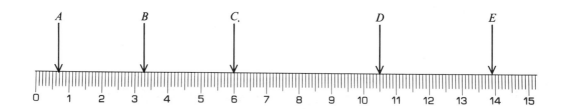

17.   Read off the numbers marked at A, B, C, D, E correct to 1 decimal place.

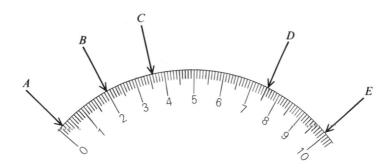

18.

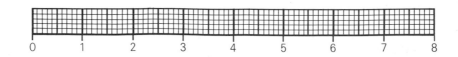

       Use a strip of graph paper to make a number-scale as shown. Mark on your strip the
       readings for the numbers A 2.5, B 5.9, C 0.2, D 7.7, E 3.1

19. Read the numbers marked at *A*, *B*, *C*, *D*, *E* correct to 2 decimal places.

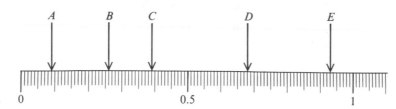

20. Use a strip of graph paper marked in millimetres, or a larger strip of 2mm graph paper, to make a number-scale as shown. Mark on your strip the readings for numbers *A* 0.67,   *B* 0.51,   *C* 0.07,   *D* 0.75,   *E* 0.99.

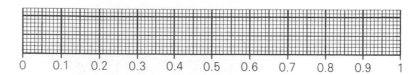

Exercise 4.2   Applications and Activities

1. Write down any number between 1 and 10. Add 2.45 and multiply the total by 2.8. Now subtract 3.5 and then divide by 5.6. Add 4.4 and double the result. Subtract the number you started with. What is your answer ?

2. Express 3207.926 correct to
    1 the nearest whole number,
    2 2 decimal places,
    3 2 significant figures.

3. In each of these calculations a mistake has been made. Find the correct answers. Can you also discover what mistake was made, in each case ?

    1 $10 - 0.726 = 2.74$ **4** $4.78 \times 8.543 = 39.913$
    2 $1.23 + 2.4 + 3.13 = 6.082$ **5** $(15.6 + 2.8) \times 4.3 = 27.64$
    3 $13.93 \div 0.07 = 19.9$

4. Use your calculator to find the numbers represented by □ in these statements.

    1 $\square + 2.45 = 19.27$ **6** $\square \div 0.34 = 7.78$
    2 $4.96 - \square = 2.93$ **7** $\square - 92.58 = 7.42$
    3 $\square \times 0.52 = 1.6328$ **8** $\square \times (3.7 + 8.5) = 85.4$
    4 $3.74 - (1.93 + \square) = 1.14$ **9** $\square + (25.8 \times 1.4) = 39.96$
    5 $54.6 \div \square = 182$ **10** $5.6 \div (2.31 - \square) = 4.375$

5.   **Square roots**

number	square root
1	1
4	2
9	3
16	4
25	5
36	6
49	7
64	8
81	9
100	10

The numbers 1, 4, 9, . . . have exact square roots. Other numbers have square roots which can be found approximately.

Numbers between 1 and 4 have square roots between 1 and 2.
Using your calculator you will find that
$$\sqrt{2} = 1.41$$
$$\sqrt{2.5} = 1.58$$
$$\sqrt{3} = 1.73, \text{ correct to 2 decimal places.}$$

Numbers between 4 and 9 have square roots between 2 and 3.
Use your calculator to find the square roots of 5, 6, 7 and 8, correct to 2 decimal places.

Similar rules work for other numbers.
e.g. 45 is between 36 and 49 so its square root is between 6 and 7, so you know it begins with 6.
Find its value correct to 2 decimal places, using your calculator.

Investigate the connection between the square roots of a number and the number which is 100 times bigger or smaller.

PUZZLE

7.   Sakina is given 15 coins for her birthday, all 10p, 20p or 50p coins. She got £5.10 altogether. How many of each coin were there ?

5 Thinking about algebra

Using algebra

Algebra is a very useful branch of mathematics. Many of the problems to be solved in our world today need the use of algebraic expressions, formulae and equations, so it is a vital subject for a very wide range of users, such as Government departments, financial businesses, industrialists, researchers, and especially for all kinds of scientific work. You are not so likely to need it in day-to-day living, although you may find some uses, but you are benefiting from the use made by others.

For example, consider the production of a motor car. Algebra is used in the designing of the car taking into account the engine performance, the costs of production and the safety aspects, and in the marketing of the car, the fixing of a price which will persuade people to buy it yet leave a profit for the producers, the spending on advertising, the planning of a distribution chain which will get the cars into the showrooms where they are needed, and so on.
Similarly, we take electricity for granted, but think of all the planning which has been necessary to bring electricity, at the right voltage and at a reasonable price, into our homes, and into the factories which make the goods we buy and use.

At present, you are just beginning to learn all about algebra, so you are going to start with easy work, but who knows where it might lead you in the future.
So, enjoy learning the basic work.

Consider the algebra involved in the production of a motor car.

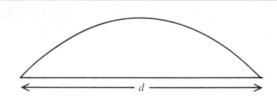

The greatest horizontal distance a projectile will travel, in metres, is given by the formula

$$d = \frac{v^2}{9.8}$$

where v is the speed of projection in m/s.

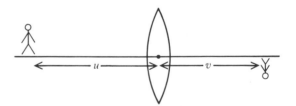

The formula giving the connection between u, the object length, v the image length and f, the focal length of the lens is

$$\frac{1}{u} + \frac{1}{v} = \frac{1}{f}$$

An algebraic expression

Here is a simple use of an algebraic expression:
Try this question with a group of friends, all starting with different numbers.
'Write down any number.
Add 12 and multiply the total by 8.
Now subtract 20 and then divide by 4.
Add 5 and halve the result.
Subtract the number you started with. What is your answer?'
What do you notice about your answers?

Now you can follow the steps with algebraic expressions.
Since we start with any number, we can let this be x.
Adding 12 gives $x + 12$.
Multiplying the total by 8 gives $8x + 96$. ($8x$ means $8 \times x$. We must multiply both **terms** by 8.)
Subtracting 20 gives $8x + 76$.
Dividing by 4 gives $2x + 19$. (We must divide both terms by 4.)
Continue with this until you get to a final answer. What is it?
Since the final answer does not involve x, it does not matter which number you begin with. (It does not even need to be a whole number. Try it again starting with a decimal.)

An algebraic formula

Here is a use of a formula:
We cannot see very far because the earth is round, not flat, and the curvature of the earth blocks our view. If we stand higher up we can see further.
Here is a formula showing how far we can see.

$$d = \sqrt{\frac{3h}{2}}, \text{ where } d = \text{the distance in miles, and}$$
$$h = \text{height of eye-level in feet.}$$

A tall man walking over level ground can see for a distance which used to be called a league. How far is this?

Assume the man's eye-level is 6 feet from the ground, so that $h = 6$. Find the value of $3 \times h \div 2$ and then take the square root. What is d? This is the distance in miles.

Castles were often built on high ground. There are various reasons for this. Can you think of some? Suppose the battlements on a castle are 96 feet above a level plain. How far could the occupants see on a clear day?

5 Algebra

Algebra is a branch of Mathematics which uses letters to represent numbers.
e.g. $3x + 2y$ is an algebraic expression. It means three times number x plus twice number y. This expression cannot be simplified but if we know particular values for x and y then we can find the value of the expression.
If $x = 4$ and $y = 7$, $3x + 2y = (3 \times 4) + (2 \times 7) = 12 + 14 = 26$.
If $x = 6$ and $y = \frac{1}{2}$, $3x + 2y = (3 \times 6) + (2 \times \frac{1}{2}) = 18 + 1 = 19$,
and so on.

Small letters a, b, c, ... are usually used to represent numbers although occasionally capital letters may be used instead. In any question, use the sort of letter which is given, do not change from small letters to capital letters or vice versa.
x and y are often used for numbers whose values have to be found. We also use them on graphs.

Write the letters carefully, otherwise your work will be difficult to read and understand. Make b different from number 6. Make ℓ different from number 1. Make x different from × (a multiplication sign). Make z different from a 2 or a 3.
o and O are not normally used as letters in Algebra as it is too easy to confuse them with number 0.

Making expressions and formulae

Examples

1   If apples cost a pence per lb, what is the cost, in pence, of 3 lb ?

Suppose the apples cost 15 pence per lb, then to find the cost of 3 lb you would multiply 15 by 3.
So if they cost a pence per lb, you multiply a by 3.
This is written as $3a$.
So 3 lb of apples costs $3a$ pence.

If the cost is c pence, then we can write a formula:
$$c = 3a$$

2   If I have £10 and spend £b, how much have I left ?

Suppose I spent £2, then to find how much I had left I would find $10 - 2$.
So if I spend £b then I have £$(10 - b)$ left.

If the amount left is £L, then we can write a formula:
$$L = 10 - b$$

3   What is the total cost, in pence, of c 15 pence stamps and d 20 pence stamps ?

The cost of c 15 pence stamps is $15c$ pence.
The cost of d 20 pence stamps is $20d$ pence.
The total cost is $(15c + 20d)$ pence.

If the total cost is t pence, then we can write a formula:
$$t = 15c + 20d$$

4   How many minutes are there in s seconds ?

If you wanted to find how many minutes there were in 240 seconds, you would divide 240 by 60.
So to find how many minutes there are in s seconds, you should divide s by 60.

This is written as $\dfrac{s}{60}$.

Therefore in s seconds there are $\dfrac{s}{60}$ minutes.

If there are m minutes, then we can write a formula:
$$m = \dfrac{s}{60}$$

Exercise 5.1

1.   If Emma is 8 years old and her younger sister Lisa is b years old, how much older is Emma than Lisa ?

2.   What is the total weight of 5 parcels weighing w kg each ?

3.   Crisps cost c pence per packet and lemonade costs 20 pence per bottle. What is the total cost of a packet of crisps and 2 bottles of lemonade ?

4.   A roll of ribbon d metres long is to be cut into 20 equal pieces. How long is each piece ?

5.   Alan gets £m pocket money and spends £2 of it. How much has he left?

6.   A rectangle is l cm long and b cm wide. What is the total length of the 4 edges ? (This is called the **perimeter** of the rectangle.)

b cm

l cm

7.   If a gardener has 3000 grams of fertilizer and it is to be spread over a lawn using
     f grams per square metre of lawn, how many square metres will it cover ?

8.   Find the total cost of 5 kg of potatoes at g pence per kg, and 2 kg of carrots, at
     h pence per kg.

9.   Tara has £1 to spend. She buys p pencils at q pence each. What is the total
     cost ? How much change, in pence, will she have ?

10. How many minutes are there from 6 minutes to 1 o'clock to m minutes past
     1 o'clock ?

Some Rules in Algebra

Multiplication

$1 \times a$ or $a \times 1$ is written as a
$2 \times a$ or $a \times 2$ is written as $2a$
(The number is always written in front of the letter. $a \times 2$ would not be written as $a2$.)
$0 \times a$ or $a \times 0$ equals 0   (Anything multiplied by zero equals zero.)
$a \times b$ or $b \times a$ is written as ab (or ba)
$a \times a = a^2$
$a \times a \times a = a^3$
$2 \times a \times a = 2a^2$
$2a \times 3b = 2 \times a \times 3 \times b = 6ab$

Addition and subtraction

$a + a = 2a$
$2b + 4b = 6b$
$8c - 5c = 3c$
$4d - 3d = d$
$7e - 7e = 0$
$f^2 + f^2 = 2 \times f^2 = 2f^2$
Expressions such as $a + b$, $3a + 4b$, $5a - b$ cannot be simplified.

Division

$a \div 1 = a$
$a \div a = 1$ (Anything divided by itself equals 1.)
$a \div 2$ is written as $\dfrac{a}{2}$ or $\frac{1}{2}a$

$2a \div 3$ is written as $\dfrac{2a}{3}$ or $\tfrac{2}{3}a$

$4a \div 3$ is written as $\dfrac{4a}{3}$ or $\tfrac{4}{3}a$

$2 \div a$ is written as $\dfrac{2}{a}$

$b \div a$ is written as $\dfrac{b}{a}$

$0 \div a = 0$ (Zero divided by any other number equals zero.)

In the examples above where numbers are divided by a, a cannot be 0 since we cannot divide by 0.

Removing brackets

$4(x + 3) = 4x + 12$
$2(a + 5b) = 2a + 10b$
$3(2c - d) = 6c - 3d$
$4(2e + 1) + 3(e - 2) = 8e + 4 + 3e - 6 = 11e - 2$
$5(f + 3g) + 2(2f - 5g) = 5f + 15g + 4f - 10g = 9f + 5g$

Substitution

If $a = 3$, $b = 5$ and $c = 0$, then

$3a + 2b = (3 \times 3) + (2 \times 5) = 9 + 10 = 19$
$4a - b + 2c = (4 \times 3) - 5 + (2 \times 0) = 12 - 5 + 0 = 7$
$abc = 3 \times 5 \times 0 = 0$
$2a^2 = 2 \times 3 \times 3 = 18$

Using formulae

Examples

1   A formula to find the perimeter of a rectangle is $P = 2l + 2b$. If $l = 12$ and $b = 8$, find P.

$P = (2 \times 12) + (2 \times 8) = 24 + 16 = 40$

2   A formula to find the cost of making some toys is $C = F + 5n$. Find C when $F = 60$ and $n = 100$.

$C = 60 + (5 \times 100) = 60 + 500 = 560$

Exercise 5.2

1. Simplify the following:

   1 $a \times 1$ **5** $2 \times f \times g$ **8** $k \times 0$
   2 $0 \times b$ **6** $h \times h \times h$ **9** $m \times n \times 3$
   3 $c \times d$ **7** $3 \times j \times j$ **10** $p \times 4 \times p$
   4 $e \times e$

2. Simplify

   1 $a + a$ **5** $6e - 5e$ **8** $5h + 2h - 7h$
   2 $5b - 3b$ **6** $9f + 3f$ **9** $6j - 4j + j$
   3 $4c - 4c$ **7** $9g - 3g$ **10** $7k - k - 5k$
   4 $d + 4d$

3. Simplify

   1 $a \div 1$ **5** $e \div 3$ **8** $3 \div j$
   2 $b \div b$ **6** $2f \div 5$ **9** $m \div n$
   3 $0 \div c$ **7** $5g \div 3$ **10** $0 \div 3p$
   4 $d \div 2$

4. If $a = 1$, $b = 5$ and $c = 7$, find the values of:

   1 $a + b$ **5** $2a + 3b + c$ **8** $a^2 + b^2$
   2 $c - b$ **6** ab **9** $2a + b^2$
   3 $3b$ **7** c^2 **10** $b^2 - a - c$
   4 $4c - 2b$

5. Remove the brackets

   1 $2(a + 2b)$ **4** $5(h + 8)$
   2 $4(c - d)$ **5** $2(j - 4k)$
   3 $3(e - 2f + 3g)$

   Remove the brackets and simplify

   6 $5(l + 4) + 2(l - 5)$ **9** $6(s + t) + 2(2s - t)$
   7 $4(m + 3) + 2(2m - 9)$ **10** $5(x - 2y - z) + 3(x + y + 2z)$
   8 $2(3p - q) + (p + 2q)$

6. **1**   A formula for finding the area of the walls of a room is $A = 4l + 4b$.
            Find A when $l = 5$ and $b = 4$.

    2   A formula for finding the speed of an object at different times is $v = 20 + 4t$.
            ·Find v when $t = 8$.

    3   A formula used to change hours into minutes is $m = 60h$.
            Find m when $h = 3$.

    4   A formula for the number of people who can be carried by m minibuses and
            c coaches of a certain firm is $n = 12m + 52c$, where n is the number of people.
            How many people visited an exhibition if they came in 6 full minibuses and
            10 full coaches of that firm ?

    5   A formula to find the cost of using an electric fire is given by $C = kpt$, where
            k is the power in kilowatts, of the fire,
            p is the price of electricity in pence per unit,
            t is the number of hours for which the fire is used,
            C is the cost, in pence.
            What is the cost of using a 2 kilowatt electric fire for 4 hours, if electricity costs
            7 pence per unit ?

Exercise 5.3 Applications and Activities

1. Simplify

1	$a + a$		**4**	$a \div a$
2	$a - a$		**5**	$\sqrt{a^2}$
3	$a \times a$			

2. Simplify

1	$6b + 2b$		**4**	$6b \div 2b$
2	$6b - 2b$		**5**	$0 \div 2b$
3	$6b \times 2b$			

3. Three parcels weigh $(2p - 3)$ kg, p kg and $(3p + 1)$ kg. What is the total weight ?

4. The time taken to cook a joint of meat is given as 20 minutes, plus an extra 40
    minutes for each kilogram. How many minutes would it take to cook a joint
    weighing 3 kg ?
    Find an expression for the time needed for a joint weighing m kg.

5.   A holiday is paid for by making an initial deposit of £50 and then paying £30 per month for 10 months. How much has been paid altogether after 3 months ?
     Find a formula for the amount £A paid after n months (where n is any whole number from 1 to 10).
     Put n = 10 in your formula to find the total cost of the holiday.

6.   The cost of hiring a car is £18 for each day the car is hired and 3 pence for each mile driven. How much would it cost to hire a car for 4 days and during that time drive 500 miles ?
     Find a formula for the cost £H of hiring the car for n days and driving it for $100m$ miles.

7.   A formula giving the distance travelled, d kilometres, when the speed is v km/hour and the time is t hours, is $d = vt$. What is the distance travelled when the speed is 70 km/hour and the time is 4 hours ?

8.   A formula to find out how much paint is needed to paint a certain area is given by
     $P = \dfrac{A}{18}$, where A is the area in square metres and P is the amount of paint in litres.
     How much paint is needed to give an area of 45 square metres two coats of that paint ?

9.   A formula to find the size of each angle in a regular polygon with n sides is $a = 180 - \dfrac{360}{n}$, where a is the size of each angle in degrees. Use this formula to find the size of the angles in a regular polygon with 10 sides.

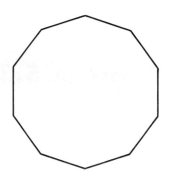

10. Here is a number pattern.

     1 × 2 × 3,   2 × 3 × 4,   3 × 4 × 5,   4 × 5 × 6,   . . .

     If it continues for n terms the expression for the last term is $n(n + 1)(n + 2)$.
     (This means the value of n multiplied by the value of $n + 1$ multiplied by the value of $n + 2$.)
     Use this expression to work out the value of the 8th term.
     A formula to work out the sum s of the numbers in the first n terms is
     $s = \frac{1}{4}n(n + 1)(n + 2)(n + 3)$.
     The sum of the first 3 terms is 6 + 24 + 60 = 90. Put n = 3 in the formula for s to check this result.
     Use the formula to find the sum of the first 8 terms.

PUZZLES

8. How many mathematical words can you find reading horizontally, vertically or diagonally, in both directions ?

S	T	A	T	I	S	T	I	C	S	Y
N	O	D	R	E	M	I	R	P	A	L
E	Q	U	I	L	A	T	E	R	A	L
T	W	O	A	S	E	R	C	A	S	A
U	E	E	N	D	T	R	T	T	M	C
C	R	N	G	I	D	A	A	D	E	I
A	A	I	L	R	R	E	N	I	T	T
R	U	L	E	R	A	Y	G	C	R	R
E	Q	U	A	L	T	M	L	E	E	E
I	S	O	S	C	E	L	E	S	P	V

9. 'All of these 9 boxes should contain the same weight of bars of gold,' said the airport cargo officer to his assistant. 'But we have been tipped off that 1 box contains some cheaper metal, and we must identify that box. It will be a bit lighter than the other ones. As the cargo must go out on the next plane, we have only time to do two weighings and we will have to use the balance scales as the other ones need repairing.'
    Can you tell the cargo officer how he can find the wrong box with the two weighings ?

10. Here is a letter from a pen-friend in Australia. Work out the sums on your calculator and, remembering that the people in Australia are upside down to us, you should be able to make these answers into words.

    $1 - 0.22 - 0.0066$
    My name is $(3 \times 4 \times 5 \times 6) - (1 \times 2 \times 3 \times 4) + 1$
    I am nearly $\sqrt{444 - 3}$
    I like to collect $555555 + 22222 - 444 + 12$
    My dog is called $(2 \times 2 \times 3 \times 3 \times 3 \times 5) - 3$
    I will put on my $234^2 - 40^2 - 111$ and take him for a walk on the $88^2 - (5 \times 6)$
    He digs $54321 - 8^3 - (3 \times 5 \times 7)$ in the $5 \times 29 \times 49$
    My sister is called $34567 - 2345 - 678 + 34 - 5$
    She is $13 \div 65$
    She works for 0.79×0.7
    She sells $27^2 - 19$
    She says I am a nuisance but $(59 \times 90) + (1469 \div 200)$

6 Thinking about the metric system

The metric system — a new beginning

In order to trade, we need a standard system of weights and measures. Most systems develop from ancient uses in a haphazard way, and values given to the various weights and measures could differ in different areas. The metric system was planned to make a new beginning, with well-defined units, the metre, the gram and the litre, and it was based on a scale of ten, as that is the basis for our numbering system. Although it was developed about 200 years ago, it was only made legal in Britain in 1864, and even then it could not be used in trade until 1897. Nearly 100 years later, we are still not fully committed to using the metric system although we are gradually using it more and more.

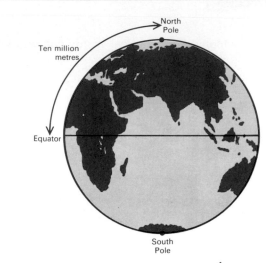

1 metre was to be measured as $\frac{1}{10\,000\,000}$ of the distance from the North Pole to the equator.

A metre is the length of the path travelled by light in vacuum during a time interval of $\frac{1}{299\,792\,458}$ of a second.

This is how a metre is defined today.

Selling in metric measures

Name some items, bought by weight, which will be weighed in kg or grams.
Name some items, bought by length, which will be measured in metres or cm.
Name some liquids which are sold in litres, centilitres or millilitres.

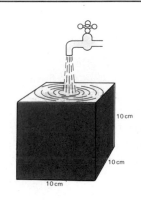

This box will hold 1 litre.
The water to fill it will weigh 1 kilogram.

Capacity in litres or ml

Weights in kg or g. Notice that the bag of potatoes holds
5 lb but the weight is also shown in kilograms.

A signpost in Canada

Metric activities

Mark out on the floor a length of
1 metre.
Find an object which weighs
1 kilogram.
Find a container which will hold
1 litre.

Using metric measures

Name some advantages which the
metric system has over the British
system of weights and measures.
Why is it used so much in
scientific work ?
Name some situations where these
people would use metric measures,
and say what units are involved:

A motorist
A person baking a cake
A surveyor
A child at school
A health visitor
A person on holiday in Europe
A builder
A greengrocer
An athlete or a swimmer
A person knitting a sweater

Think of some other people who
use metric weights and measures
in their jobs or leisure activities,
and say what units are involved.

The Metric System

Length

The main unit is called the **metre** (m)
One-thousandth part of a metre is a millimetre (mm)
One-hundredth part of a metre is a centimetre (cm)
One thousand metres is a kilometre (km)

i.e.
$$1000\,mm = 1\,m$$
$$100\,cm = 1\,m$$
$$1000\,m = 1\,km$$

(so 10 mm = 1 cm)

Weight

The main unit is the **gram** (g)
One-thousandth part of a gram is a milligram (mg)
One-hundredth part of a gram is a centigram (cg)
One thousand grams is a kilogram (kg)
Since a kilogram is rather a small weight, a larger unit is often needed.
One thousand kilograms is a tonne, sometimes called a metric ton.

i.e.
$$1000\,mg = 1\,g$$
$$100\,cg = 1\,g$$
$$1000\,g = 1\,kg$$
$$1000\,kg = 1\,tonne$$

Capacity

The main unit is the **litre** (ℓ)
One-thousandth part of a litre is called a millilitre (ml)
One-hundredth part of a litre is a called a centilitre (cl)
One thousand litres is a kilolitre (kl)

i.e.
$$1000\,ml = 1\,\ell$$
$$100\,cl = 1\,\ell$$
$$1000\,\ell = 1\,kl$$

It is useful to know that 1 millilitre of water weighs 1 gram,
1 litre of water weighs 1 kilogram.

To change from one unit to another

centimetres into millimetres

1 cm = 10 mm, so to change cm into mm multiply by 10.
5 cm = 50 mm
6.2 cm = 62 mm

mm into cm

10 mm = 1 cm, so to change mm into cm divide by 10.
30 mm = 3 cm
24 mm = 2.4 cm

metres into cm

1 m = 100 cm, so to change metres into cm multiply by 100.
3.2 m = 320 cm
5.61 m = 561 cm

cm into metres

100 cm = 1 m, so to change cm into metres divide by 100.
62 cm = 0.62 m
560 cm = 5.6 m

metres into mm

1 m = 1000 mm, so to change metres into mm multiply by 1000.
2 m = 2000 mm
1.5 m = 1500 mm
0.07 m = 70 mm

mm into metres

1000 mm = 1 m, so to change mm into metres divide by 1000.
2500 mm = 2.5 m
6 mm = 0.006 m

The methods are similar for changing units of weight and capacity.
e.g. To change grams into kg, divide by 1000.
    To change litres into ml, multiply by 1000.

Accuracy of measurements

If you had to measure the width of a field then your first problem would be to decide where the exact boundaries were. It would probably be sufficient for your purpose to measure it in metres, and if this was not accurate enough you could measure it to the nearest 0.1 m. It is easier to measure the floor of a room, because it is clearer to see where to begin and end the measurement. You could measure this to the nearest 0.1 m (10 cm). If you needed a more accurate measurement, for example, to buy a fitted carpet, you could measure it to the nearest cm. When measuring lines in geometry, we usually measure to the nearest mm.

Therefore, the accuracy that you must choose depends on what you are measuring, for what purpose you need the measurement, and how accurate your measuring instruments are.

Similar ideas apply to weighing. With many heavy objects it might be sufficient to weigh in kg, but lighter objects need to be measured correct to 100 g, 25 g or 10 g. You would need to measure more accurately for scientific experiments.

Shopkeepers and others who sell goods by weight, length or capacity have to have accurate weighing and measuring instruments. However, many goods are supplied pre-packed nowadays, so that the quantity is stated on the package and the shopkeeper does not need to weigh or measure anything.

Drawing and measuring lines

This is the line *AB*

A ——————————————————————————————————— B

A and *B* are the points at the ends of the line.

If a line *AB* has to be drawn to an accurate length it is useful to draw the line slightly longer than needed and then mark *A* and *B* by small marks crossing the line.

Examples

1   Draw a line *AB*, 6.2 cm long.
    This is 6 cm 2 mm.
    Draw a line longer than needed, and put a cross-mark for *A* near one end.
    First count along 6 cm and then another 2 mm, and mark *B* there.
    The part of the line between the cross-marks for *A* and *B* should be exactly 6.2 cm long.

2

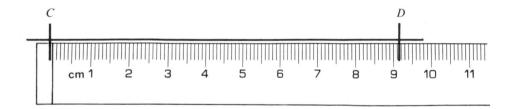

To measure the line *CD*, first decide how many whole cm it is (9) and then count how many mm to the nearest mm mark (2).
So the measurement is 9 cm 2 mm.
This would be written as 9.2 cm or 92 mm.

Readings on a weighing-scale

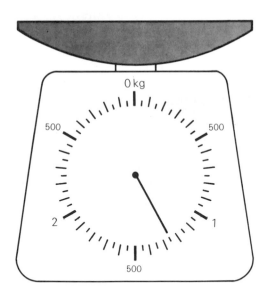

This is a weighing-scale which weighs in kg from 0 to 3 kg. The half-kilogram marks are marked 500 for 500 g. Between 0 and 500 there are 4 larger marks. These represent 100, 200, 300 and 400 g. The smaller marks between each of these represent 50 g.

The measurement shown is between 1 kg and 2 kg. Counting the longer marks it is between 200 g and 300 g. It is halfway between them, making it 250 g. So the weight is 1 kg 250 g.
This would be written in grams as 1250 g, or in kilograms as 1.25 kg.

Exercise 6.1

1. How many
    1 mm in 8 cm   **5** mg in 3 g   **8** ml in $1\frac{1}{2}$ litres
    2 g in 4 kg   **6** mm in 5 m   **9** cm in 60 mm
    3 cm in $\frac{1}{2}$ m   **7** kg in 10 tonnes   **10** kg in 2000 g ?
    4 m in 2 km

2. Write
    1 2560 g in kg   **5** 2.3 m in cm   **8** 800 cl in ℓ
    2 25 cm in m   **6** 3.5 kg in g   **9** 356 cm in m
    3 4 ℓ in ml   **7** 36 mm in cm   **10** 0.75 kg in g
    4 8 cm in mm

3. Give the readings shown on these instruments.
    1 Weight in kg.

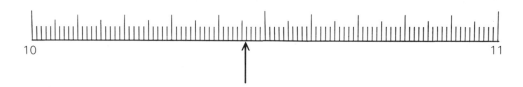

    2 Weighing scale in kg and g   **3** Measuring jug

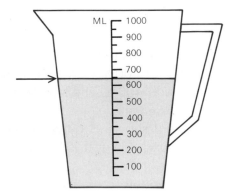

4.   Measure the lines *AB*, *CD*, *EF*, *GH* in cm, to the nearest mm.

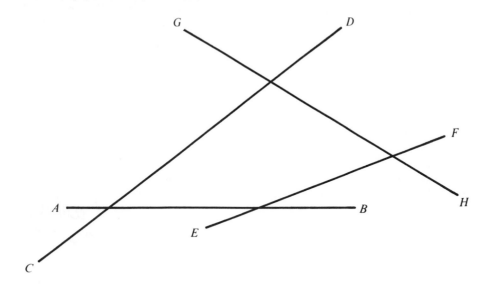

5.   Using the ruler shown in the diagram,
   1   what is the reading shown at *A*,
   2   what is the reading shown at *B*,
   3   what is the length of the elephant, in cm ?

Exercise 6.2   Applications and Activities

1.   If 1 washer weighs 7 g, what do 1000 washers weigh, in kg ?

2.   An urn contains 8 ℓ of tea. A cup holds 160 ml of tea. How many cups can be filled from the urn ?

3.   A roll of cloth contains 75 m. A pattern for a dress uses 4.5 m. How many of these dresses can be made from 3 rolls of cloth ?

4.   Helen has 4 packets of seeds.
      She wants to plant the seeds in rows 5 m
      long. How many rows can she plant ?

5.   A charity collected 60.5 kg of knitting wool. They plan to use this to knit baby garments, which each take 110 g of wool. How many garments will it make ?

6.   A chemist has 5 cartons of bottles of cough medicine. How many litres of medicine are there altogether ?

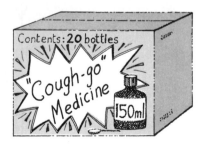

7.

The diagram shows a piece of wood with 5 screw holes marked. The distance between each pair of holes is 11.5 cm and the distance between the end holes and the edge of the wood is 4.2 cm. (The measurements are taken to the centres of the holes.) How long is the piece of wood ?

8. A fence is made by placing 12 posts, 2.6 m between each pair, and joining them with 3 strands of wire. How long is the fence, and how much wire is needed ?

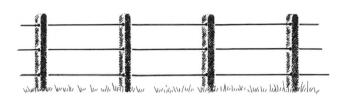

9. A cupboard is placed along a wall of a room, as shown. The wall is 3.7 m long. How wide is the cupboard ?

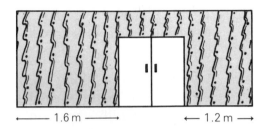

←—— 1.6 m ——→   ←— 1.2 m —→

10. A grocer buys tea in bulk, blends it, and then sells it in 120 g packets. How many packets can he make from 54 kg of tea ?

11. A bag of damp sand weighed 5.5 kg. After it dried out it weighed 4.7 kg. What was the loss of weight, in grams ?

12. A box of sweets weighed 550 g. The box weighed 70 g and there were 80 sweets inside. What was the average weight of 1 sweet ?

13. A tin of powdered food contains a plastic measuring scoop, which holds 9 ml of the powder. The tin contains 0.45 litres of powder. How many scoopfuls can be taken out ?

14. A surveyor used a chain 20 m long to measure out the line for a fence of length 300 m. The chain was actually 20.1 m long. How long was the fence likely to be ?

15. Krishna measured the length of a room as 4.77 m. What was this length, correct to the nearest 10 cm ?

16. A recipe for a cake uses these ingredients:

> 100 g butter
> 100 g caster sugar
> 3 eggs
> 125 g flour
> 50 g chopped nuts

Taking 1 egg to weigh 55 g, find the total weight of the ingredients.

17.   A piece of ribbon is 5 m long. 5 pieces of length 85 cm are cut from it. How long is the piece that is left, in cm ?

18.   Party glasses hold 160 ml. How many glasses can be filled from a 3 litre bottle of lemonade ?
      A 2 litre bottle of orange squash is diluted with four times as much water. How many glasses can be filled from this diluted squash ?

19.   **Estimation**

      It is useful to be able to make good estimates of weights and measurements. Here are some suggestions to improve your skill. You should think of others.

      Length. Find out the measurements of your thumb as far as the knuckle, the width of your hand across four fingers, the length of your hand-span, the length of your foot with a shoe on, your height, the distance you can reach with arms stretched out, the height you can reach on tiptoe, and so on. Use a measured distance of 100 m to find the length of your pace when you walk normally, and how long your stride is. Practise estimating distances by comparing them with these lengths.
      You could make your own measuring instruments by getting a length of rope and marking it off every metre. Then get a length of wood 1 metre long and mark it off every 10 cm or 5 cm. Use your ruler as well, and you should be able to measure lengths quite accurately.

      Weight. Get used to the weight of 1 kg (a bag of sugar) and 2.5 kg (a bag of potatoes). For smaller weights, a 20 p coin weighs 5 g, so 20 of them weigh 100 g. Find your own weight in kg and the weight of a small child. Estimate other weights by comparing them with these known weights.

      Capacity. Estimate how much water various containers hold and check by using a measuring jug or a litre bottle. A bucket or a watering can may have measuring lines marked on it. It is useful to remember that 1 litre of water weighs 1 kg.

      Estimate the following and then check as many as possible by making accurate measurements or weighings.

      1   The width of the doorway.
      2   The weight of your calculator.
      3   The height of the step on the nearest staircase.
      4   The amount of water to fill a washbasin.
      5   The length of a piece of string which will just go round your waist.
      6   The weight of a chair.
      7   The weight of a pencil.
      8   The amount of liquid to fill a small glass.
      9   The height of the ceiling.
      10 The width of your house frontage.

20. **Capacity**

Look in your home for containers which have the capacity marked on them.
Then make a list, from the smallest to the largest.

e.g.   Bottle of Tipp-Ex   20 ml
       Antiseptic liquid   200 ml
       Washing-up liquid   500 ml
       Tin of motor oil   5 ℓ
       Watering can   8 ℓ

21. **The Metric System**

Find out as much as you can about this and design a poster about it.
Here are some of the things you can consider:
When was it introduced ? In which country ?
What was the original definition of a metre ? What is the present definition of a metre ?
Although we usually use the prefixes milli-, centi-, kilo-, there are others,
e.g. deci-. Find out about these. Why were these words chosen for the prefixes ?

PUZZLE

11. Mr and Mrs McLean have three household jobs to do before they can set off on holiday.
(1) Their house must be vacuumed. They have one vacuum cleaner, and the task will take 30 minutes.
(2) The lawn must be mowed. They have only one mower, and this task also takes 30 minutes.
(3) Their baby must be bathed, dressed, fed and settled in his carry-cot for the journey. This, too, will take 30 minutes.
How long will it take them to do all these jobs ?

7 Thinking about statistics

Statistics through the ages

We know that in the Old Roman Empire, 2000 years ago, a count was made of the population. We read in the Bible that Mary and Joseph had to go to Bethlehem to be counted. In England, 900 years ago, the king, William the Conqueror, sent out commissioners to survey his new kingdom, and they collected information about the people and their land holdings. This record survives today in the Domesday Book. So statistics, the collecting and analysing of data, is not a new subject. What use can a Government make of the figures when it has counted the population? Today, this is called taking a census. In Britain it has been taken every 10 years from 1801. When do you think the next one will be? (There was no census taken in 1941. Why do you think this one was left out?) As well as counting the population, what other information about the population will the government find useful, and for what purposes?

With the use of computers, it is much easier and quicker to process the data than it used to be, so that much more use is being made of statistical data now than even a few years ago.

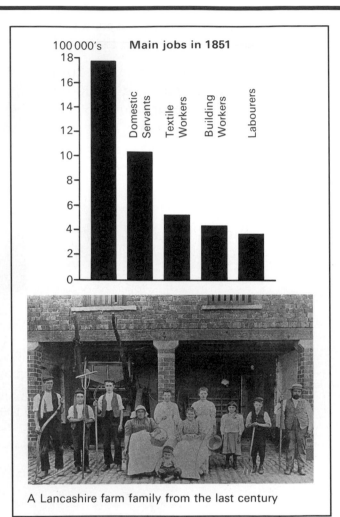

A Lancashire farm family from the last century

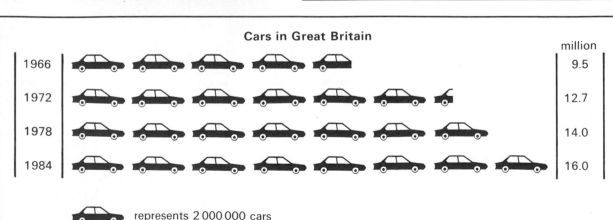

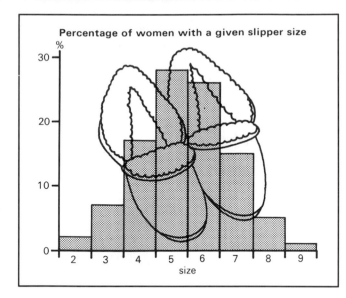

Percentage of women with a given slipper size

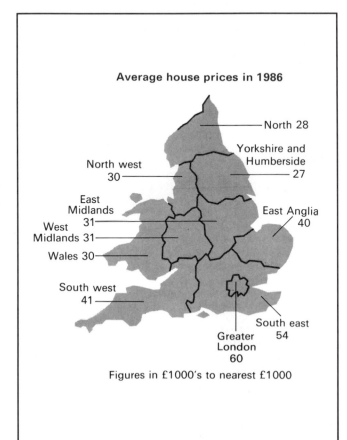

Average house prices in 1986

North 28
Yorkshire and Humberside 27
North west 30
East Midlands 31
West Midlands 31
East Anglia 40
Wales 30
South west 41
Greater London 60
South east 54

Figures in £1000's to nearest £1000

Using statistics

Name some sorts of numerical data which these people might find useful:

A shoe manufacturer
An athletics coach
A farmer
A football manager
Someone new to the district, who wanted to choose which school to send their children to
A scientist doing medical research
An insurance company, for car insurance
A person wishing to buy a new washing machine

Think of some other people who make use of statistics, and say what sort of data they use.

Statistical diagrams

One thing we can do with the data is to represent it by a diagram. It is often easier to get a general idea from a diagram than by reading a list of figures, and a diagram is more interesting than a list of figures. Get some newspapers and magazines and cut out all the items which involve statistics. This will give you some idea of the range of topics using statistics nowadays. There should be some diagrams included. Arrange your cut-outs to make a poster about statistics.

7 Statistics

We often need to collect and use numerical facts.

Your teacher needs to know the number of children in your class, how many boys and how many girls, and the range of ages. He/she needs this information to plan ahead. Are there enough desks or tables ? How can the class best be split into suitable groups for group work ? Is the work which has been planned suitable for the age-range ?

At home, you know how many children there are in your family and their ages, and how much pocket-money you get.

Your parents need to know the family earnings, and the plan for using this money, so much for rent or mortgage payments, fuel bills, food, clothing, etc.

The branch of Mathematics concerned with collecting numerical data and then using it, often to make decisions for future action, is called **Statistics**.

The word **statistics** is also used for the actual numbers collected, i.e. the data.

Statistics is a subject which has a wide variety of uses. The Government collects many kinds of statistics which are published in journals. Scientists use statistics in their research. Industry uses statistics to plan future action. Insurance companies use statistics to fix the premiums they must charge. Sports' associations keep statistical records.

After data is collected, it is often displayed in the form of a list, a table or a graph. Then it can be studied, in order to make conclusions from it.

Tally tables

Example 1

Workers in an office were asked which method of transport they used to get to work that morning. Their replies were as follows:

Walk, bus, car, walk, walk, walk, car, walk, bus, bus, walk, car, car, motorbike, car, car, bus, car, car, walk, car, walk, car, car, walk, car, motorbike, walk, walk, car, motorbike, car, bus, motorbike, walk, car, bus, car.

The items are entered in a tally chart as they occur.

		Total
Car	ЖНŤ ЖНŤ ЖНŤ I	16
Motorbike	IIII	4
Bus	ЖНŤ I	6
Walk	ЖНŤ ЖНŤ II	12
		38

Notice that the numbers are grouped in fives, the fifth number going through the first four. ЖНŤ
The groups of 5 are kept in neat columns. This makes the totals easy to count.

Presenting the data in a table

Example 2

Method of transport to and from school

	Morning			Afternoon		
	Boys	Girls	Total	Boys	Girls	Total
Walk Cycle Motorbike Car Bus						
Total						

Copy this table and fill in the figures to satisfy this information.
Of the 50 boys, 10 walk to school, 5 cycle, 3 come on their motorbikes and 8 come by car. The rest come by bus. All go home by the same method except that 2 who walk to school go home by car and 3 who come by car go home by bus.

Of the girls, 12 walk to school, 8 cycle, 1 comes on her motorbike, 3 come by car and 16 come by bus. 4 of the girls who come by bus walk home and 2 others go home by car instead of by bus.
Fill in the remaining spaces in the table.

How many pupils come to school by bus ?
How many pupils go home by bus ?

Statistical diagrams

You will already have drawn simple diagrams. These diagrams of the data of example 1 will remind you about pictograms and bar charts.

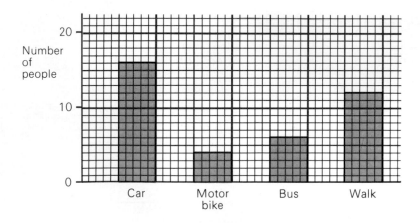

Pictogram showing how office workers get to work

Car	16	𝄞𝄞𝄞𝄞𝄞 𝄞𝄞𝄞𝄞𝄞 𝄞𝄞𝄞𝄞𝄞 𝄞
Motorbike	4	𝄞𝄞𝄞𝄞
Bus	6	𝄞𝄞𝄞𝄞𝄞 𝄞
Walk	12	𝄞𝄞𝄞𝄞𝄞 𝄞𝄞𝄞𝄞𝄞 𝄞𝄞

Bar chart showing how office workers get to work

Frequency Distributions

Example 3

This list gives information about the size of households, in a sample of 50 households.

1	2	2	4	1	4	3	4	2	4
5	1	3	5	2	5	2	2	2	2
1	1	1	2	3	2	3	4	2	6
2	2	2	3	3	3	2	4	1	3
6	3	4	2	2	2	3	1	5	2

Copy and complete this tally table showing this information.

f is short for **frequency**, the number of times each item occurs. This list showing the frequency of each item is called a **frequency distribution**.

Size of household	Tally	f
1		
2		
3		
4		
5		
6		
		50

The graph we use to illustrate a frequency distribution is called a **histogram**. It is very similar to a bar chart, with the bars in order and no spaces between them.

Histogram to show the distribution of size of family, in 50 families

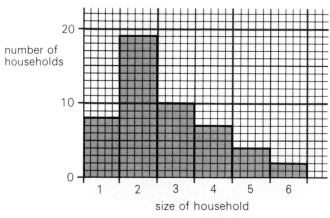

Alternatively, a **bar-line graph** can be drawn

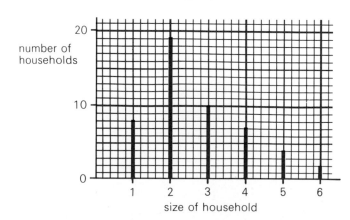

This is more appropriate because it shows clearly that there is no value for in-between numbers such as $1\frac{1}{2}$.

Collecting information for an investigation

If you are going to collect information:

1   Decide what you are trying to find, and the questions you must ask or the observations you must make, to get this information.
2   Decide how you are going to record the information as you get it. This may be on a tally chart, you may just write it down in order, or you can decide on a different method.
3   When you have collected all the data you need, you can make a summary of it. This may be in a simple list or in a more complicated table.
4   Illustrate your results with diagrams, which may be pictograms, bar charts, bar-line graphs or histograms. You could also use pie charts which are explained in Chapter 10. Give each diagram a heading to explain what it is about.
5   Study your results and the diagrams and see if you can make any comments about them. Are they as you would have expected, or are there any unusual features ?

Note

If you are getting information by asking people, decide who you are going to ask. This could be the pupils in your class and possibly other pupils or teachers in your school. At home you could ask parents and friends. You should not approach strangers unless your teacher is supervising you. You should decide what questions you are going to ask. Some people may not wish to give you answers which they regard as personal or private information. For example, if you asked people how much money they earned they might not want you to know. So choose your investigation carefully and plan to ask questions which people will be willing to answer. Then check with your teacher before you go ahead.

If you are doing an observation out-of-doors yourself, for example doing a traffic survey on a busy road, then do be careful to keep well away from the road. Accidents can happen ! It is also sensible to be with friends, not alone. In school hours, your teacher should be in charge of you. Out of school hours you should have your parents' permission.

Exercise 7.1

1. This list shows the number of cats in five European countries.

Italy	69
France	65
U.K.	65
West Germany	39
Netherlands	21

    Figures are in 100 000's.

    Show this information in a pictogram or bar chart.

2. The top 5 paying tourist attractions in 1988 were:

1.	Madame Tussaud's	27
2.	Alton Towers	25
3.	Tower of London	22
4.	Blackpool Tower	15
5.	Natural History Museum	14

    The numbers are admissions in 100 000's, to the nearest 100 000.

    Show this information on a bar chart.

3. The land surface of the Earth is divided as follows:

Europe	11
Asia	44
Africa	30
North and Central America	24
South America	18
Oceania	9
Antarctica	14

    The numbers are in 1 000 000's of km^2, to the nearest 1 000 000.

    Show this information on a bar chart.

4.   The colours of 100 cars passing along a road were noted. Make a tally table of this information and then show it on a bar chart.

Red, red, beige, pale blue, grey, beige, brown, grey, grey, beige, pale blue, grey, white, dark blue, white, beige, green, red, dark blue, white, white, black, pale blue, red, brown, black, pale blue, grey, red, white, white, black, red, grey, red, white, green, white, red, green, white, white, pale blue, grey, red, pale blue, red, grey, red, dark blue, beige, pale blue, red, black, white, yellow, red, beige, red, black, red, grey, pale blue, black, grey, grey, beige, white, green, pale blue, dark blue, dark blue, white, red, red, beige, pale blue, dark blue, pale blue, white, red, red, yellow, black, white, brown, red, white, red, beige, white, brown, white, red, pale blue, pale blue, brown, green, dark blue, grey.

5.   Some families were asked to say what was the main method of transport to their holiday destination this summer. Their replies were:

Canal barge, plane, coach, train, car, plane, car and ferry, plane, plane, plane, car and ferry, car, car, car, plane, car, car, cruise ship, car, coach, car, car, plane, car, car, car, car and ferry, car and ferry, plane, plane, car, car and ferry, car, train, car, car, car.

Show this information in a list and on a suitable diagram.
Can you use this information to estimate how many of these families went abroad for their holiday ?

6.   35 girls were asked which sort of crisps they preferred. Here are their replies:

plain, prawn, onion, vinegar, cheese, onion, tomato sauce, plain, prawn, prawn, plain, cheese, prawn, prawn, prawn, bacon, prawn, prawn, beef, onion, beef, prawn, cheese, tomato sauce, prawn, vinegar, onion, plain, onion, chicken, cheese, prawn, vinegar, vinegar, vinegar.

List this information and illustrate it by a suitable diagram.

At a summer fair, crisps will be sold. The organisers have decided that they will order 12 boxes, but they don't know which sorts to get. Using the result of this survey, and your own preference, which sorts would you order, and how many boxes of each ?

7.   The number of people in each car was noted for 100 cars returning from a seaside town on a Saturday evening. The results were:

1	3	2	4	3	4	2	1	1	3
1	2	4	2	1	1	4	3	2	1
1	3	2	1	2	4	3	2	3	2
1	1	3	5	2	1	3	3	2	1
1	1	3	1	1	3	2	4	3	3
1	2	4	2	2	1	5	3	1	1
2	2	1	4	3	1	1	2	4	1
2	4	3	2	2	1	5	3	2	4
2	5	2	4	1	3	2	2	3	3
1	3	5	1	1	1	2	2	3	1

Make a tally table of this information and then represent the frequencies in a bar-line graph or histogram.

8.   In an experiment with dice, 3 dice were thrown 200 times and the sum of the 3 numbers noted. These sums were:

14	10	17	8	13	10	8	12	9	15
10	13	14	8	13	9	10	14	7	9
13	12	11	13	8	9	7	14	15	8
4	9	8	7	5	13	9	10	12	7
8	3	9	11	8	9	12	8	6	11
12	17	15	4	11	9	12	7	9	14
10	7	11	8	13	11	14	11	9	15
11	8	14	12	9	9	16	11	9	8
8	13	16	12	12	7	6	8	11	8
11	10	11	12	12	13	13	13	18	10
9	14	15	8	8	12	3	12	8	9
13	9	12	11	15	7	15	5	13	6
13	14	12	16	8	15	12	9	12	10
7	13	14	18	4	12	7	18	11	15
12	13	10	7	9	11	10	13	8	11
4	11	12	7	5	13	11	16	7	12
11	10	14	15	11	9	8	10	14	14
10	14	6	12	11	16	9	13	18	10
8	5	14	11	11	12	17	12	13	5
9	10	13	14	13	10	12	12	7	9

Show these sums in a list and draw a bar-line graph or a histogram of the data. Which sum has occurred most ? Which has occurred least ?
Describe the shape of the graph. Are these results what you would have expected, or are they surprising ?

9.   The table gives the frequency distribution of the marks of 60 pupils in an examination.

Mark	Number of pupils
40–49	3
50–59	8
60–69	16
70–79	21
80–89	7
90–99	5

Draw a histogram to represent this information. (Label the blocks on the horizontal axis 40–49, 50–59, etc.)

10.   In the seven cricket matches played on a Sunday, in the Refuge Assurance League, these were the runs scored by the first five batsmen in each of the teams.

33	8	56	39	3	66	26	5	10	3
8	33	31	1	0	1	31	3	24	22
4	31	38	63	67	46	8	19	46	1
35	0	17	27	39	13	66	7	10	46
7	30	0	5	102	22	24	38	10	1
26	8	24	67	5	17	97	26	20	—
17	21	2	83	56	32	23	19	4	56

(The missing score is because in one team only 4 players batted.)

Group these runs into classes 0–14, 15–29, 30–44, etc. and show the distribution in a table and on a histogram. Comment on the scores.

Exercise 7.2   Applications and Activities

1.   The scores in 44 matches in Barclays League on a particular Saturday were as follows:

Div I.   0–0 1–1 4–0 0–1 2–0 3–0 0–0 1–1 1–0 0–0
Div II.   1–0 5–4 1–1 2–2 2–2 1–1 0–0 2–1 2–0 3–2 1–1
Div III. 0–0 1–1 1–0 0–1 0–1 2–3 4–2 1–1 3–0 2–3 0–3
Div IV.   0–1 0–0 0–1 4–3 2–2 0–0 0–3 4–1 0–1 0–3 3–3 1–0

Copy and fill in this table showing the **number of teams** in each category.

Number of teams		Goals by home team						
		0	1	2	3	4	5	Total
Goals by away team	0							
	1							
	2							
	3							
	4							
	Total							

Draw two bar-line graphs or histograms, one showing the distribution of goals by the home teams and the other showing the distribution of goals by the away teams. Comment on these graphs.

2. Using the table of question 1, make a frequency distribution table of the total scores in each match. Represent these frequencies in a bar-line graph or histogram. Comment on the graph.

3. A group of girls in a Youth club gave information about the number of children in their families. The numbers include themselves.
(The number of girls is given first, so 3,2 means 3 girls, 2 boys.)
Here is the list:

2,1	2,0	1,1	1,2	1,1	2,0	2,1	2,0	2,1	2,1
2,1	2,1	1,1	4,2	2,1	2,1	2,2	3,2	2,0	1,0
2,0	2,1	2,1	1,1	1,1	1,1	1,0	1,1	3,0	3,1
2,0	5,1	1,1	1,1	2,0	3,1	1,1			

Why must the first number be at least 1 ?
Design a table to show this information. Also make a list showing the distribution of the total number of children in each family.
Illustrate your results by suitable diagrams.

4. Run a competition using 10 table-tennis balls which have to be thrown into a bucket. Record the scores of competitors, (how many out of 10 which land in the bucket,) in a tally table. Repeat with the same competitors, but this time they should use the hand they don't normally use, to throw.
Draw bar-line graphs or histograms of the two sets of results and comment on them.
Perhaps you can plan further competitions of a similar kind.

5.   Here is an experiment for you to do.
      Put 10 discs in a bag, with two of them coloured differently to the others. (We
      will call these the red ones.) Take the discs out one at a time, until you get a red
      one. If it is the first disc out, record that result as 1, if it is the second disc out,
      record the result as 2, and so on.
      Replace the discs in the bag, mix them up, and repeat this process about
      100 times.
      Before you begin it is interesting to guess which result will occur most.
      Put your results in a tally table, and then draw a histogram or bar-line graph.
      Comment on the results.
      Was your guess a good one ?

6.   Do an experiment of tossing sticks over a set of parallel lines.
      Use the floorboards of the room if they form parallel lines, otherwise draw
      equally-spaced parallel lines on the floor. Find 10 thin sticks of equal length, with
      length about $\frac{3}{4}$ of the distance between the lines.
      Toss the sticks one at a time, but without taking particular aim. They may either
      land across (or touching) a line, or land completely between two lines. Record
      how many of the 10 land completely between lines.
      Repeat the experiment about 50 times. Make a frequency distribution table of the
      results, and draw a bar-line graph or histogram. Comment on the shape of the graph.

7.   Get about 120 dried peas, or something similar, and put them in a jar. Ask other
      people to estimate how many peas there are. (It is best if they do not hear other
      people's answers first.) Write the results down. Get about 50 results.
      You should then put the numbers in groups (called classes). For example, 60–69,
      70–79, 80–89, etc. However, you may have to choose different classes if these do
      not fit the answers you have. You need about 7 classes with an equal range of
      numbers in each.
      Make a frequency distribution table using these classes and illustrate it with a
      histogram. Comment on the guesses and the shape of the histogram.

8.   Adults sometimes grumble about the amount of coinage they carry around.
      Mother's purse can get too full of small change, and coins can make a hole, by
      wear and tear, in father's pocket.
      Carry out an experiment to see how much change people have, at the time
      when you ask them. Record the results. There are two things you can count, the
      number of coins in purse or pocket, or the amount, in pence, of these coins.
      Decide beforehand whether you are going to include £1 coins in your survey.
      Since you will have to use adults for this survey, it is best to combine with others
      in the class so that you can all ask your parents and a few other adults whom you
      know.
      You might do a separate survey of the pupils in your class.
      Investigate the results and comment on them.

9.   There are many investigations you can do, collecting data from your own class. Here are a few suggestions, but you should think of others.

1   Methods of travelling to school.
2   Arrangements at lunch time:- school dinner, bring own lunch, go home, etc.
3   Shoe sizes of boys, and of girls.
4   Choice of favourite sports, if playing and if watching.
5   Number of pets at home, and what they are.

PUZZLES

12.   Jodie had £20 to spend on her 4 days' holiday. She kept a total like this:

1st day spent	£8.00	which left her with	£12.00
2nd day spent	£6.50	which left her with	£5.50
3rd day spent	£3.00	which left her with	£2.50
4th day spent	£2.50	which left her with	£0
	£20.00		£20.00

Kevin kept his accounts also:

1st day spent	£8	which left him with	£12
2nd day spent	£6	which left him with	£6
3rd day spent	£3	which left him with	£3
4th day spent	£3	which left him with	£0
	£20		£21

He couldn't understand why he had an extra £1 in the 2nd column. Can you explain ?

13.   There were 200 runners in a road race. A trainer was asked who would come 1st, 2nd and 3rd, and he replied:

'If x is the number worn by the winner,
x does not divide by 2, 3, 4, 5, 6 or 8,
x is not a prime number,
x is 2 less than a square number.

If y is the number worn by the second runner,
the sum of y's digits is 9,
when y is divided by 11 there is a remainder of 1,
y is the product of 2 square numbers.

If z is the number worn by the runner coming third,
z is a cube number,
z is the sum of 2 square numbers, and also the sum of 2 other square numbers.'

The trainer's predictions turned out to be correct. What numbers were worn by the first three in the race ?

8 Thinking about money and time

From barter to money

We use money throughout our lives. Perhaps if we lived on a desert island we might manage to use bartering methods instead. Even there a time might come when, if we were bartering with coconuts, our neighbours might have enough coconuts for the near future, and might prefer some token instead, to be used later to buy some fish from us. Our other neighbours might need some of our coconuts but could not give us vegetables in exchange until they were ready for harvesting, so again they would give us some token for us to 'spend' later, and so we would start a money system with these tokens.

Earning and spending money

Name some of the things you have bought in the last week. Where does the money you spend come from ? Do you earn it, possibly by doing small jobs around the house, or are you just given it as a gift ?
Name some of the expenses your family have had in the last week.
Do you think it is a good idea to save some money 'for a rainy day' ?
Do you think you ought to give a proportion of your money to deserving charities ?
Suppose that you need to raise some money for a school fund. Can you think of some ideas for raising this money ? For each idea, where does the money come from, the pupils, the parents or members of the public ?
The Government needs money to run the country, to pay for education, defence, transport, health services, etc. Where does this money come from ?
The local council needs money to run its local services, such as education (the expenses not paid by the Government), police, fire and ambulance services, street lighting, etc. Where does this money come from ?

Children's expenses

Family expenses

A traditional clock, in a Swiss village

A modern digital clock

Government and Local Authority expenses

Time

Were you 'on time' for school today ? In a modern country our lives are regulated by time.
Make a timetable for tomorrow, starting with the time you will get up, and the times of the various activites into which the day is divided. Approximately what fractions of the day will you spend on sleeping, eating, working (at school or elsewhere), leisure activites, and any other activities ? Approximately how many hours in a week do you spend watching television ? How many hours in a year is this ? Do you think this is making good use of your time ?

Time at work

Most people who go out to work have to put in a certain number of hours at the job. Why is this ?
In some jobs, time is very important. How do these people use time in their jobs or activities, apart from putting in the hours at work ?

A bus driver
A TV producer
A teacher
A mother with a young child
A boxer
An athlete
A farmer
A deep-sea diver

Name some other people whose jobs or activities involve the use of time to a large extent.

8 Money and Time

Money

Since there are 100 pence in £1, our money calculations use the decimal system.
£3 and 67 pence is £3.67
£4 and 8 pence is £4.08
£4 and 80 pence is £4.80. On a calculator this may be recorded as 4.8
This means £4.80, not £4.08.

Examples, working in £'s.

Addition   £2.36 + £4.54   £
2.36
4.54
6.90   Answer £6.90

(On a calculator this will be recorded as 6.9)

Subtraction   £10 − £3.96   £
10.00
3.96
6.04   Answer £6.04

(On a calculator there is no need to enter 10.00 for £10.00. 10 will do.)

Multiplication   £6.25 × 8   £
6.25
8
50.00

Answer £50 or £50.00, whichever is more appropriate.
(A calculator will just show 50)

Division   £45 ÷ 6   £
6)45.0
7.5   Answer £7.50

(A calculator will just show 7.5)

Division How many books at £6.40 can be bought for £60 ?

This is £60 ÷ £6.40
On your calculator do 60 ÷ 6.4

The answer is 9.375, showing that 9 books can be bought and there is some money left over.

To find how much is left, multiply £6.40 by 9 and subtract the total from £60.

60 − (9 × 6.4) = 2.4, so there is £2.40 left.

Examples, working in pence.

1   63p + 97p

$$\begin{array}{r} \text{p} \\ 63 \\ 97 \\ \hline 160 \end{array}$$ Answer £1.60

2   £1 − 54p

$$\begin{array}{r} \text{p} \\ 100 \\ 54 \\ \hline 46 \end{array}$$ (£1 is 100p)

Answer 46p

3   37p × 3

$$\begin{array}{r} \text{p} \\ 37 \\ 3 \\ \hline 111 \end{array}$$ Answer £1.11

4   75p × 8

$$\begin{array}{r} \text{p} \\ 75 \\ 8 \\ \hline 600 \end{array}$$ Answer £6 or £6.00

5   £2 ÷ 5

$$\begin{array}{r} \text{p} \\ 5\overline{)200} \\ \hline 40 \end{array}$$ Answer 40p

Amounts to the nearest penny

If you are working in pence,

29.3 pence = 29p, to the nearest penny.

12.62 pence = 13p, to the nearest penny.

(If the figure in the 1st decimal place is 5 or more, round up to the next penny.)

If you are working in £'s,

£3.776 = £3.78, to the nearest penny.

£2.494 = £2.49, to the nearest penny.

(The figures in the first two decimal places give the pence, if the figure in the 3rd decimal place is 5 or more, round the pence up to the next penny.)

Multiplying pence by 100

Since $100 \times 1p = £1$, multiplying by 100 changes pence into £'s.
If a packet of sweets cost 12p, then 100 packets cost £12.
If the coach fare per child is 75p, then for 100 children it is £75.
If 1 pencil costs 6p, then 100 cost £6, so 200 cost £12.

Articles costing 99p, £1.99, £2.99, etc

To find the cost of 7 articles at 99p each, this is 7 at £1 less $7 \times 1p = £7 - 7p = £6.93$.
To find the cost of 4 articles at £5.99 each, this is 4 at £6 less $4 \times 1p = £24 - 4p = £23.96$.

Approximations and estimations

When you go shopping, it is useful to make an approximate calculation of any bill so that you can see if you have enough money, and you can check that you do not get the wrong change.
For example, in a shop suppose you select 3 articles at £1.99 each, 2 at £2.95 each and 1 at £4.90. Before you go to the cash desk you could do an approximate calculation to see if you had enough money to pay for them. It is nearly 3 at £2, 2 at £3 and 1 at £5 so you would need nearly £17. You also expect to get just over £3 in change if you pay with a £20 note.
(When the exact amount is shown on the till you can check your exact change.)

Subtraction, by the method of adding on.

This is useful when subtracting from an exact amount such as £1, £5, £10.
e.g. £5 − £1.83
£1.83 and 7p makes £1.90, and 10p makes £2, and £3 makes £5.
The answer is 7p + 10p + £3 = £3.17
This is the way a shopkeeper would count out the change as you are given it.

Exercise 8.1

1. **1** If 1 article costs 3p, what do 100 cost ?
    2 If 1 article costs 14p, what do 300 cost?

2. **1** Find the cost of 8 articles at 99p each.
    2 Find the cost of 7 articles at £2.99 each.

3. Find the change from £1 if I spend:
    42p,   17p,   53p,   66p,   81p.

4.   Find the change from £5 if I spend:
     48p,   £3.61,   £4.11,   £2.30,   £1.73.

5.   If you have to pay 67p, what is the least number of coins you can use, and what
     are they ?
     If instead you pay with a £1 coin, what is the least number of coins you can
     receive in change, and what are they ?

6.   James has several 2p and 5p coins but no more change. On the bus he must
     pay the exact fare. What coins must he use for a journey costing
     1   16p   **2**   19p ?

7.   Mrs Fraser spent £7.84 on meat and £2.36 on vegetables. How much was this
     altogether ? What change did she get from a £20 note ?

8.   Find the total cost of 3 bottles of milk at 31p per bottle, 2 packets of tea at 58p
     per packet, and $\frac{1}{2}$ dozen eggs at £1.18 per dozen.

9.   From a mail-order catalogue Caroline orders 3 items at £2.99 each and 2 items
     at £9.99 each. What is the total cost ?

10. Mrs Harris buys 8 m of curtain material at £5.45 per metre. What is the total cost ?

11. Petrol costs 191.9p per gallon. What is the cost of 4 gallons, to the nearest
     penny ?

12. Two books together cost £5.70, one being £1.80 more than the other. What did
     each one cost ?

13. What is the total cost of 12 notebooks at 16p each and 12 pens at 14p each ?

14. Mrs Desai makes 200 soft toys. The material for each toy costs 66p. Other
     expenses amount to £15. She sells the toys for £1.99 each. What profit does she
     make ?

15. Mr Grant spends £6 on petrol for his car and this takes him 120 miles. What is
     the cost per mile ?

16. 12 people win a competition and share the prize money of £500 equally. How
     much do they each get, to the nearest penny ?

17. 35 bars of chocolate cost £9.45. What would be the cost of 7 similar bars ?

18. How many 17p packets of sweets can be bought for £10, and how much
     change is there ?

19.   Equal numbers of 20p and 15p stamps were bought for £11.20. How many of each kind were there ?

20.   Mr Douglas has a £20 voucher to spend at the garden centre. He decides to buy 3 bushes for £2.35 each and spend the rest on bulbs at 35p each. How many bulbs can he buy ?

Time

The units for time are unlikely to be changed in the near future although since they are not based on ten they are not easy to use on a calculator. Perhaps, eventually, things will be changed so that there could be 10 new hours in a day, 10 new minutes in an hour, and even 10 days in a new week. But we cannot change the length of a year because that is the length of time that the earth takes to go round the sun, and that is approximately $365\frac{1}{4}$ days.

Here is the present table for time:

Time

```
60 seconds = 1 minute
60 minutes = 1 hour
24 hours = 1 day
7 days = 1 week
52 weeks = 1 year
365 days = 1 year
366 days = 1 leap year
12 months = 1 year
```

Recording the time of day can either be by the 12-hour clock, when morning times are denoted by a.m. and afternoon times by p.m., or by the 24-hour clock. To avoid confusion, timetables are often printed with times using the 24-hour clock.

Examples

	12-hour clock	*24-hour clock*
1 o'clock early morning	1.00 am	1.00 or 01.00
5 past 1 early morning	1.05 am	1.05 or 01.05
Noon	12.00 pm	12.00
Quarter-to-1 early afternoon	12.45 pm	12.45
1 o'clock early afternoon	1.00 pm	13.00
Half-past 8 in the evening	8.30 pm	20.30
One minute to midnight	11.59 pm	23.59
Midnight	12.00 am	0.00 or 00.00
One minute past midnight	12.01 am	0.01 or 00.01

(The day changes at the instant of midnight so when the time is shown as 12.00 am or 0.00 the date has changed.)

On a timetable the 24-hour times would be printed as 4-figure numbers. The full stop separating the hours and minutes could be left out.
e.g. 1.23 am would be printed as 0123,
      1.23 pm would be printed as 1323.

1323 would be pronounced as thirteen twenty-three or thirteen twenty-three hours. But 1300 would be pronounced as thirteen hundred hours.

The calendar

A year has 365 days.
Every 4th year is a leap year and has an extra day, 29th February.

There are 52 weeks (+ 1 extra day) in a year.
There are 52 weeks (+ 2 extra days) in a leap year.

There are 12 months in a year:-
January, February, March, April, May, June, July, August, September, October, November, December.

April, June, September and November have 30 days.
February has 28 days, and 29 days in leap years.
All the other months have 31 days.

Thirty days hath September,
April, June and dull November,
All the rest have 31,
Excepting February alone,
Which has 28 days clear,
And 29 in each leap year.

FEBRUARY 1992						
Sun	Mon	Tu	Wed	Th	Fri	Sat
						1
2	3	4	5	6	7	8
9	10	11	12	13	14	15
16	17	18	19	20	21	22
23	24	25	26	27	28	29

Leap years are years whose dates are divisible by 4, e.g. 1988 and 2000.

(A number divides by 4 if its last 2 figures divide by 4.
e.g. to check if 1992 divides by 4, just check if 92 divides by 4. Does it? If so, 1992 is a leap year, if not, 1992 is not a leap year.)

The exceptions to the leap year rule were the years 1700, 1800 and 1900 which were not leap years. However, 2000 will be a leap year.
(The reason for these exceptions is that the actual length of a year is nearly $365\frac{1}{4}$ days, but not precisely.)

There are 4 weeks (+ usually some extra days) in a month.
There are 7 days in a week:-
Sunday, Monday, Tuesday, Wednesday, Thursday, Friday, Saturday.

Use of a calculator

You cannot use your calculator directly for mixed calculations involving hours and minutes, minutes and seconds, days and weeks, etc. since these are not based on a scale of ten. You will have to do the calculations for the different units separately. Here are some examples:-

1   A plumber does two jobs. The first one takes 1 hour 37 minutes and the second takes 2 hours 46 minutes. What is the total time taken ?

$$\begin{array}{r} 1\,\text{hr}\ 37\,\text{min} \\ \underline{2\,\text{hr}\ 46\,\text{min}} \\ \underline{4\,\text{hr}\ 23\,\text{min}} \end{array}$$

Use your calculator to add 37 and 46. This gives 83. 83 min = 1 hr 23 min so write down 23 min and carry 1 hr forward, making 4 hours altogether.

2 Of a school day of 5 hours, 2 hours 25 minutes was spent on rehearsals for a display. How much time was left for lessons ?

$$\begin{array}{r} 5\,\text{hr} \;\; 0\,\text{min} \\ \underline{2\,\text{hr}\; 25\,\text{min}} \\ \underline{2\,\text{hr}\; 35\,\text{min}} \end{array}$$

Use your calculator to take 25 from 60, since you cannot take 25 from 0. This gives 35 min. Then adjust for the 1 hour you changed into 60 minutes, so, depending on the way you normally do subtraction, you will have either 5 hr − 3 hr or 4 hr − 2 hr. This gives 2 hours.

3 12 hr 22 min ÷ 7

$$\begin{array}{r} 7)\overline{12\,\text{hr}\; 22\,\text{min}} \\ \underline{1\,\text{hr}\; 46\,\text{min}} \end{array}$$

Do the hours part first. 7 into 12 goes 1 remainder 5. Write down 1 hr. Change the remainder, 5 hr, into 5 × 60 min = 300 min, so altogether there are 322 min. 322 ÷ 7 = 46, so the answer is 1 hr 46 min.

Exercise 8.2

1. Change these times to the 24-hour clock.

    2.10 am,   7.00 pm,   2.15 pm,   4.05 pm,   11.50 pm.

    Change these times to the 12-hour clock.

    0350,   7.30,   12.05,   18.18,   2210.

2. Write down the time shown on this clock when it is in the afternoon,
    1 in the 12-hour system,
    2 in the 24-hour system.

3. Work out the answers to these calculations.
    1 2 min 23 sec + 1 min 48 sec + 4 min 16 sec
    2 12 hr 15 min − 5 hr 40 min
    3 10 yr 8 mth × 4
    4 57 yr 11 mth ÷ 5
    5 (12 hr 14 min + 1 hr 12 min) × 5

4. A train left London at 11.15 am and arrived at Manchester at 1.58 pm. How long did the journey take ?

5. Sandra works in a local shop from 2.30 pm to 6 pm on five afternoons each week. She is paid £3.20 per hour. How much is her weekly wage ?

6. Naresh set off on a training ride at 10.55 am and cycled for $4\frac{1}{4}$ hours. At what time did he stop ?

7. On a timetable, a plane was due to leave an airport at 2235 and arrive at its destination at 0205 the next day. How long should the journey take ? It actually arrived 15 minutes early. At what time did it arrive ?

8. A school's lessons begin at 8.50 am and end at 2.50 pm with an hour's break at lunchtime and 20 minutes break mid-morning. If there are 7 lessons of equal length, how long is a lesson ?

9. Philip started school on his 5th birthday in 1989. In which year will he have his 16th birthday ?

10. In a particular year, April 1st is on a Monday. On which day of the week are these dates in that year ?

   1 April 9th
   2 April 25th
   3 March 25th
   4 What date will it be on the Monday 5 weeks after April 1st ?

11. How many days will there be/were there in February in these years ?
   1 1908   **2** 1976   **3** 1866   **4** 2016   **5** 1990

12. Use a calendar of the present year to answer these questions.

   1 On what day of the week is 12th September ?
   2 How many weeks are there from 1st May to 31st July ?
   3 The financial year (for income tax purposes) begins on 6th April. What day of the week is this ?
   4 How many 'shopping days' are there from 1st October to Christmas ? (Sundays and Christmas Day, 25th December, are not counted.)

Exercise 8.3   Applications and Activities

1. The electricity bill for a certain householder was worked out as follows:-
   a standing charge of £7.30 per quarter plus a cost of 5.8p per unit used. The meter reading was 49616, and the previous reading was 48516.
   How many units had been used, and what was the total cost for that quarter ?

2. Write down any sum of money less than £100 which includes £'s and pence.
    Write it down again, interchanging £'s and pence, e.g. £63.47 becomes £47.63.
    You may have to put in or lose a 0, £9.26 becomes £26.09 and £18.03 becomes
    £3.18.
    Subtract the smaller amount from the larger one and write down your answer.
    Write down the answer again with the £'s and pence interchanged.
    Find the sum of the last two amounts you have written down.
    What is your final answer ?

3. Tea is sold in packets of 125 g for 58p, or
    packets of 250 g for £1.10.
    Which size of packet represents the better
    value for money ?

4. Mrs Wilson wants to buy 2 curtains size 54 × 46, and 4 curtains size 72 × 66.
    1 Show how she can find a quick estimate of the cost, and give the estimated
        total.
    2 Use your calculator, or another method, to find the exact cost.

Very good value! Price per pair			
54 × 46	£29.99	54 × 66	£49.99
72 × 46	£42.99	72 × 66	£59.99
90 × 46	£49.99	90 × 66	£74.99
108 × 46	£59.99	108 × 66	£89.99
54 × 90	£68.99	90 × 90	£99.99
72 × 90	£86.99	108 × 90	£124.99

5. Find the total cost of the ingredients used in making a cake from 150 g of butter,
    150 g of sugar, 3 eggs and 200 g of flour, when flour costs 80p for a 2 kg bag,
    butter 65p for 250 g, sugar 60p for a kg and eggs £1.16 per dozen.

6.   This is the **Fares Table** on the local bus.

Town centre				
25	Pollard Street			
35	30	Victoria Road		
40	37	25	Addison Road	
55	50	40	35	Long Lane

Fares in pence

1   What is the total cost for Mr and Mrs Lambert to travel from Addison Road to the town centre ?

2   What is the total cost for 3 children to travel from Pollard Street to Long Lane? (Children pay half-fare.)

7.   A man worked 40 hours in a week. For the first 36 hours he was paid £3.60 an hour. For the rest he was paid at the overtime rate of £5.40 an hour.

1   What were the man's wages that week ?

2   How many hours altogether had he worked in a week when he earned £178.20 ?

8.   This is an evening's programmes on a local TV station.

    5.55   Weather
    6.00   News
    6.25   Sport Today
    6.50   Double treble quiz show
    7.20   Film: The Silver Arrow
    9.35   The Wayfarers
   11.05   Local Lives
   11.45   Closedown

1   How long did the film last ?

2   If someone switched on at the end of Sport Today and watched TV until closedown, for how long had they been watching ?

9.   Here is part of a bus timetable:

Ashmead School	1554	1602	1608	1616	1622	1629
Brook Lane	1604	1612	1618	1626	1632	1639
Carlton Village	1619	1627	–	1641	–	1654
Denham Station	–	–	1640	–	1654	–

1   Saria finishes school at 3.50 pm. What is the time of the next bus she can catch to get to her home in Carlton Village ? How long does the journey take ?
   If she just misses her usual bus how long will she have to wait for the next one ?

2   Her teacher, Mr Bishop, wants to catch the 5 pm train from Denham station. Which bus must he catch at school, and how long is the journey to the station ?

10.   A plumber does three repair jobs as follows:- the first from 9.35 am to 11.15 am, the second from 11.45 am to 12.50 pm and the third from 2.05 pm to 4.50 pm. Find the total time taken on the three jobs.

11.   **Estimations of time**

   Ask your friends, one by one, to estimate 1 minute of time. Use your watch to record their estimates, in seconds. Comment on the results.
   You can also choose a task, such as running round the playing field. Ask your friends to estimate how long it will take you, and then do the task and compare the result with the estimates.

PUZZLE

14.   In an election one term for the post of football captain, Oliver got 22 votes and Lee got 10. Next term two of the boys who voted for Lee vote for Oliver instead, but several boys who voted for Oliver now vote for Lee. What is the smallest number of boys who must change their minds like this and now vote for Lee if Lee is to be elected captain ?

Miscellaneous Section A

Aural Practice

Often in life you will need to do quick calculations without using pencil and paper or calculator. Sometimes you will **see** the numbers written down, and sometimes you will just **hear** the questions. These aural exercises will give you some practice in **listening** to questions.

These aural exercises, A1 and A2, should be read to you, probably by your teacher or a friend, and you should write down the answers only, doing any working out in your head. You should do the 15 questions within 10 minutes.

Exercise A1

1.   What is the value of 11 squared ?

2.   5 similar pairs of stockings cost £3. How much does one pair cost ?

3.   A maths lesson starts at one thirty five and finishes at two twenty. How many minutes long is the lesson ?

4.   Write correct to 2 decimal places the number 4.378.

5.   Roy measured the height of a doorway as 200 cm. What is this height in metres ?

6.   Write down the number which is 2 less than 2000.

7.   Simplify the algebraic expression $7b - b$.

8.   Add 15 and 9 and divide the result by 8.

9.   Emily thought of two numbers. When she added the numbers together she got 12, when she multiplied the numbers together she got 32. What were the two numbers she thought of ?

10.   There are two adjacent angles on a straight line. One of them is 130°, how big is the other ?

11.   Sunil is 8 years old and his father's age is 4 times his age. How old will Sunil's father be when Sunil is 12 ?

12.   What is the value of $a^2 + b^2$ when $a = 3$ and $b = 1$?

13.   A piece of wood is one hundred and thirty seven centimetres in length. What is this length to the nearest 10 cm ?

14.   If today is Friday the thirteenth of June, what will be the date next Friday ?

15.   2 angles are corresponding angles made by parallel lines. One is 63°, how big is the other ?

Exercise A2

1.   A box of pencils was labelled 'Contents one dozen'. How many pencils would there be in 7 boxes ?

2.   The attendance at a football match was thirty thousand and fifty-six. Write this number in figures.

3.   Mr Robinson buys a tool costing £7.99. How much change should he get from a £10 note ?

4.   What is the name given to an angle between 90° and 180° ?

5.   These numbers follow a pattern. What are the next 2 numbers in the sequence ? 2, 5, 8, 11, 14.

6.   A formula for area is $A = bh$. What is the value of A if $b = 9$ and $h = 6$?

7.   Write down the cube root of 27.

8.   The admission charges for a museum were 50 pence for father, 40 pence for granny and 25 pence each for the 2 children. How much is this altogether ?

9.   Sheila has to take 2 spoonfuls of medicine 3 times each day. How much does she take daily, if a spoonful is 5 ml ?

10.   What time is 3.30 pm in the 24-hour clock ?

11.   A coach holds 40 people. How many people will 20 such coaches hold ?

12.   What is an expression for the cost of 15 books at £y each ?

13.   What number is a factor of both 35 and 77 ?

14.   Write the number 42.684 correct to 3 significant figures.

15.   One record costs £6.50 and another costs £2.50. How much is this altogether ?

Exercise A3   Revision

1.   Find the values of
      1 2^5 **2** 4^3 **3** $\sqrt{81}$ **4** $\sqrt[3]{125}$ **5** 10^6

2.   If $a = 60°$ and all the other angles are equal,
      what size are they ?

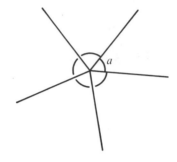

3.   Write these numbers correct to the nearest 100.
      1 10 365   **2** 7495   **3** 43 310   **4** 3649   **5** 4962

4.   Bakula buys 5 packets of biscuits at x pence each, and 3 packets of sweets at
      y pence each. What is an expression for the total cost ?
      If the total cost is c pence, write down a formula for c.

5.   Some sugar was taken from a 1 kg bag to bake a cake. 0.7 kg of sugar remained.
      How many **grams** of sugar had been used ?

6.   The diagram shows the goals scored
      by some football teams.
      1   How many football teams were
            there ?
      2   What was the total number of
            goals scored ?

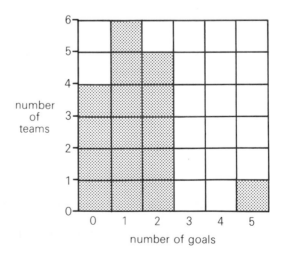

number of goals

7.   It is 6.15 pm and my train is due at 1950 according to the timetable. How long
      have I to wait ?

8.   Which of these numbers are prime numbers ?   31, 33, 35, 37, 39.

9.   What size is angle a ?

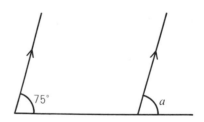

10.   Simplify
      1 $3a + 3a$ **2** $3a - 2a$ **3** $a^2 + a^2$ **4** $a^2 \times a$ **5** $a \div a$

11.   Write these numbers correct to 2 decimal places.
      1   7.182   **2**   6.2845   **3**   2029.157   **4**   46.789   **5**   0.03527

12.   How many
      1   mm in 6 cm,   **4**   ml in 5 ℓ,
      2   g in 2 kg   **5**   cm in 4 m ?
      3   m in 3 km,

13.   The opening hours of a shop are shown on this
      poster.
      For how many hours each week is the shop open ?

Mon	9.30– 5.30
Tues	9.30– 5.30
Wed	9.30–12.30
Thurs	9.30– 8.00
Fri	9.30– 8.00
Sat	9.00– 5.00
Sun	—

14.   If $V = x^2 h$, what is the value of V when $x = 8$ and $h = 10$?

15.   If oranges are packed 80 to a box, 30 boxes are needed. How many boxes are
      needed if they are packed 200 to a box ?

16.   The bar chart shows how some money is divided
      among 3 charities A, B and C. The bar A is
      11 cm long, B is 9 cm and C is 5 cm. If the amount
      A gets is £165, how much are the shares of B
      and C ?

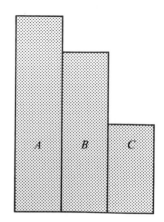

17.   The number of insects in a colony doubles each week. If there were 10 insects
      at first, in how many weeks would there be more than 10 000 ?

18.   Calculate the sizes of angles *a*, *b* and *c*.

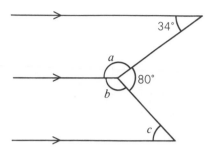

19.   Write these numbers correct to 3 significant figures.
       1   253.312   **2**   56 752   **3**   7.0829   **4**   0.03514   **5**   290.751

20.   If 600 cups which should cost 95 p each are bought at a reduced price of
       65 p each, what is the total saving ?

Exercise A4   Activities

1.   **Elevens**, a 'patience' game with a pack
      of cards.
      Shuffle the pack of 52 cards and put
      down 9 cards face upwards (usually
      in three rows of three, but this is not
      essential). Keep the rest of the pack in
      your hand.
      Using the next 2 cards from the pack,
      put cards face upwards to cover any
      2 cards whose numbers add up to 11,
      such as 7 and 4 in the diagram. It does
      not matter which number 7 you cover
      up, just choose one of them. Repeat this
      with other pairs which add up to 11.
      You can use the new cards in the same
      way as the original ones, using only the
      top card of each pile. Aces count as 1's
      and pair with 10's.

      Do not count the picture cards as numbers. Instead, if a jack, queen and king
      are all visible, cover up all three with the next three cards.
      You win the game if you use up all the cards in the pack. If you get to a
      situation where you cannot find any more pairs, or sets of jack, queen, king,
      you lose.
      Try the game a few times and see how many times you win.

Now we are going to change the rules to carry out a statistical experiment.
Amended rules:– If you get to a situation where you cannot cover up any
more cards, use the next card from the pack to make an extra pile so that you
are now using 10 piles. This extra card may help to get things going again,
if not, put another one down so as to make 11 piles, and so on every time you
cannot cover any cards up. When you have used all the pack of cards, count
how many piles there are. Record this number as the score, on a tally chart.
It will be at least 9, and sometimes gets as big as 16. (The smaller, the better.)
Repeat this experiment several times.
Finally, draw a histogram to show the distribution of scores. Comment on its
shape, and on the results.

2.   **Parallelograms**

This figure has two pairs of parallel sides and it is called a **parallelogram**.

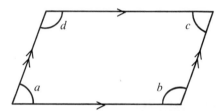

If angle a = 75°, calculate the sizes of angles b and d.
Using angle b, calculate the size of angle c.
Can you deduce anything about the angles of a parallelogram ?

To draw a parallelogram accurately

Begin by drawing a line AB.
Draw a slanting line AD through A.
Using your ruler and set-square draw
a line through D parallel to AB.
Draw a line through B parallel to AD.
Let these lines intersect at C.
Then $ABCD$ is a parallelogram.
Measure its angles.
What can you discover about the lengths
of the sides?

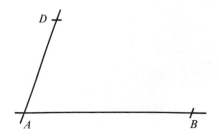

3. **Planning a party** or an adventure afternoon for younger children.
    This can be in your own home, for a younger brother or sister, or it may be for members of a children's club, held in the clubroom. It can be for a birthday, for Christmas, or for some other festival time or celebration.

    First, decide on what sort of afternoon you are planning, how many children there will be, the ages of the children involved and when and where it will be held. You could have a theme for the afternoon, such as 'pirates' or 'clowns'. Design an invitation card.

    Find out how much you can spend, perhaps as an over-all total or as 'so much a head'.

    Plan a menu and decide how much of each item must be bought. Don't forget to include soft drinks.

    Plan a timetable for the afternoon with the time of beginning and the time it will end, times for various activities such as games and entertainment, and time for eating.

    Decide what other things must be bought, other than food, e.g. balloons, decorations, small prizes. Are there any other expenses such as hire of an entertainer or hire of a room ? Find the total cost of everything.

    Write all these details in a booklet and illustrate it with pictures.

4. **Cube numbers and multiples of three**

1 Write down a list of the cubes of numbers from 0 to 9.

2 Here is a rule for a number chain.

For a 1-figure number, cube the number. For other numbers, cube each figure of the number and find the sum of these cubes.

Repeat this rule as long as you get to a different number.

e.g. for $126 \rightarrow 1^3 + 2^3 + 6^3 = 1 + 8 + 216 = 225$

then $225 \rightarrow 2^3 + 2^3 + 5^3 = \ldots$, and so on.

Investigate this number chain, but only start with any numbers which are multiples of 3.

3 There is a slight connection with triangular numbers. Can you say what it is ?

4 If you have a Bible, you may be interested to look at St. John, chapter 21, verse 11.

5. **Multiplication**

This is a multiplication table chart using the numbers 3, 6, 9 only.

	3	6	9
3	9	18	27
6	18	36	54
9	27	54	81

Now copy the table, but change all the 2-figure numbers, such as 18, to 1-figure numbers, by adding the 2 figures together.

e.g. for 18, $1 + 8 = 9$, so write down 9.

Comment on the table.

Now make a similar multiplication table, with 2-figure numbers changed to 1-figure numbers, using the numbers 1, 2, 4, 5, 7, 8.

For a result such as 56, change 56 to $5 + 6 = 11$, then change 11 to $1 + 1 = 2$.

Look for patterns in the table and comment on them.

6. **A number pattern**

Make a pattern involving 4 consecutive numbers. Multiply them all together and add 1. Investigate the results.

Numbers	Product	Add 1
1, 2, 3, 4	24	25
2, 3, 4, 5	120	121
3, 4, 5, 6	. . .	
. . .		

7. **The Earth**

The Earth makes 1 complete revolution about its axis every 24 hours. How long does it take to rotate through 1° ?

London is on longitude 0°, New York is on longitude 74° West. These measurements in degrees correspond to the degrees of rotation. When the sun rises in London, the Earth must rotate another 74° before it rises in New York. How much later will this be ?

This is why different countries keep different times. Many countries keep the same time throughout the whole country, but in a large country, such as USA, there is too much difference between the Eastern and Western sides, and the country is divided into different time zones. See if you can find in an atlas a map showing time zones in different countries.

People who have business dealings with another country will need to know the time difference so that they can telephone during working hours. This also matters to anyone who has relations abroad who may not appreciate being woken up by the telephone at 4 am ! Choose 10 cities and make a table showing the times there when it is 9 am, 12 noon, 3 pm and 6 pm in London.

If you visit Greenwich, East London, you can stand on longitude 0°. Why was the 0° line chosen to go through this place ?

Try to find out where the International Date Line is, why it is not a straight line, and what happens when you travel across it. Does it make any difference whether you go eastwards or westwards ?

8. **Measurement of time**

Before modern clocks were invented, people used other devices to measure time. These included sundials, water clocks, candles and pendulums. Many people today will use an egg-timer, and that is a very simple idea.
Find out about these and other instruments and make some of them yourself. You can investigate how the timing of a pendulum's swing varies with the length of the string.

9. **To draw perpendicular lines** with a set-square.
    e.g. Draw a line through *P* at right angles to *PQ*.

If you are not drawing accurately, it is sufficient just to put your set-square
along the line *PQ* with the corner at *P*. However, to make an accurate line
going exactly through *P* you can use this method.

(1)
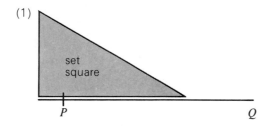

(2) slide down ruler   (3) draw the line along this side through → point *P*

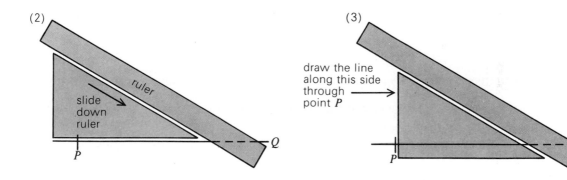

Now you can use your set-square to draw an accurate rectangle.
Begin with a line *AB*.
Make accurate right angles at *A* and *B*, to the
line *AB*.
Choose a point *D* on the line through *A*. At *D*
draw a line at right angles to the line *AD*. Let
this meet the line through *B* at *C*.

You can check whether your drawing is accurate by measuring the angle at *C*
and the lengths of the 4 sides.

10. **To bisect an angle**

This means 'to cut it exactly in half'.

1 Draw an acute angle and bisect it by using your protractor. Repeat using an obtuse angle.

2 Draw an acute angle on tracing paper and bisect it by folding the paper. Repeat using an obtuse angle.

3 This method shows how to bisect an angle using the straight edges of a ruler, without measurement.

Place the edge of the ruler along AC with the ruler on the side of the line nearer B. Draw a line along the opposite edge. Then place the edge of the ruler along BC with the ruler on the side of the line nearer A. Draw a line along the opposite edge. If the two lines you have drawn cross each other at Z, join CZ, which is the bisector of the angle at C.

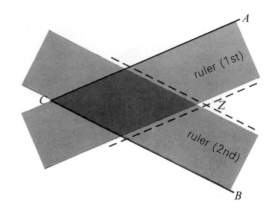

Practise this method, bisecting an acute angle and also an obtuse angle.

Can you also discover another way of bisecting an angle using a ruler, if you make measurements?

4 This method shows how you can bisect an angle using a ruler (without measurement) and compasses.

With centre C, draw arcs to cut CA and CB at X and Y.

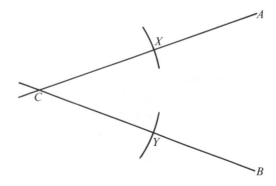

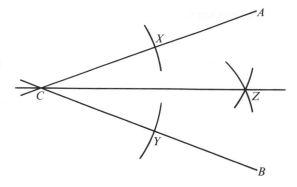

With centres X and Y in turn, and a suitable radius, draw arcs to cut at Z. Join CZ, which is the bisector of the angle at C.

Practise this method, bisecting an acute angle and then an obtuse angle.

5 Draw an acute angle at a point C, and bisect it. Choose a point D on the bisector.
Through D draw a line at right angles to CD, meeting the sides of the original angle at E and F.
Measure CE and CF.
Measure DE and DF.
What do you notice about these measurements ?

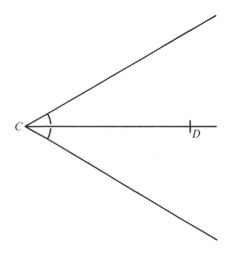

11. **The cost of a child**

How much does it cost to keep a child of your age for a year ?
You will not be able to work this out exactly, but you can get an approximate value. Think of all the expenses. Here are some of them:- Food, clothes, fares to school, school meals, pocket money, money for clubs and leisure activities, holidays, presents. What others can you think of ?
Many parents would say that 'You are worth your weight in gold'. Find the up-to-date price of gold and work out how much you would be worth.

12. **Christmas Decorations**

Here is an idea for do-it-yourself models. They are made from thin cardboard and do not need glueing. They can be pulled apart for storage.

Build-a-star

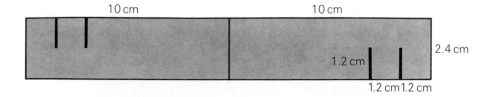

To begin with, make a 5-pointed star. For this you need 5 strips like the one shown. By using a cardboard rectangle 20 cm by 12 cm you can make the measurements for the 5 strips together and then cut them into separate strips. The slots are 1.2 cm high, and are 1.2 cm and 2.4 cm from each end, from the bottom edge on the right and from the top edge on the left. A slot should be a thin double slot so that it is just wide enough for a similar piece of cardboard to fit in it, and it should go halfway across the strip. Enlarged, a slot would look like this ⊓ rather than this ⋀

To make a pointed star the centre line is **scored**. That means that you put your ruler along the line and then drag your compass point along it. This will make a nick in the cardboard. Then the cardboard will bend along this nick. Always bend cardboard away from the side you have scored on, not towards it.
Later on you can make some pieces which are not scored, to use as curved pieces, and you can make sets of larger or smaller pieces.

To assemble a star

Stand two pieces together to form a W. Put the inner slot of the 1st into the inner slot of the 2nd. Join a 3rd piece to the 2nd in the same way.

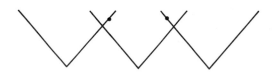

Now slot the 1st piece to the 3rd using the slots shown by the dots. These slots should be put in 'backwards' so that it looks like this

and not like this

Join the 4th piece to the 3rd in the inner slots, and then into the 2nd's slots. Join the 5th piece to the 4th in the inner slots, and then into the 3rd's slots. Complete the star by joining the inner slots of the 5th and 1st pieces, and the remaining other slots.

If you make a star with only 4 points it is more secure if the second slots are not put in backwards.

Once you have used point pieces and can assemble them correctly, try making a 'flower' by using 5 or 6 unscored pieces.

You can then invent your own designs, perhaps using scored and unscored pieces alternately, or making some longer pieces to go alternately with shorter pieces. For Christmas decorations, make them in different colours and dangle tinsel from them.

13. **Computer programming**

If you have the use of a computer at home or at school, and have learnt how to write programs for it, then you may like to write some programs to link with mathematical ideas.
If you are a beginner, start with simple programs. Keep the listings of all programs. As your skill develops you may be able to improve your earlier work. For anyone really interested in computing it will not take long before you are writing quite interesting and useful programs, some of which can be used for mathematical investigations. You can also invent games which use mathematical ideas.

One difficulty in including programs in a book such as this, is that we do not know what make of computer you will be using. Although we can write in BASIC, which is a programming language suitable for most machines, and which beginners can use, your machine may have slightly different rules of BASIC, so that without changing the instructions slightly the program will not work. So we will just include a few simple programs, making them as straightforward as we can. These may encourage you to try them on your computer, and then you may be able to improve them. They may also give you ideas for other programs which you could use in your own investigations and activities.

Here is a program to improve your mental arithmetic by testing your multiplication tables up to 12 × 12. All it does is get the computer to choose two numbers and ask you to multiply them, and then it will tell you whether your answer is correct.

```
10    REM prog: mentl
20    REM mental arithmetic
30    CLS
40    RANDOMIZE TIMER
50    LET A =  INT(RND*13)
60    LET B =  INT(RND*13)
70    PRINT "What is ";A;" × ";B;
80    INPUT C
90    PRINT
100   LET D=A*B
110   IF C=D THEN PRINT "     YES ";
120   IF C<>D THEN PRINT "     NO ";
130   PRINT ,A;" × ";B;" = ";D
140   PRINT
150   PRINT "Press S to stop, and any other letter to
      continue"
160   A$=INKEY$
170   IF A$="" THEN 160
180   IF A$<>"S" and A$<>"s" THEN 30
190   END
```

Try the program and see how well you know your tables.
Now you can improve the program in several ways. You could include keeping a score, so that you know how many answers you have got right. You could include a 'pause', so that you have only a short time in which to answer the question. You could change some of the questions to addition instead of multiplication.

14.   **Prime numbers**

Here is a computer program which will find prime numbers. It works in a similar way to the method used by Eratosthenes (see question 6, page 12). We find prime numbers up to a number n by dividing by all the lower prime numbers up to $\sqrt{n}$.

```
10   REM prog:primel. To find prime numbers up to 500.
20   DIM A(100)
30   CLS
40   INPUT" What number do you want to search to . . .";N
50   PRINT
60   PRINT " The primes up to ";N; "are . . ."
70   PRINT
80   PRINT 2,:IF N>2 THEN PRINT 3,
90   LET R = 2
100  LET A(2)=3
110  FOR X=5 TO N STEP 2
120  FOR Y=2 TO R
130  IF A(Y)*A(Y)>X THEN 170
140  LET F=INT(X/A(Y))
150  IF X = F*A(Y) THEN 200
160  NEXT Y
170  LET R=R+1
180  LET A(R)=X
190  PRINT X,
200  NEXT X
210  PRINT
220  PRINT
230  PRINT "Finished"
240  END
```

Here are some investigations you could do with prime numbers. By altering the program you might be able to use the computer to help you.

1   Are there less prime numbers occurring the further we go in searching for them ? Find the number of primes between 1 and 100, 101 and 200, etc, and plot your results in a histogram.

2   Make a list of prime pairs. These are prime numbers which differ by 2, e.g. 17 and 19, 29 and 31, 41 and 43.
     It is thought that there is an infinite number of these. Find how many there are between 1 and 100, 101 and 200, etc. Plot your results in a histogram.

3   For numbers greater than 5, all prime numbers end in the figures 1, 3, 7, 9. For prime numbers up to 500, see how many of each type there are, and show the results in a bar chart.

15. **Guess the number**

Here is a computer program for a simple number game. You have to guess a number, which is between 1 and 100. You can play the game with a friend, not looking while you take it in turns to enter a number, or you can play it by yourself with the computer entering the number.

Try to improve your strategy for finding the number in as few guesses as possible. You could find a method that will give you the number with 6 guesses at most, and often less.

You probably use a similar kind of strategy when you try to find a certain place in the middle of a video tape.

After playing this game, try to invent a number game yourself, and write a program for it.

```
10    REM prog: game1. Number guessing game
20    CLS
30    PRINT"Enter a whole number between 1 and 100. For a
      secret number press 999"
40    INPUT N
50    PRINT
60    RANDOMIZE TIMER
70    IF N = 999 THEN LET N = INT(RND*100+1)
80    IF INT(N)<>N THEN PRINT "     Enter a WHOLE
      number":GOTO 40
90    IF N<1 OR N>100 THEN PRINT "     A number in range
      1 to 100 please":GOTO 40
100   CLS
110   LET B=1
120   LET TR=0
130   LET T=100
140   GOSUB 320
150   GOSUB 450
160   IF G=N THEN GOTO 290
170   IF G<N THEN 230
180   PRINT " Sorry, too high . . ."
190   LET T=G-1
200   GOSUB 320
210   GOSUB 450
220   GOTO 160
230   PRINT " Sorry, too low . . ."
240   LET B=G+1
250   GOSUB 320
```

```
260 PRINT
270 GOSUB 450
280 GOTO 160
290 PRINT "Correct. Number of guesses = ";TR
300 PRINT:PRINT
310 END
320 PRINT " Choose numbers from the following : "
330 PRINT
340 LET K=B
350 FOR L=1 to 16
360 IF K<10 THEN PRINT " ";
370 PRINT K;
380 IF K=T THEN 430
390 LET K=K+1
400 NEXT L
410 PRINT
420 IF K<=T THEN 350
430 PRINT
440 RETURN
450 PRINT : INPUT" Enter your guess ";G
460 IF G>=B and G<=T THEN 490
470 PRINT " Your guess is out of range. . .re-enter "
480 GOTO 450
490 LET TR=TR+1
500 RETURN
510 END
```

16. **Write your own computer programs** based on the ideas of Chapter 1. Here are some suggestions:
    1   To find the prime factors of any number.
    2   To find all the factors of any number.
    3   To test whether any number is a prime number.
    4   To find the sequence of triangular numbers. To find which triangular numbers are also square numbers.
    5   To make number patterns.

PUZZLE

15. If a chiming clock takes 2 seconds to strike 2 o'clock, how long does it take to strike 3 o'clock ?

9 Thinking about fractions and percentages

Using fractions

You are already familiar with simple fractions such as $\frac{1}{2}$, $\frac{1}{4}$, $\frac{3}{4}$. Other fractions such as $\frac{1}{3}$, $\frac{2}{3}$, $\frac{1}{5}$, $\frac{1}{6}$, are not used in practical situations quite so often.

Think of situations where you have used fractions, or seen fractions used.

Name some situations where these people would use fractions:

A shoe retailer
A grocer selling cooked meats
A child learning to tell the time
A musician
A mother dividing a cake among 5 children
A milkman supplying milk to school for the children to drink
A publican selling beer, and spirits
A mechanic using spanners
A photographer

A fractions problem

Sam was trying to reduce the fraction $\frac{16}{64}$ to its lowest terms but instead of doing it the correct way he carelessly cancelled the 6's, $\frac{16}{64}$ and he got the answer $\frac{1}{4}$. When he found out that was the correct answer he thought he had discovered a good way to do such questions. But unfortunately for him, it doesn't usually work out right. Can you find the three other fractions with denominators less than 100 for which this wrong method would work? (In one of them the fraction is still not in its lowest terms.)

For distances less than a mile, fractions are used.
What is odd about the way the fractions are written?

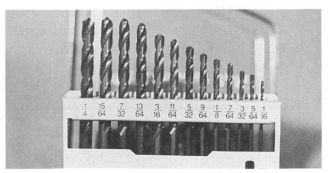

What is the difference in size between each bit and the next larger?

Which of these two notices do you think is better ?

Special offers on goods are a way to persuade you to buy.

Using percentages

Percentages are simply fractions, with the % sign meaning 'out of 100'. They are used extensively nowadays in a variety of situations, but especially where finance is involved.

One advantage of using percentages is that it is easier to compare them with each other, than it is to compare fractions with different denominators.

For instance, which is the larger, $\frac{2}{3}$ or $\frac{3}{5}$?

Which is the larger, $66\frac{2}{3}\%$ or 60% ? What is 1% of £1 ? What is 1% of £100 ?

The rate of VAT (value added tax) is 15%, (at present). What does this mean ?

A shop has a sale and reduces all its prices by 25%. Why will a shopkeeper do this ? How will he work out the new prices ?

Why do manufacturers make some products whose containers have such labels as '10% extra free' ? What fraction are you getting extra ? What does 'She gives 100% effort' mean ?

For what purpose are percentages often used in schools ?

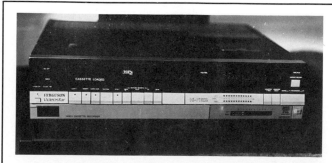

Percentage of households with video recorders	
1982	7%
1983	14%
1984	24%
1985	30%
1986	37%
1987	44%

Fractions and Percentages

Fractions

Fractions are numbers such as $\frac{1}{4}$ (one-quarter), $\frac{1}{3}$ (one-third), $\frac{2}{5}$ (two-fifths), $\frac{5}{9}$ (five-ninths).

The number underneath is called the **denominator**. It tells us how many smaller equal parts the whole unit is divided into.

The number on top is called the **numerator**. It tells how many of the smaller parts are counted.

e.g. $\frac{5}{9}$ Divide a whole unit into 9 equal parts.

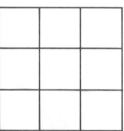

Take 5 of these parts.
The shaded region is $\frac{5}{9}$ of the whole square,
(and the unshaded region is $\frac{4}{9}$ of the whole square).

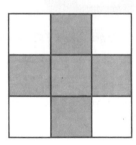

The shaded part represents $\frac{1}{4}$ (one-quarter) of the circle. (The whole circle is divided into 4 equal parts and 1 part is shaded.)
The unshaded part represents $\frac{3}{4}$ (three-quarters) of the circle.

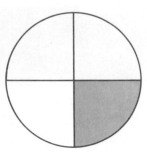

The shaded part represents $\frac{2}{5}$ (two-fifths) of the rectangle.
(The whole rectangle is divided into 5 equal parts and 2 parts are shaded.)
The unshaded part represents $\frac{3}{5}$ of the rectangle.

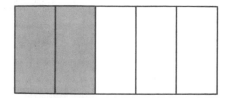

This diagram shows that $\frac{2}{5}$ is equivalent to $\frac{4}{10}$.

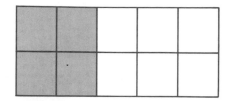

This diagram shows that $\frac{2}{5} + \frac{1}{10} = \frac{4}{10} + \frac{1}{10} = \frac{5}{10} = \frac{1}{2}$.

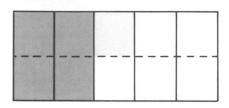

Improper fractions and mixed numbers

Improper fractions are numbers with a greater numerator than denominator, such as $\frac{6}{5}$ and $\frac{5}{2}$.

Mixed numbers are numbers with a whole number part and a fraction part, such as $1\frac{1}{5}$ and $2\frac{1}{2}$.

This diagram shows that $\frac{6}{5} = 1\frac{1}{5}$.

This diagram shows that $\frac{5}{2} = 2\frac{1}{2}$.

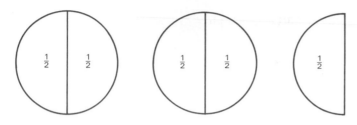

Examples

1   Change $3\frac{7}{8}$ into an improper fraction.

(Multiply the whole number 3 by 8 to change it into eighths. This is 24 eighths and another 7 eighths make 31 eighths.)

$3\frac{7}{8} = \frac{24}{8} + \frac{7}{8} = \frac{31}{8}$

2   Change $\frac{45}{7}$ into a mixed number.

(Divide 7 into 45. It goes 6 times so there are 6 whole ones. 6 × 7 = 42 and the remainder is 3, so there is also $\frac{3}{7}$.)

$\frac{45}{7} = \frac{42 + 3}{7} = \frac{42}{7} + \frac{3}{7} = 6 + \frac{3}{7} = 6\frac{3}{7}$

Using fractions

Examples

1   Reduce $\frac{60}{75}$ to its lowest terms.

60 and 75 both divide by 5 so reduce the fraction by dividing both the numerator and the denominator by 5. This process can be called **cancelling**.

$\dfrac{\overset{12}{\cancel{60}}}{\underset{15}{\cancel{75}}}$ This gives the fraction $\frac{12}{15}$ but this is still not in its lowest terms because

12 and 15 both divide by 3.

So divide both the numerator and the denominator by 3.

$\dfrac{\overset{4}{\cancel{\overset{12}{\cancel{60}}}}}{\underset{5}{\cancel{\underset{15}{\cancel{75}}}}} = \frac{4}{5}$ This is the fraction in its lowest terms.

2 Change $\frac{5}{6}$ into a fraction with denominator 18.

6 becomes 18 when multiplied by 3, so multiply the numerator and the denominator by 3.

$\frac{5}{6} = \frac{5 \times 3}{6 \times 3} = \frac{15}{18}$

3 Find $\frac{2}{3}$ of £3.90

$\frac{1}{3}$ of £3.90 is £1.30
So $\frac{2}{3}$ of £3.90 is £1.30 × 2 = £2.60

4 Find $\frac{3}{5}$ of 1 hr 20 min

1 hr 20 min is 80 min
$\frac{1}{5}$ of 80 min = 16 min
So $\frac{3}{5}$ of 80 min = 16 × 3 min = 48 min

Using your calculator:
$\frac{3}{5} = \frac{6}{10} = 0.6$ so you need 0.6 × 80 = 48

Fractions with denominators 3, 6, 9 or 7 do not have exact decimal equivalents. You can still use your calculator to work out fractional parts, but because the fractions are not exact decimals it is better to do the multiplication first and division last.

5 Find $\frac{5}{6}$ of £6.50, to the nearest penny.

You must find $\frac{5}{6}$ × 650 pence
Do it in this order:- 5 × 650 ÷ 6 rather than 5 ÷ 6 × 650
The answer is 541.666. . .
This is £5.42, to the nearest penny.
(You could have worked in £'s, using 6.5 instead of 650.)

6 Find $1\frac{3}{4}$ times 25 m

$\frac{1}{4}$ of 25 m = 6.25 m
$\frac{3}{4}$ of 25 m = 6.25 × 3 m = 18.75 m
$1\frac{3}{4}$ of 25 m = (25 + 18.75) m = 43.75 m

Or do it this way:
$1\frac{3}{4}$ is the same as $\frac{7}{4}$
$\frac{7}{4}$ of 25 m = 6.25 × 7 m = 43.75 m
Using your calculator, $1\frac{3}{4} = 1.75$ so you need 1.75 × 25 = 43.75

Exercise 9.1

1. What fraction of the shape is shaded ?

   1   **2**   **3**

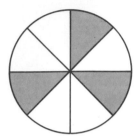 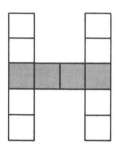 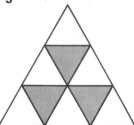

                4   **5**

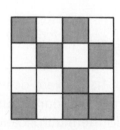 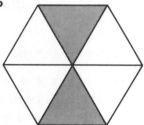

2. Copy the diagrams and shade the fraction stated.

   1 $\frac{2}{5}$ **2** $\frac{4}{7}$ **3** $\frac{3}{4}$

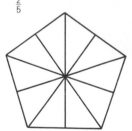 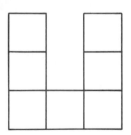 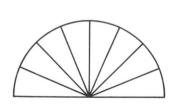

       4 $\frac{5}{6}$ **5** $\frac{3}{8}$

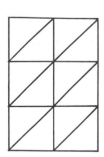 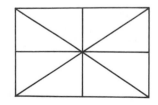

3.   Reduce these fractions to their lowest terms.

1 $\frac{3}{9}$ **2** $\frac{24}{36}$ **3** $\frac{9}{12}$ **4** $\frac{27}{54}$ **5** $\frac{12}{30}$

6 $\frac{5}{20}$ **7** $\frac{70}{100}$ **8** $\frac{21}{56}$ **9** $\frac{60}{80}$ **10** $\frac{35}{45}$

4.   **1**   Change $\frac{3}{8}$ into a fraction with denominator 24
      2   Change $\frac{5}{6}$ into a fraction with denominator 12
      3   Change $\frac{2}{3}$ into a fraction with denominator 15
      4   Change $\frac{3}{4}$ into a fraction with denominator 36
      5   Change $\frac{3}{10}$ into a fraction with denominator 50
      6   Change $\frac{1}{2}$ into a fraction with denominator 6
      7   Change $\frac{2}{5}$ into a fraction with denominator 20
      8   Change $\frac{7}{8}$ into a fraction with denominator 48
      9   Change $\frac{2}{9}$ into a fraction with denominator 27
      10   Change $\frac{1}{4}$ into a fraction with denominator 32.

5.   Change these mixed numbers to improper fractions.

1 $4\frac{2}{5}$ **2** $2\frac{5}{6}$ **3** $2\frac{1}{10}$ **4** $3\frac{3}{4}$ **5** $6\frac{2}{3}$

6 $2\frac{3}{5}$ **7** $4\frac{1}{4}$ **8** $8\frac{1}{3}$ **9** $3\frac{1}{7}$ **10** $1\frac{9}{10}$

6.   Change these improper fractions to mixed numbers.

1 $\frac{7}{4}$ **2** $\frac{7}{3}$ **3** $\frac{17}{12}$ **4** $\frac{37}{10}$ **5** $\frac{29}{6}$

6 $\frac{100}{9}$ **7** $\frac{42}{5}$ **8** $\frac{25}{8}$ **9** $\frac{11}{2}$ **10** $\frac{20}{3}$

7.   **1**   Find one-half of each of these numbers.

      60   20   44   10   80   16   34   70   56   200

      2   Find one-third of each of these numbers.

      6   15   24   66   33   48   18   90   9   36

      3   Find one-quarter of each of these numbers.

      88   16   8   24   84   48   32   52   120   200

      4   Find two-thirds of each of these numbers.

      3   21   75   18   99   60   12   45   27   30

      5   Find three-quarters of each of these numbers.

      4   20   160   36   12   28   80   100   44   60

8.   Find the values of

1 $\frac{1}{2}$ of £5.70   **5** $\frac{7}{10}$ of 200 g   **8** $\frac{1}{4}$ of 2 kg

2 $\frac{2}{3}$ of 3.75 km   **6** $\frac{1}{3}$ of £2.91   **9** $\frac{3}{8}$ of 4 hr

3 $\frac{3}{4}$ of 180°   **7** $\frac{3}{5}$ of 6 ℓ **10** $\frac{4}{5}$ of £125

4 $\frac{2}{5}$ of 1 m

9.   Use your calculator to find these amounts to the nearest penny.
     1 $\frac{5}{6}$ of £5   **4** $\frac{1}{6}$ of £11.49
     2 $\frac{2}{7}$ of £10.30   **5** $\frac{7}{9}$ of £23
     3 $\frac{3}{8}$ of £1.05

10. Find the values of
     1 $1\frac{3}{4}$ times 5 m   **4** $4\frac{1}{2}$ times £10.60
     2 $1\frac{2}{3}$ times 300 g   **5** $2\frac{2}{5}$ times 7.5 ℓ
     3 $3\frac{1}{3}$ times 12 min

Percentages

The symbol % stands for 'per cent', which means 'out of 100'.
So, 7% means 7 out of 100.
As a fraction this is $\frac{7}{100}$
As a decimal it is 0.07

If in an election 61% of the voters have voted for a certain candidate, this means that out of the total number of voters, 61 out of every 100 voted for that candidate.
If in an examination you got 77 marks out of a total of 100 marks, this can be stated as a mark of 77%.

To find a percentage of a sum of money

Change the percentage into a fraction, if it is a simple fraction such as $\frac{1}{2}$, $\frac{1}{4}$, $\frac{1}{5}$, $\frac{1}{10}$, $\frac{1}{20}$, or change it into a decimal and use your calculator.

Example

Find 20% of £360.

$20\% = \frac{20}{100} = \frac{1}{5}$, so find $\frac{1}{5}$ of £360.
$\frac{1}{5}$ of £360 = £72.

To find a percentage of a sum of money, using your calculator

Examples

1   Find 24% of £35

To do this if there is no %⃞ key on your calculator:
24% as a decimal is 0.24, so find 0.24 × 35. Your calculator gives 8.4 so 24% of £35 is £8.40

If there is a $\boxed{\%}$ key on your calculator then press 24 $\boxed{\times}$ 35 $\boxed{\%}$
(The order of the two numbers does not matter, but press $\boxed{\%}$ last, instead of $\boxed{=}$.)
You should get 8.4. If you do not, then perhaps your calculator works in a different way. Look at its instruction booklet, or try to find out how it works. Perhaps, on your calculator, you have to press $\boxed{=}$ also.

2   Find 70% of £216

70% as a decimal is 0.7 so find 0.7 × 216. Your calculator gives 151.2 so 70% of £216 is £151.20
Using the $\boxed{\%}$ key you can press 70 $\boxed{\times}$ 216 $\boxed{\%}$

3   Find 4% of £52.40

4% as a decimal is 0.04 so find 0.04 × 52.4 (or 0.04 × 52.40)
Your calculator gives 2.096. To 2 decimal places this is 2.10, so 4% of £52.40 is £2.10 correct to the nearest penny.
Using the $\boxed{\%}$ key you can press 4 $\boxed{\times}$ 52.4 $\boxed{\%}$

To find a percentage of a quantity

Example

Find 44% of 250 kg

44% as a decimal is 0.44 so find 0.44 × 250. Your calculator gives 110, so 44% of 250 kg is 110 kg.
Using the $\boxed{\%}$ key you can press 44 $\boxed{\times}$ 250 $\boxed{\%}$

Increase or decrease by a percentage

Examples

1   Increase £75 by 9%

You can work out what 9% of £75 is, and add this to £75.
9% of £75 = £(0.09 × 75) = £6.75
Add this to the original £75, making £81.75

Another way to do this is to say that the original amount was 100%, so if we increase it by 9% we get 109%
So the new amount is 109% of £75 = £(1.09 × 75) = £81.75

Your calculator may give you this answer if you press 75 $\boxed{+}$ 9 $\boxed{\%}$

2   Decrease £54 by 5%

You can work out what 5% of £54 is, and take this from £54.
5% of £54 = £(0.05 × 54) = £2.70
Take this from the original £54, leaving £51.30

Doing this the other way, the original amount was 100% and if we decrease it by 5% we get 95%
So the new amount is 95% of £54 = £(0.95 × 54) = £51.30

Your calculator may give you this answer if you press 54 ⊟ 5 ％

Exercise 9.2

1. Express these percentages as fractions in their simplest forms.

   1   30%   **2**   75%   **3**   15%   **4**   24%   **5**   40%

2. Express these percentages as decimals.

   1   18%   **2**   95%   **3**   6%   **4**   11%   **5**   60%

3. Find the value of

   1   48% of £5.50   **4**   12% of £95
   2   5% of £12   **5**   80% of £23.40
   3   25% of £13.20

4. Find the value of

   1   4% of 3 m   **4**   9% of 50 cm
   2   15% of 2 kg   **5**   21% of 5 ℓ
   3   60% of $\frac{1}{2}$ hour

5. **1**   Increase £2.50 by 6%   **4**   Increase £106 by 10%
   2   Increase £75 by 20%   **5**   Decrease £300 by 8%
   3   Decrease £6.50 by 4%

Exercise 9.3   Applications and Activities

1. William spends half of his pocket money on Saturdays, and one-third on Sundays. This leaves him with 75p for the rest of the week. How much pocket money does he get ?

2. June and her mum went to pick mushrooms. June found 18 and her mum found $2\frac{1}{2}$ times as many. How many did they find altogether ?

3. A farmer decided to check and repair a wall which was 240 m long. On the first day he did a length of 96 m, the second day he did $\frac{3}{4}$ of that distance and on the third day he did $\frac{2}{3}$ of the distance of the second day. What fraction of the complete length remained to be done ?

4. At a football match one-third of the spectators were seated. The other 16 800 stood up. How many spectators were there altogether ?

5. In an election there were 3 candidates, Mr A, Mr B and Mr C. 3150 people voted and Mr A got $\frac{1}{5}$ of the votes. How many votes did he get ?
Mr B got $\frac{4}{9}$ of the votes. How many did he get ?
Mr C got the rest of the votes. How many did he get ?
Who won the election ?
How many more votes did the winner get, than the runner-up ?

6. Mira was trying to save £12 to buy a sweater. For 7 weeks she saved £1.20 a week. What fraction of the £12 had she still to save ?

7. On a farm there were 280 animals. $\frac{5}{8}$ of them were sheep, $\frac{1}{10}$ of them were pigs, there were 2 ponies, 4 dogs, 3 cats, 5 rabbits and the rest were cows. How many cows were there ? What fraction of the total were cows ?

8. Mrs Evans won £450 in a competition. She gave $\frac{1}{3}$ of it to her husband and $\frac{2}{5}$ of the remainder to her daughter. She kept the remaining money for herself. How much did she keep ?

9. A water tank held 720ℓ of water. The gardener used $\frac{1}{4}$ of it on Monday, $\frac{1}{3}$ of the remainder on Tuesday and on Wednesday he used $\frac{2}{3}$ of what was left. How much water remained ?

10. A joint of meat weighed $3\frac{1}{4}$ kg. The cooking time was recommended as 40 minutes per kg plus an extra 20 minutes.
What total cooking time was needed ?
It was planned to have lunch at 1 pm. At what time should the joint have been put in the oven ?

11. The foreman put in a report that 12% of the machines in the workshop needed repairing. If there were 225 machines altogether, how many were working properly ?

12.   This seed packet contained 250 seeds.
       At least how many seeds can you expect
       to germinate ?

13.   A couple stay in a hotel for 3 nights at a cost of £18 per person per night. A
       service charge of 10% is added to the bill. What is the total cost for both of
       them ?

14.   A brass bar weighing 40 kg is made of 55% copper and the rest of zinc. How
       many kg of zinc does it contain ?

15.   A group of 5 boys do a job for which they earn £60. The organiser takes 25%
       of this and the rest of the money is shared equally among the other four. How
       much does each boy receive ?

16.   A furniture store had a dressing table for sale at £120. Since it was slightly
       damaged the price was then reduced by 15%. How much was it sold for ?

17.   It is estimated that some gravel will lose 12% of its weight when drying.
       A load weighed 350 kg. What will it weigh when dry ?

18.   The insurance premium for a car is £240. It is reduced by 60% for 'no claim
       discount'. How much does the motorist have to pay ? He pays this in
       12 monthly instalments. How much does he pay per month ?

19.   A holiday company has decided to improve its accommodation and services and
       to do this it raises its prices by 9%. What is the new cost of a holiday previously
       costing £260 ?

20.   A house was bought for £18 000. It is estimated that since that time house
       values have risen by 40%. What is the house worth now ?

21.   **Percentages in daily life**

       Get a copy of a daily newspaper and cut out all the references to percentage
       that you can find. You should find quite a few, in the articles themselves, in the
       financial pages and in the advertisements. Arrange these cut-outs on a poster.

22. **Fractions in order of size**

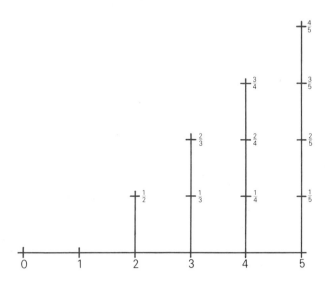

Look at this diagram. The points 0 to 5 are marked off along a horizontal line. Vertical lines are drawn upwards and the fractions have been marked off, those with numerator 1 on level 1, those with numerator 2 on level 2, and so on.

To write these fractions in order of size, put your ruler on the base line. Keeping the ruler passing through 0, turn it gradually until it also passes through one of the fraction points. The first fraction it comes to is $\frac{1}{5}$, because $\frac{1}{5}$ is the smallest fraction of these ten, and so its line is the least steep. As you let the ruler turn more, still keeping it passing through 0, it will pass through all the other fractions, in order of size.

Two of the fractions are equivalent, that is, the same size, and the ruler passes through both together. Which are they ?

Write down all the fractions in order of size. For the equal fractions, write down the one which is in its lowest terms.

This kind of sequence is called a **Farey sequence**.

Using squared paper or graph paper, make your own diagram, but going as far as point 10. Write down all your fractions in order of size.

You can make discoveries about these fractions.

If two consecutive fractions in the list are $\dfrac{a}{b}$ and $\dfrac{c}{d}$, investigate $b \times c$ and $a \times d$.

If three consecutive fractions in the list are $\dfrac{a}{b}, \dfrac{c}{d}$ and $\dfrac{e}{f}$, investigate $a + e$ and $b + f$.

10   Thinking about pie charts

Looking at pie charts

Why do you think the name pie chart was chosen ?
Here is a bar chart and a pie chart showing how the price you pay for a record album is divided among the people who are involved in its manufacture and sale.

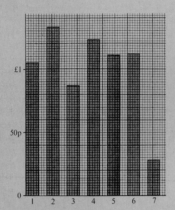 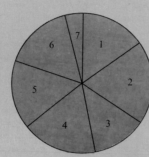

Record Album

1 VAT £1.05
2 Shop profit £1.33
3 Dealer profit 87p
4 Royalty and copyright £1.23
5 Design, manufacturing, promotion £1.11
6 Record company costs £1.12
7 Record company profit 28p
Total cost £6.99

Look at the diagrams and state some facts which they tell you about these records.
Has the bar chart got any advantages over the pie chart ?
Has the pie chart got any advantages over the bar chart ?
Here is a pie chart showing the proportions of costs for a compact disc. Compare it with the pie chart for the album.
Why is the angle for VAT nearly the same on both diagrams ?
Which sectors are much greater for compact discs, and why do you think this is ?

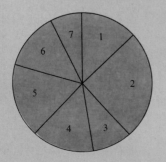

Compact Disc

1 VAT £1.43
2 Shop profit £2.81
3 Dealer profit £1.02
4 Royalty and copyright £1.59
5 Design, manufacturing. promotion £1.89
6 Record company costs £1.47
7 Record company profit 78p
Total cost £10.99

Favourite activities ?

Using pie charts yourself

Think of some data which you have collected, or could collect, which you could represent on a pie chart. The pictures may give you some ideas.

Favourite magazines ?

Favourite soft drinks ?

John Barnes
Favourite sports personality ?

10 Pie Charts

One way of showing how a whole item is split up into several parts, is to draw the whole as a circle and divide it into sectors for the different parts.
This kind of diagram is called a **pie chart**.

Example 1

In a survey, 180 people were asked to name their favourite leisure pursuit chosen from these five categories. The results are as shown:

Watching television	70
Reading	50
Taking part in sports	25
DIY and car maintenance	15
Entertaining and visiting friends	20
	180

The working for the pie chart

Since 180 people are represented by 360°,
    1 person is represented by 2°.

Television	70 × 2° =	140°
Reading	50 × 2° =	100°
Sports	25 × 2° =	50°
DIY, etc.	15 × 2° =	30°
Entertaining	20 × 2° =	40°

Pie chart to show leisure pursuits of 180 people

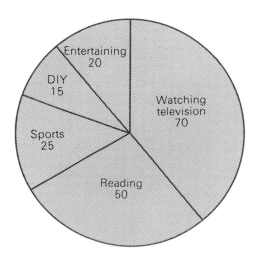

One advantage of a pie chart is that it is easy to see approximately what fraction of the whole is involved. Here, the largest part is 'watching television', and this, together with 'entertaining', makes half. Reading is just bigger than $\frac{1}{4}$, and sports and DIY together are just less than $\frac{1}{4}$.

Example 2

An advertisement gives these facts about eggs.
12.1% of the egg is protein
11.8% of the egg is carbohydrates, minerals and vitamins
10.5% of the egg is fat
65.6% of the egg is water

The working for the pie chart

To find the angle for 12.1% we need 12.1% of 360°.
Use your calculator to work out $\frac{12.1}{100} \times 360°$, giving the answer to the nearest degree.

Protein	$\frac{12.1}{100} \times 360° =$	44°
Carbohydrates, etc.	$\frac{11.8}{100} \times 360° =$	42°
Fat	$\frac{10.5}{100} \times 360° =$	38°
Water	$\frac{65.6}{100} \times 360° =$	236°

Pie chart to show the composition of eggs

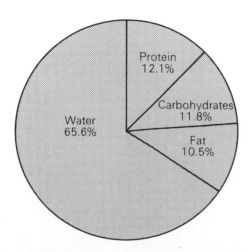

Exercise 10.1

1. The pie chart shows the time Marie
   spends on different subjects in each
   week.
   There are 7 lessons on 4 days and 8
   lessons on the 5th day. How many
   lessons are there in a week ?
   What size of angle represents 1 lesson ?
   Which subject has most lessons ?
   How many lessons are there for Maths ?
   How many lessons are there for P.E. ?
   How many lessons are there for foreign
   languages ?

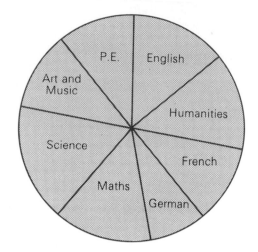

2. The 30 children in a class were asked how they came to school. The results
   were represented on a pie chart and the angles of the sectors were:

   Bus   132°
   Car   48°
   Cycle   24°

   The remaining sector represented the children who walked to school. What was
   the angle in this sector ?
   What size of angle represents 1 child ?
   How many children were there in each category ?

3. This list shows the vehicles used by a 'typical' police force. Show this
   information on a pie chart.

Large cars	80
Small cars	160
Vans	55
Motorcycles	35
Coaches	25
Lorries, etc.	5
	360

4. 36 girls were asked to name their favourite colour. Here are their replies:

    Blue, blue, blue, pink, green, white, pink, black, pink, pink, yellow, red, pink, black, black, black, yellow, green, black, yellow, pink, blue, blue, red, black, blue, red, blue, red, blue, pink, blue, blue, red, yellow, pink.

    Make a list of these replies and draw a pie chart to show the information.

5. According to a survey, an 'average' family spends £30 a week on transport. This shows how the money is spent, (amounts to nearest 50 p).

Cost of buying a car	£11.50
Cost of running a car	£13.50
Bus fares	£1.50
Other fares	£3.50

    ('Other fares' includes train fares, air fares, taxis, ferries and cycles.)

    Represent this information on a pie chart.

6. A survey on soft drinks showed the percentages of each type sold.

Fizzy drinks	52%
Squash	33%
Fruit juice	15%

    Calculate the sizes of the angles in the sectors of a pie chart, to the nearest degree.
    Show this information on a pie chart.

7. The estimated cost of running a car for 20 000 miles per year is split up into the following amounts:

Petrol	£1250
Oil, tyres, servicing	£265
Licence	£100
Insurance	£185

    What is the total cost ?
    On a pie chart, what amount would be represented by an angle of 1° ?
    Draw a pie chart to show the information.

8.   The bar chart illustrates the weekly budget of a family.

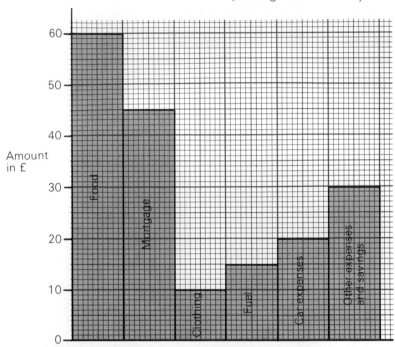

Use the chart to calculate the family's weekly income, and the fraction of the weekly income used on each item.
Draw a pie chart to show the same information.

9.   When petrol cost £1.80 per gallon, the cost was made up of these items:

Tax (duty and VAT)	£1.16
To retailers	8p
To oil company	56p

Draw a pie chart to represent these figures.

10.   The supply of platinum in 1988 came from these countries:

South Africa	80%
USSR	13%
Canada	4%
Other countries	3%

Calculate the sizes of the angles in the sectors of a pie chart, giving them to the nearest degree.
Show the information on a pie chart.

Exercise 10.2 Applications and Activities

1. The pie chart represents the houses built by 3 builders, *A*, *B*, *C*.
    1 Measure the angles of each
         sector, to the nearest 5°.
    2 If builder *A* built 30 houses,
         what was the total number
         of houses built ?
    3 What sector angle
         represents 1 house ?
    4 How many houses were
         built by *B*, and by *C* ?
    5 Represent this information
         in a pictogram.

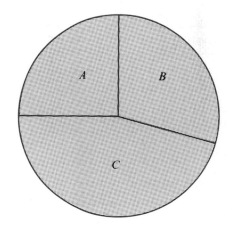

2. A survey of 15 year-old girls showed the most popular part-time jobs were:

Shopwork	49%
Hotel or cafe work	17%
Paper rounds	11%
Other jobs	23%

    From boys, the answers were:

Paper rounds	36%
Shopwork	27%
Manual work	16%
Other jobs	21%

    Draw two pie charts showing this information. Comment on the results of the
    survey.

3. The weekly spending in a small business firm was listed, and represented on a
    pie chart.

	Amount in £	Sector angle in degrees
Wages	600	b
Materials	400	c
Transport	d	60
Other expenses	e	f
Total	1800	a

Find the missing numbers represented by letters a, b, c, d, e, f, working in that
order.
Draw the pie chart.

4. Here are some figures which show how former countryside in Britain is now
    being used for building and commercial uses.

What the land was used for:		What the land is now used for:	
Farmland	61%	Housing	66%
Unused	17%	Transport	13%
Woodland	16%	Outdoor recreation	9%
Other uses	6%	Industry	8%
		Health and Education	4%

Draw two pie charts to show these figures.

5. Here are some suggestions for data you can collect yourself and represent by
    pie charts.

    1 Make a list of how you spend your time on an average weekday of 24 hours,
    including time spent sleeping, eating, at school, on homework, watching
    television, etc. You could compare this with how you spend your time at
    weekend.

    2 Make a list of how you spend your weekly pocket money.

3 From the TV timetables in the newspaper or magazines, choose an evening from 5 pm to 11 pm and find how much time is devoted to news, sport, drama, music, etc. on one of the channels. You can compare the results for the different channels.

4 Do a traffic survey at a safe place. Classify the traffic into categories, such as cars, buses, heavy goods vehicles, etc.

You should think of other ideas for yourself. There are also suggestions in Chapter 7 which you could use for pie charts.

PUZZLES

16. A spy smuggled two messages to his leader.
One said '3263426   702   2498   729841'
The other had this division sum:

```
          E P F
Y P ) D R I O
      F D
      A I
      P I
      Y O O
        I Y
        I
```

Decode the sum and thus decide what the first message was.

17. Here is a pattern of triangles. By considering the pattern of numbers, find how many triangles there are in the last two drawings.

1

5

?
(More than 10)

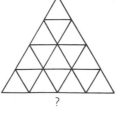
?

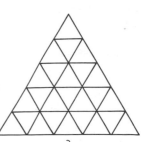
?

11 Thinking about negative numbers

What is a negative number ?

I have £35 and I get a bill for £13. If I pay the bill, how much money will be left ?
This is an ordinary subtraction sum and you can do it on your calculator by pressing
35 ⊟ 13 ⌑. What is the answer ?
I have £35 and I get a bill for £43. If I pay the bill, how much money will be left ?
Now, commonsense tells me that I can't pay the bill. But the calculator does not have
any commonsense so I will enter the calculation in the same way as before, pressing
35 ⊟ 43 ⌑.
What is the answer ? What does it mean ?
This is a negative number, called 'minus 8' or 'negative 8'.
I tell my mother how hard up I am and she gives me £8. On my calculator there is −8
shown. If I add 8 to this, what do I get ?

Negative numbers need not just be whole numbers, they can be fractions or decimals
such as $-\frac{3}{4}$, −3.3, etc.
The ordinary numbers 1, 2, 3, . . . as well as the fractions and decimals such as $\frac{2}{3}$, 0.3,
can be called positive numbers. If we want to emphasise that they are positive
numbers rather than negative numbers we can write +1, +2, +3, $+\frac{2}{3}$, +0.3, etc. There
is one number which is neither a positive nor a negative number. Which is it ?
On most calculators minus 8 is shown as −8 and there is a special key used for
entering negative numbers. Find out how to use this.

The temperature in Arctic regions can go as low as
−90°F.

The lowest point in the Western Hemisphere, 282 feet
below sea level, is in Death Valley, California.

In summer 1989, the water level in Hafren reservoir in Wales was 60 feet below normal.

Examples of negative numbers

There are many situations where we use negative numbers in our lives. What examples can you think of ? The pictures may give you some ideas.

Delta II rocket lifting off at Cape Canaveral in 1988. Times before lift-off are counted down as 10 9 8 7 6 5 4 3 2 1 zero.

Curtis Strange with a score of 2 below par, shown on scoreboards as −2.

11 Negative Numbers

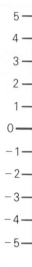

Here is a number line where the numbers go below 0.

Example

This is a thermometer marked in the Celsius scale.
0°C is the temperature at which water freezes, and the
temperature can drop below that level, so temperatures below
zero are given as −1°, −2°, −3°, etc.
Temperatures above zero are given as ordinary numbers,
1°, 2°, 3°, etc, or they can be given as plus numbers,
+1°, +2°, +3°, etc. (+3° is the same as 3°.)

Examples of calculations

1 The temperature last night was −4°. It has risen by 10°. What is the temperature
now ?

Start on a number line at −4. You are adding 10 so go upwards. Count out 10 and
you should get to 6. So the temperature now is 6°.

You can write this calculation as $(-4) + 10 = 6$.

You can do this calculation on your calculator. If you want to enter a negative number on your calculator, use the $\boxed{+/-}$ key, e.g. to enter -4, press 4 $\boxed{+/-}$. To calculate $(-4) + 10$, press 4 $\boxed{+/-}$ $\boxed{+}$ 10 $\boxed{=}$ and you will get the answer 6.

2 If on a calculator you press 5 $\boxed{-}$ 8 $\boxed{=}$, what answer will the calculator show ?

Start on the number line at 5. You are taking away 8 so go downwards. You count out 8 and you should get to -3.
You can write this calculation as $5 - 8 = -3$.
Now try this question on your calculator.

3 On the harbour wall there is a line showing the depth of the water in feet.
0 was marked at the average water level so if there is less water, negative numbers have to be used.
How much has the water level fallen if it was at 6 feet and later it was at (-3) feet ?

Count down from 6 to -3.
You count down 9 altogether so the water level has fallen by 9 feet.
You could write this calculation as
$6 - (-3) = 9$, and do it on your calculator by pressing 6 $\boxed{-}$ 3 $\boxed{+/-}$ $\boxed{=}$

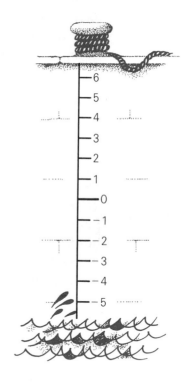

Exercise 11.1

1.   Where do you get to on the number scale by following these instructions ?

1   Start at 3 and go down 3.   **6**   Start at 5 and go down 6.
2   Start at -6 and go up 4.   **7**   Start at -3 and go up 2.
3   Start at -4 and go down 7.   **8**   Start at 2 and go down 2.
4   Start at 1 and go up 2.   **9**   Start at 3 and go down 5.
5   Start at -3 and go down 2.   **10** Start at -5 and go up 1.

2.   Say whether you should go up or down, and by how many:

    1   to get from 5 to 2,   **6**   to get from 2 to − 4,

    2   to get from − 4 to 3,   **7**   to get from 3 to 6,

    3   to get from 1 to − 4,   **8**   to get from −1 to 0,

    4   to get from − 2 to − 5,   **9**   to get from − 5 to −1,

    5   to get from − 4 to 0,   **10**   to get from 7 to −1.

3.   Where did you begin in these situations ?

    1   If having gone down 3 you get to 6.

    2   If having gone up 2 you get to 5.

    3   If having gone up 5 you get to 0.

    4   If having gone down 2 you get to − 3.

    5   If having gone up 4 you get to 0.

4.   Find the new temperature in the following cases.

    1   The temperature is +8° and it rises 3°.

    2   The temperature is +6° and it falls 9°.

    3   The temperature is − 4° and it rises 6°.

    4   The temperature is − 9° and it rises 2°.

    5   The temperature is 0° and it falls 6°.

    6   The temperature is +10° and it falls 24°.

    7   The temperature is − 8° and it rises 10°.

    8   The temperature is − 3° and it rises 3°.

    9   The temperature is +5° and it falls 4°.

    10   The temperature is −1° and it falls 3°.

5.   Say how many degrees the temperature has risen or fallen in the following cases.

    1   It was 0° and is now + 4°.

    2   It was − 5° and is now − 7°.

    3   It was + 3° and is now + 6°.

    4   It was −1° and is now 0°.

    5   It was − 4° and is now − 2°.

    6   It was 0° and is now − 5°.

    7   It was − 3° and is now − 7°.

    8   It was + 2° and is now − 3°.

    9   It was − 6° and is now −1°.

    10   It was − 2° and is now + 6°.

Exercise 11.2   Applications and Activities

1. Kate and Anne are playing a
    number game on this set of
    steps.
    They call the longer step 0, and
    the ones above 1, 2, 3, . . .
    From step 0 they number the
    ones below as −1, −2, −3, . . .
    Kate is on step 3 and Anne on step −1. Anne
    would have to go up 4 steps to reach Kate.
    This instruction is given as +4. Kate would
    have to go down 4 steps to reach Anne. This
    instruction is given as −4.
    (i.e. To go up, +. To go down, −.)

    What is the instruction to get from

    1   −3 to 3,   **4**   −2 to 5,
    2   0 to −2,   **5**   −3 to −1 ?
    3   1 to −4,

    Where does Anne finish if she was

    6   on step 4 and Kate said −3,   **9**   on step 0 and Kate said −1,
    7   on step −1 and Kate said +4,   **10** on step −5 and Kate said +2 ?
    8   on step −2 and Kate said −2,

2. (In this question give the answer in the form
    '10 minutes to 1' or '10 minutes past 1'.)

    1   If the time is 12 minutes to 1 o'clock,
        what will be the time in 20 minutes ?
    2   If the time is 5 minutes to 2 o'clock,
        what was the time 5 minutes ago ?
    3   If the time is 4 minutes past 3 o'clock,
        what was the time 2 minutes ago ?
    4   If the time is quarter past four, what
        was the time 20 minutes ago ?
    5   If the time is quarter to five, what will
        be the time in 25 minutes ?

3.   **1**   If the time is 12 minutes past 1 o'clock, how many minutes have passed since it was 5 minutes to 1 o'clock ?

    2   If the time is 5 minutes to 2, in how many minutes will it be 2.15 ?

    3   If the time is twenty to three, in how many minutes will it be five to three ?

    4   If the time is 6 minutes to 4, how many minutes have passed since it was quarter to 4 ?

    5   If the time is ten to five, in how many minutes will it be ten past five ?

4.   Mr Collins has an agreement with his bank to overdraw money, that is, to spend more money than is in his account.

    1   If he has £400 in his account and writes a cheque for £650, how much will his account be overdrawn ?

    2   If his account is overdrawn by £200 and he puts £80 into the account, how much is he overdrawn now ?

    3   If his account is overdrawn by £70 and he puts £130 into the account, how much is his account in credit ?

    4   If his account is overdrawn by £150 and he takes out another £30, how much is he overdrawn now ?

    5   If he has £250 in his account and writes a cheque for £400, and then puts £80 into the account, is his account overdrawn or in credit, and by how much ?

5.   Vijay and Amul are playing a game with cards marked with + numbers or − numbers. At the end of the game they score according to the numbers on their cards.

e.g. For $\boxed{+8}$ $\boxed{-6}$ $\boxed{-3}$ Vijay scores $8 - 6 - 3 = -1$

What do they score with these cards ?

1    **4**

2    **5**

3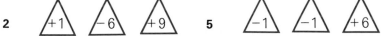

6.   **1**   If the temperature is $+3°$ and it falls by $8°$, what is the new temperature ?

    2   If the temperature is $-4°$, by how many degrees must it rise to become $+7°$?

    3   If the temperature is $+9°$ and it falls to $-6°$ overnight, through how many degrees has it fallen ?

    4   After rising 8 degrees the temperature is $+1°$. What was it originally ?

    5   After falling 6 degrees the temperature is $-9°$. What was it originally ?

7. Number patterns can use negative numbers.
   e.g. 10, 7, 4, 1, −2, −5, −8, . . . (Taking 3 off each time).

   Write down the next three terms in these sequences.

   1 20, 15, 10, 5, . . .   **4** −22, −17, −12, −7, . . .
   2 −10, −8, −6, −4, . . .   **5** 18, 14, 10, 6, . . .
   3 −3, 0, 3, 6, . . .

8. Here is a multiplication number pattern.

4	0	4	8	12	16
3	0	3	6	9	12
2	0	2	4	6	8
1	0	1	2	3	4
0	0	0	0	0	0
	0	1	2	3	4

Here is a similar pattern extended to include negative numbers.

	−4	−3	−2	−1	0	1	2	3	4
4					0	4	8	12	16
3					0	3	6	9	12
2		−6			0	2	4	6	8
1				−1	0	1	2	3	4
0					0	0	0	0	0
−1									−4
−2					0				
−3									
−4			8						

Copy it and use the number patterns in rows and columns to complete it. Some numbers have been filled in, to help you.

The spaces filled in show that $1 \times (-1) = -1$
$$(-2) \times 0 = 0$$
$$2 \times (-3) = -6$$
$$(-1) \times 4 = -4$$
$$(-4) \times (-2) = 8$$

This last result seems rather strange but it is the true result.
Now you know how to multiply negative numbers.
Write down the answers to these questions:
$0 \times (-6)$, $5 \times (-7)$, $(-1) \times 10$, $(-8) \times 0$, $(-5) \times (-6)$.

12 Thinking about triangles

What is a triangle ?

What is a triangle ?
Where is the word derived from ?
What other words begin with the letters 'tri', for a similar reason ?

Triangle facts

You may have made some discoveries about triangles in chapter 2. What facts do you already know about them ?

Triangles in everyday life

Look for examples of triangles in daily life. The road traffic signs enclosed in a triangle are **warning** signs. Can you find any other examples of triangles being used as warning symbols ?
Why in structures like scaffolding are diagonal pieces put in to form triangles ?
Why did a milkmaid traditionally sit on a 3-legged stool rather than a 4-legged one ?

Why are all these warning signs needed here ?

This is a warning symbol used on clothing and other materials. What does it mean ?

Counting triangles

How many triangles can you find in this drawing ?

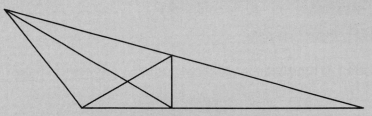

Draw some triangles of different shapes. What different kinds of triangles are there, and what are they called ? Look for some of these in the drawing above.

168

12 Triangles

A figure with 3 straight sides is called a **triangle**.

Acute-angled, right-angled and obtuse-angled triangles

These are **acute-angled triangles**, since all their angles are acute angles (less than 90°).

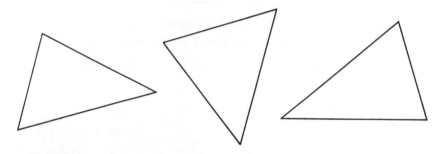

These are **right-angled triangles**, since one of the angles in each triangle is a right angle.

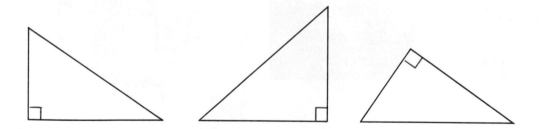

These are **obtuse-angled triangles**, since one of the angles in each triangle is an obtuse angle.

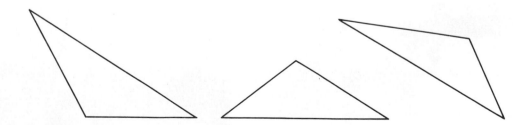

An exterior angle of a triangle

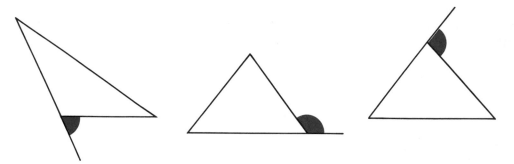

These shaded angles are called exterior angles of the triangles.
They are made by producing (i.e. extending) one of the sides of the triangle.

Angles of a triangle

1 An exterior angle is equal to the sum of the two opposite interior angles.

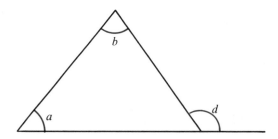

In the diagram, $d = a + b$

2 The sum of the angles of a triangle is 180°.

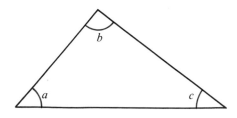

In the diagram, $a + b + c = 180°$

Scalene, isosceles and equilateral triangles

These triangles have all sides of different lengths and they are called **scalene triangles**.

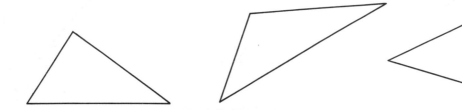

These triangles have two equal sides and they are called **isosceles triangles**.

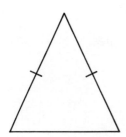 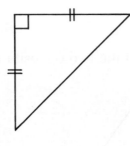 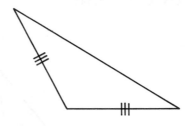

This is an
acute-angled
isosceles triangle

This is a
right-angled
isosceles triangle

This is an
obtuse-angled
isosceles triangle

(The small marks crossing the sides is the sign that those lines have equal length.)

A triangle with all three sides equal is called an **equilateral triangle**.

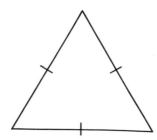 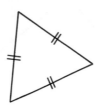 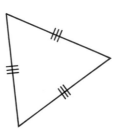

These are equilateral triangles.

Angles in isosceles triangles

The angles opposite the equal sides are equal.

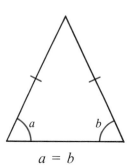

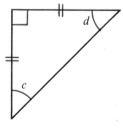

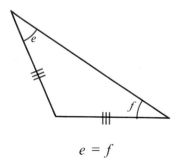

$a = b$ $c = d$ $e = f$
                  (and they are 45°)

Angles in an equilateral triangle

Each angle is 60°.

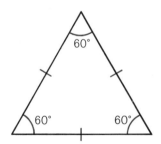

Naming of triangles

A triangle with vertices at points A, B, C is
called triangle ABC.
This can be written as $\triangle ABC$.

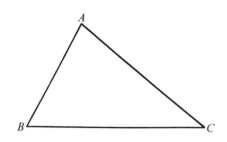

Naming of angles

Sometimes it is not convenient to label angles with small letters.

Instead we can label an angle by naming the point
where the angle is.
This is angle B or $\angle B$ because it is at point B.

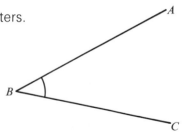

There may be more than one angle at point *B*, so
that we need further information.

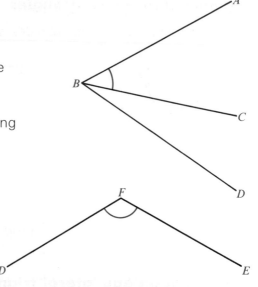

Here the **marked** angle is called an angle *ABC* or
$\angle ABC$ or $\widehat{ABC}$. It could also be called $\angle CBA$. The
middle letter tells us at which point the angle is.
Here it is at *B* so the middle letter is *B*. The other
two letters, each with *B*, tell us the two lines making
the angle. Here they are *BA* and *BC*.
The unmarked angle is $\angle CBD$ (or $\angle DBC$).
The complete angle is $\angle ABD$ (or $\angle DBA$).

This angle is at *F*, so the middle letter is *F*.
The lines are *FD* and *FE*, so the angle is $\angle DFE$
(or $\angle EFD$).

Examples

1   Find the sizes of angles *b* and *c*.

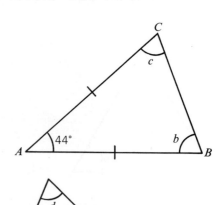

$b + c + 44° = 180°$ (sum of angles of
                                               a triangle = 180°)

$b + c = 136°$
$\triangle ABC$ is isosceles, $AB = AC$, so $b = c$
$b = 68°, c = 68°$

2   Find the sizes of angles *d* and *e*.

$d = 76°$ (isosceles triangle,
                                     equal angles)

$e = d + 76°$ (exterior angle
                                    of triangle)

$e = 152°$

3   Find the sizes of angles *f* and *g*.

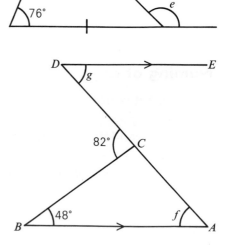

$f + 48° = 82°$ (exterior angle of
                                      $\triangle ABC$)

$f = 34°$
$g = f$ (alternate angles)

$g = 34°$

Exercise 12.1

1. Measure the angles in these triangles, using your protractor. Check that the sum of the angles of each triangle is 180°. (Because you are measuring to the nearest degree, the sum may not be exactly 180°.)

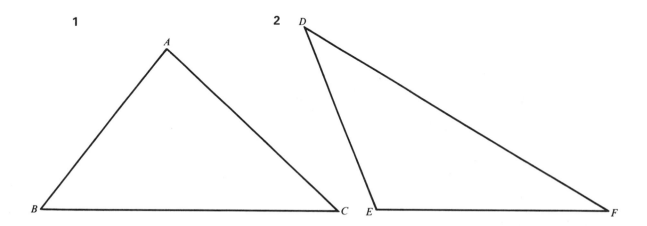

2. Check that these triangles are isosceles, by measuring their sides (in cm, to the nearest mm). Measure the angles in the triangles, using your protractor. Check that the sum of the angles of each triangle is 180°, and that the angles opposite the equal sides are equal.

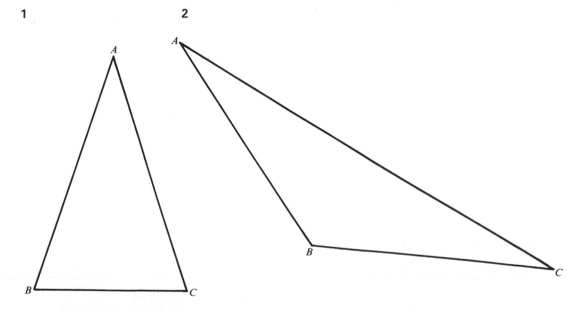

3.   Calculate the sizes of the 3rd angles in these triangles.

1

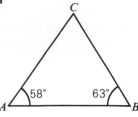

2

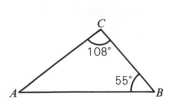

3

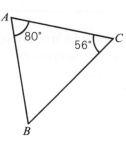

4

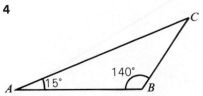

5

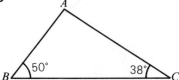

4.   Calculate the marked angles in these figures.

1

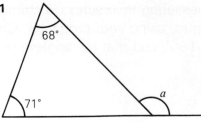

2

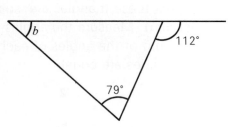

3

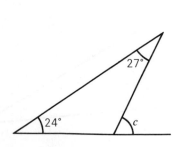

4

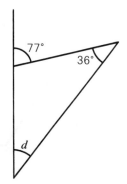

5

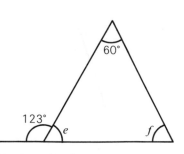

5.   Calculate the 3rd angle in these triangles and say whether the triangle is acute-angled, right-angled or obtuse angled, or if it is isosceles or equilateral.

    1   Two angles are 130°, 32°.   **4**   Two angles are 28°, 32°.

    2   Two angles are 58°, 32°.   **5**   Two angles are 74°, 32°.

    3   Two angles are 60°, 60°.

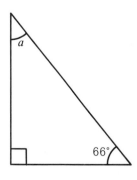

6.   Find the size of angle *a*.

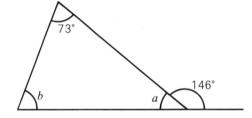

7.   Find the sizes of *a* and *b*.
      What sort of triangle is it ?

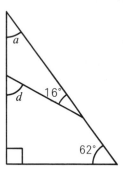

8.   Find the size of *a*, and then
      find the size of *d*.

9.   Give the small letter names of these angles.
      1 ∠*BAC*   **2** ∠*DCB*   **3** ∠*ADC*
      Name these angles using 3 capital letters.
      4 *f*   **5** *d*

    6   Name ∠*B* using 3 letters, in 4 different
      ways.

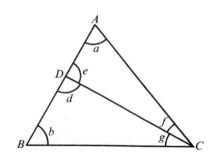

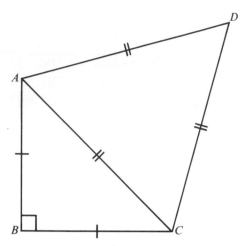

10. △*ABC* is a right-angled isosceles triangle
     with ∠*B* = 90°.
     △*ACD* is an equilateral triangle.
     Calculate the sizes of
     1   ∠*BAC*   **2**   ∠*CAD*   **3**   ∠*BAD*

Exercise 12.2   Applications and Activities

In questions 1 to 4, find the sizes of the marked angles.

1.

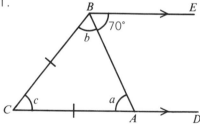

2.

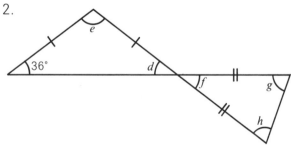

3.

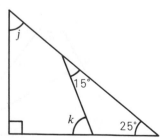

4.

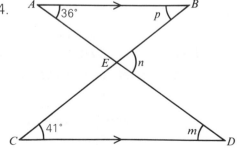

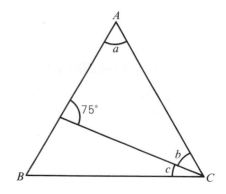

5. $\triangle ABC$ is equilateral. Find the sizes of angles a, b and c.

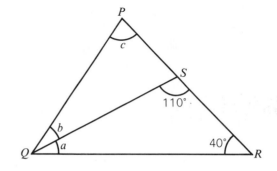

6. In the diagram the line QS bisects the angle PQR. (This means it cuts it exactly in half.) Calculate the sizes of angles a, b and c.

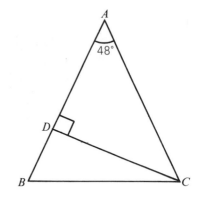

7. If $AB = AC$, which two angles are equal ?

    Find the sizes of $\angle ABC$, $\angle BCA$, $\angle ACD$, $\angle CDB$, $\angle BCD$.

PUZZLE

18. Mr English, Mr French and Mr German teach English, French and German. However, not one of them teaches the subject which is the same as his name.
    If Mr French's wife is the English teacher's sister, what does Mr German teach ?

13 Thinking about probability

What is probability ?

'The family next door will probably go to Spain for their holidays.'
Think of some sentences which include the word 'probably'.
I'll probably go . . .
I'll probably buy . . .
The bus will probably be late again.
My mother will probably let me come.
These are predictions for the future, but they are not definite predictions.
Consider these statements:
'The family next door are going to Spain for their holidays.'
Unless something unforseen happens, it is certain that they will go.
'The family next door may go to Spain for their holidays.'
There is nothing certain here, it is not even as likely as 'probably'.
Perhaps you can tell from the tone of voice of the speaker, or you know from past experience, how likely the event is to happen.
Which of these events are more likely to happen ? Put the statements in order, with the more likely ones last.

   You will have chips for tea tonight.
   It will rain today.
   Someone in your family will have a large win on the pools.
   It will go dark tonight.
   If you toss a coin, it will come down heads.
   You will be involved in a road accident within the next month.
   You will travel abroad within the next year.

You are making a judgement about the likelihood or the probability of the event happening.
In Mathematics we give this a numerical value varying from 0, (completely unlikely to happen), to 1, (absolutely certain to happen). Try to give a numerical value to your previous answers. If not 0 or 1, give them as decimals, to 1 or 2 decimal places.
Sometimes you can alter the probability by taking certain actions. What action could you take to lessen the probability that you will be late for school ?
Suggest some actions that you could take to lessen the probability that you will be involved in a road accident.

Investing money in stocks and shares means judging how well a company will do.

Will a by-pass be needed in the future ?

The insurance company may decide that there are likely to be less burglaries.

Using probability

Probability is often associated with gambling. A professional gambler will work out how likely he is to win a game or a bet. And for you to learn about probability, the simple questions are often based on the probabilities of the results of tossing coins, throwing dice or picking cards out of a pack. But, in real life, probability has many, more important, uses.

Government departments, business firms, industrialists, scientists, medical researchers and many other people and organisations use the figures from past events to predict what is likely to happen in the future, and thus they can plan ahead. For example, Insurance Companies use their knowledge of past claims to predict future ones, and they can then decide what premiums they must charge.

Finish of the 1989 Grand National. Some people gamble on horse racing.

13 Probability Experiments

Probability is the likelihood of an event happening, for example, a tossed coin showing heads. It is measured on a numerical scale from 0 to 1 and can either be given as a fraction, e.g. $\frac{1}{2}$ or as a decimal, e.g. 0.5.

An experiment

If we have a number of beads in a bag, some red and some blue, but otherwise identical, and we pick one out at random (i.e. without looking), record its colour, replace it in the bag and give the bag a shake to mix the beads up again, and keep repeating this, then after a few trials we can work out the fraction

$$\frac{\text{number of trials giving a red bead}}{\text{total number of trials}}.$$

These are the results from one such experiment when the bag contained less red beads than blue ones.

number of trials (n)	number of red beads (r)	fraction $\dfrac{r}{n}$	$\dfrac{r}{n}$ to 2 decimal places
10	3	$\frac{3}{10}$	0.30
25	9	$\frac{9}{25}$	0.36
50	16	$\frac{16}{50}$	0.32
100	31	$\frac{31}{100}$	0.31
200	56	$\frac{56}{200}$	0.28
300	93	$\frac{93}{300}$	0.31
500	143	$\frac{143}{500}$	0.29
1000	302	$\frac{302}{1000}$	0.30

Here are the first 100 results, worked out after every 10 trials, plotted on a graph.

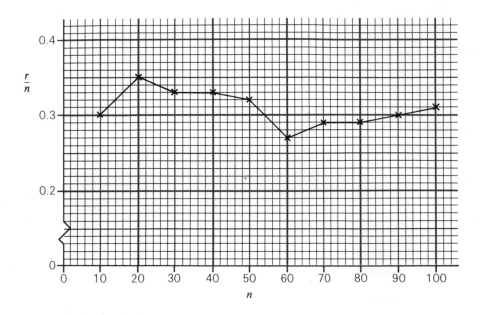

Here are the results for 1000 trials, worked out after every 100 trials.

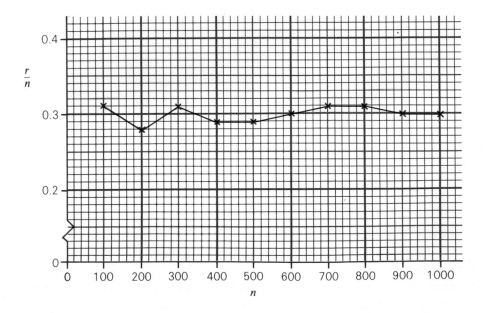

Although the results may be erratic after only a few trials, they then settle down around 0.3 so that in the long run red appears in 0.3 of the trials.

$$\text{The probability of a red bead} = \frac{\text{number of red beads drawn out}}{\text{total number of beads drawn out}} = 0.3$$

We can only use this method for estimating probability if we do enough trials to show that the fraction is settling down to a steady value. If the event was unpredictable the fraction would not settle down and we could not find a value for the probability.

When we know the probability of an event happening we can use its value to predict the likelihood of a future result.

In many cases we can **calculate** probabilities. (See Chapter 20.) For instance, if we had known that the bag of beads contained 30 red and 70 blue beads, we could calculate that the probability of a red bead = $\frac{30}{100}$ = 0.3, without doing the experiment.

In other cases it is not possible to do a calculation. If you are entering for a race, the probability that you will win cannot be calculated by a mathematical formula. It will depend on how well you can run, compared with the speeds of the other runners, and this may be affected by such things as the length of the race, the weather, how comfortable your shoes are, etc. Perhaps someone will estimate that the chance of you winning is 75%. This means that according to them, you are more likely to win than not, but not certain to win. In the long run, in similar races, they think that you would win in 75% or $\frac{3}{4}$ of them.

Experiments to try

Here are some suggestions for experiments. We have chosen simple equipment such as coins, dice and playing cards. If you have not got proper equipment it is often possible to think of a substitute.
All the trials should be done randomly and fairly. Toss a coin properly. Give a die (dice) a good shake before rolling it out onto a flat surface. With a pack of cards, take out the jokers first so that the pack contains the 52 cards of the 4 suits, and then shuffle them properly.
If you can combine other people's results with yours to give more trials, then do so. Keep a proper record of all your results because you may be able to use them again later.

Exercise 13.1

1. **Tossing coins**

   There are several experiments you can do using the results of tossing coins, so instead of continually having to toss coins again, start off by tossing a coin 200 times. Record your results in order, in a grid of 10 columns by 20 rows. Put H for head and T for tail.

   The grid starts like this:

H	H	T	H	T	T	H			

   1 What is the probability of a toss showing a head ?

   If you toss a coin 200 times, guess how many heads you are likely to get.

   Using the results you have recorded, make a table similar to this and fill it in.

number of tosses (*n*)	number of heads (*h*)	fraction $\frac{h}{n}$	$\frac{h}{n}$ to 2 decimal places
1			
2			
3			
4			
5			
10			
20			
50			
100			
150			
200			

   Was your guess a good one ?
   From your results, what value would you give for the probability of a toss showing a head ?
   Often a coin is tossed at the beginning of a game, such as in football or cricket matches. Why is tossing a coin chosen at such times ?

2   If two coins are tossed, what is the probability that both of them will show heads ?

If two coins are tossed 100 times, guess how many times you are likely to get two heads.

Now use the results in your grid in pairs. You could write down in a tally chart the number of heads in each pair of tosses.
e.g. If your table begins

H H   T H   T T   H H   T T   . . .

Number of heads   2   1   0   2   0
in two tosses

Tally chart

Number of heads in two tosses		f
0 1 2	//.. /... ///.	
		100

Was your guess a good one ?
The estimated probability of getting two heads

$$= \frac{\text{number of trials giving two heads}}{\text{total number of trials}} = \frac{. . .}{100} = . . .$$

You can investigate in a similar way taking coins 3 at a time, or 4 at a time.

2.   **Throwing a die**

(Although you probably talk about playing with a *dice*, the correct word is a *die*. Two or more are called *dice*.)

Instead of throwing a die for every different experiment, start off by recording your throws (the numbers which land on the top face) as you throw a die 400 times.
Make a grid of 20 columns by 20 rows.

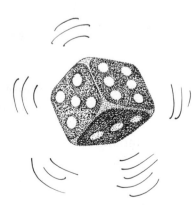

1   What is the probability of a die showing a six ?

If you throw a die 400 times, guess how many sixes you are likely to get.

Using the results you have recorded, make a table similar to this and fill it in.

number of throws (n)	number of 6's (s)	fraction $\dfrac{s}{n}$	$\dfrac{s}{n}$ to 2 decimal places
10 20 50 100 200 300 400			

From your results, what value would you give for the probability of a throw showing a six ?

2   If you throw two dice and add the two numbers together, what is the most likely total, and what is the probability of getting that total ?

Guess the most likely total, and also guess how many times that total will occur if you throw two dice 200 times.

Now use the results in your grid in two's. Make a new grid and put the totals in that.
e.g. If your table begins

$$\underbrace{6 \quad 4}_{} \quad \underbrace{1 \quad 2}_{} \quad \underbrace{3 \quad 5}_{} \quad \underbrace{1 \quad 4}_{} \quad \ldots$$

Totals for   10   3   8   5
the pair

You could also record the totals in a tally chart and represent them by a histogram. According to these results, the most likely total is . . .

The estimated probability of getting this total

$$= \frac{\text{number of trials giving this total}}{\text{total number of trials}} = \frac{\ldots}{200} = \ldots$$

(200 trials is not really enough to give a reliable answer so your most likely total may not be the correct one. Do not feel annoyed at this. The important thing is that it is correct according to your experiment. Not all dice are fair ones. Maybe the one you used is not perfect, and favours some numbers more than others. You could investigate this. You could also combine someone else's results with yours, to see if this affects the answers. The more trials there are, the closer the results should be to the mathematically correct ones.)

3   Is it true that, if you throw a die 6 times, you **must** get at least one six ?

What is the probability of getting at least one six if you throw a die 6 times ?

Guess how many times this will happen out of 66 sets of results.

Use the results in your 1st grid in groups of 6 at a time. Record √ if the group of 6 contains at least one six and x if it does not. From the 400 results you will have 66 groups of 6 (with 4 left over). Count how many √'s you have. Compare the results with your guess, and work out the estimated probability.
Again you may get answers which are closer to the mathematically correct ones if you combine your results with those of other people to give you more trials.

Exercise 13.2   Applications and Activities

1.   Put 10 similar drawing-pins into a cup and holding it approximately 20 cm above a table, gently tip the drawing-pins out so that they land on the table. They come

to rest point upwards, like this ⊥ or on their side, like this ⟨⟨ Count and

record how many land point upwards. Repeat the experiment 50 times. Find the total number point upwards after 1, 5, 10, 20, 30, 40 and 50 goes.

Make a table similar to this and fill it in.

total number tipped out (n)	number point upwards (s)	fraction $\frac{s}{n}$	$\frac{s}{n}$ to 2 decimal places
10			
50			
100			
200			
300			
400			
500			

If the results are settling down to a certain value this gives the value of the probability that a drawing-pin in this type of experiment will land point upwards. (There is no theoretical way of checking this result.)
The height through which the drawing-pins fall may affect the result. You could investigate this by repeating the experiment from different heights. Different makes of drawing-pins may also give different results.

2. **Marbles in a circle**

You need 7 marbles, 2 of which are coloured
differently. (We will call these the red ones.) You
also need two polythene cups. The marbles should
fit in the bottom of a cup like this:-
If they don't all touch the bottom of the cup, give it
a gentle shake.

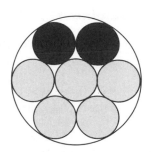

If you put the 7 marbles in at random, what is the probability that the 2 red
marbles are next to each other ?

yes

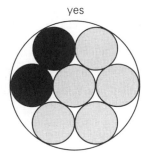

yes

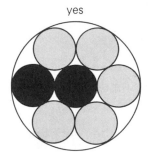

no

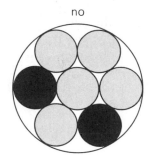

Make a guess first.
When you have carried out one trial, record the result as √ or x
Then pour the marbles into the other cup for the next trial. Repeat about 100
times.
Estimated probability of the 2 red marbles being next to each other

$$= \frac{\text{number of successful results}}{\text{total number of results}}$$

Was your guess a good one ?

3.   If you are playing a card game where you begin with 3 cards, what is the
      probability that they include at least one which is an Ace, King, Queen or Jack ?

Make a guess first.

Shuffle a pack of cards and pick out 3 cards.
Record as √ if they contain at least one of those cards
and as x if they do not.
Replace the cards, shuffle and repeat 100 times
altogether.

Estimated probability $= \dfrac{\text{number of successful results}}{\text{total number of results}}$

Was your guess a good one ?

4.   **Dominoes**

You can do probability experiments
with dominoes.

If you have a set going up to double
six then the numbers on them are

0–0 0–1 0–2 . . . up to 0–6
1–1 1–2 1–3 . . . up to 1–6
2–2 2–3 and so on, up to 6–6

How many dominoes are there
altogether ?
Put the dominoes in a bag and draw
them out without looking.

If you pick out 2 dominoes at random, what is the probability that they will
match ?

They match if they have one number the same.
e.g.

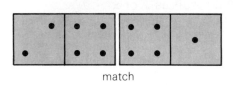

match

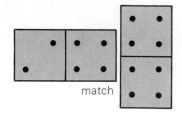

match

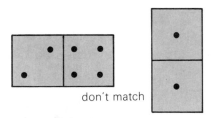

don't match

Make a guess first.
You can estimate the probability by drawing out 2 dominoes. Record √ if they
match and x if they do not. Put the two dominoes back, give the bag a good
shake and repeat about 100 times.

$$\text{Probability of 2 dominoes matching} = \frac{\text{number of results which match}}{\text{total number of results}}$$

Was your guess a good one ?

5.   Archie, Bertie and Charlie were playing a game where they had to throw a six with a die to begin. They argued about wanting to go first, because they thought that the first player had a better chance of throwing a six before the others. Is this correct ? What is the probability of the first player to begin being the first to throw a six ?

Use the beginning of your dice grid as the scores of the 3 boys in turn, starting with A, then B, then C, then A again, etc. When you reach a six, record which boy has thrown it. Then begin again, starting with the next throw on your grid as belonging to A. When you have used all your results, borrow someone else's grid to use as well. Try to get 100 results. Then you can estimate the probability of A getting a six first.

$$\text{Probability} = \frac{\text{number of results for A}}{\text{total number of results}}$$

You can also estimate the probability of B and C getting a six first.
Suggest a fair way for the boys to decide who shall go first.

PUZZLES

19.   Put the numbers 1 to 8 in these circles so that no number is joined by a line to the next consecutive number.

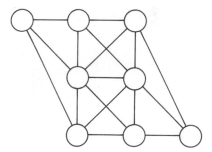

20.   Here is a magic square using numbers 1 to 16 that adds up to 34 both down and across as well as diagonally. So do the 4 corners, and the 4 centres.
Copy it and fill in the missing numbers.

13	8		
12		14	
		4	
			16

14 Thinking about coordinates

Coordinates in the classroom

If someone was trying to describe where you were sitting in the classroom, they might say something like 'in the 2nd row of desks from the doorway, 3rd from the front'. In that case they are using a system very similar to that which we use in plotting points on graphs, although we plot points, rather than rectangles such as desks.

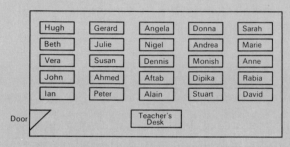

In the plan of the classroom shown, who is sitting at the desk described above ?
To simplify the wording, we shall call this desk (2, 3), so that, like in our coordinate system, we measure, in this case from the doorway, along first and then up.
Susan's friends are sitting at three desks, (1, 4), (3, 5), (5, 2). What are their names ?
Can you think of situations where we use a similar system (sometimes using letters rather than numbers) to pin-point a position ?

Here is a game where the squares are described by a coordinate system.

In chess, how are the squares numbered to record games ?

Positive and negative coordinates

Now that you have used negative numbers you can use them on a graph as well.
The x-axis is numbered like this:

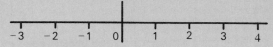

The y-axis is similar, going up the page.
Together, they look like this.

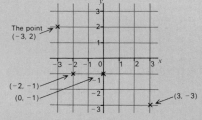

Here is a picture to draw, so that you can practise using negative coordinates.
On graph paper label the x-axis from -30 to 40, and the y-axis from -20 to 20, using a scale of 2 cm to 10 units on both axes.
Join each point to the next one with a straight line, except where there is a cross after the point.

$(22, -5)$, $(32, 13)$, $(-13, 13)$, $(-8, 1)$x $(-8, -2)$, $(-8, -16)$, $(-5, -16)$, $(-5, -2\frac{1}{2})$x $(-28, 2)$, $(-28, 5)$, $(32, -7)$, $(32, -10)$, $(-28, 2)$x

Complete the diagram with most of a circle, centre at $(30, -8)$ and radius 8 units $(1.6 \, \text{cm})$.

Houston, Texas is a city built in a rectangular pattern so it is easy to direct someone using a coordinate system.

14 Coordinates

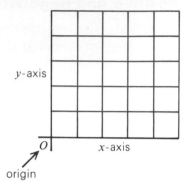

A point on a graph can be fixed by giving its coordinates, i.e. its x-value and its y-value.

Examples

1 Point A has x-value 1 and y-value 2.
   This can be written as the point (1, 2).
   (The x-value is always written first.)

   A is (1, 2)
   B is (3, 0)
   C is (6, 3)

   Copy this diagram and plot the point D (4, 5).
   Join AB, BC, CD, DA.
   What sort of figure is $ABCD$?

Graphs including negative numbers

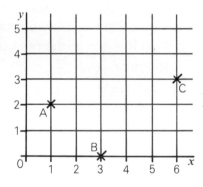

2 Point *P* has *x*-value −1 and *y*-value 3.
   P is (−1, 3)
   Q is (−2, −2)
   R is (3, −3)

   Copy the diagram and plot the point *S* (4, 2).
   Join *PQ*, *QR*, *RS*, *SP*.
   What sort of figure is *PQRS* ?

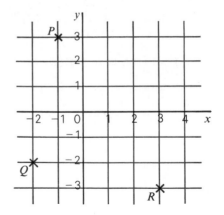

Exercise 14.1

For each question, draw axes for *x* and *y* from −3 to 3, using equal scales on both axes.

1. Plot points *A* (1, 3), *B* (−2, 2) and *C* (3, −3).
   Join *AB*, *BC* and *AC*.
   What sort of triangle is triangle *ABC* ?

2. Plot points *D* (−2, 0), *E* (1, 2) and *F* (−1, −1).
   Join *DE*, *EF* and *DF*.
   What sort of triangle is triangle *DEF* ?

3. Plot points *G* (3, 2), *H* (−1, 1) and *J* (−2, −3).
   Join *GH*, *HJ* and *GJ*.
   What sort of triangle is triangle *GHJ* ?

4. Plot points *K* (−1, 2), *L* (2, 3), *M* (0, −2) and *N* (3, −1).
   Join *KL* and *MN*.
   What do you notice about these lines ?

5. Plot points *P* (0, −2), *Q* (2, 3), *R* (3, −2) and *S* (−2, 0).
   Join *PQ* and *RS*.
   What do you notice about these lines ?

Exercise 14.2   Applications and Activities

1. Draw axes for *x* and *y* from −1 to 4 using equal scales on both axes.
   Plot the points *A* (−1, 1), *B* (0, 4) and *C* (3, 3). Join *AB* and *BC*.
   Mark a point *D* and join *AD* and *CD*, such that *ABCD* is a square.
   What are the coordinates of *D* ?

2.   For this question, use graph paper with x from -2 to 3 and y from -4 to 6 using scales of 1 cm to 1 unit on both axes.

   1   This is a pattern of numbers connecting x and y.

x	-2	-1	0	1	2	3
y	-2	-1	0	1	2	3

   To represent this pattern on graph paper, plot the points $(-2, -2)$, $(-1, -1)$, $(0, 0)$, $(1, 1)$, $(2, 2)$, $(3, 3)$.
   These points lie on a straight line. Draw it.

   2   Here is another pattern of numbers.

x	-2	-1	0	1	2	3
y	-4	-2	0	2	4	6

   To represent this, plot the points $(-2, -4)$, $(-1, -2)$, $(0, 0)$, etc., on the same graph as before, and draw the straight line through these points.

3.   For this question, draw the x-axis from -4 to 3 using a scale of 1 cm to 1 unit, and the y-axis from -6 to 12 using a scale of 1 cm for 2 units.

   1   Here is a pattern of numbers.

x	-4	-3	-2	-1	0	1	2	3
y	-5	-3	-1	1	3	5	7	9

   To represent this pattern plot the points $(-4, -5)$, $(-3, -3)$, etc.
   If the points lie on a straight line, draw the line.

   2   Copy and complete this pattern for x and for y.

x	-4	-3	-2	-1				
y	-2	0	2	4				

   Plot the points representing this pattern on the same graph and if they lie on a straight line, draw the line.
   What do you notice about your graphs?

4. Draw the x-axis from -2 to 6 and the y-axis from 0 to 6.
    Plot the points E $(-2, 0)$, F $(0, 3)$, G $(2, 4)$ and H $(4, 6)$.
    Three of these points lie on a straight line. Draw this line.
    Write down the coordinates of 4 more points which lie on the same line.

    Complete this pattern:

    $(-2, 6)$, $(-1, 5)$, $(0, 4)$, $(1, 3)$, $(2, \ )$, $(3, \ )$, $(4, \ )$.
    Plot these points and join them with a straight line.
    What are the coordinates of the point where the 2 lines cross each other ?

5. Continue the pattern of numbers:
    $(0, 0)$, $(1, 1)$, $(2, 4)$, $(3, 9)$, $(4, 16)$, $(\ \ )$, $(\ \ )$, $(\ \ )$, $(\ \ )$.
    If the first number in the bracket is x and the second one y, what is the
    connection between y and x in any bracket ?
    On graph paper, use a scale of 2 cm to 1 unit on the x-axis, with x from 0 to 8,
    and a scale of 2 cm to 10 units on the y-axis, with y from 0 to 70.
    Plot the 9 points given above and join them, without using a ruler, to form
    a smooth curve.
    On this curve, what is the value of y when $x = 5\frac{1}{2}$?
    On the curve, what is the value of x, correct to 1 decimal place, when $y = 40$?

PUZZLE

21. What is this ? On graph paper label the x-axis from -30 to 20 and the y-axis from -30 to
    30, using equal scales on both axes. Mark these points. Join each point to the next one
    (working downwards in columns). Add shading or any other lines you think necessary.

$(5, 5)$	$(14, -15)$	$(9, -29)$	$(-9, -28)$	$(-22, 28)$
$(10, 3)$	$(16, -19)$	$(7, -29)$	$(-9, -29)$	$(-22, 30)$
$(13, 0)$	$(16, -26)$	$(8, -27)$	$(-11, -29)$	$(-21, 28)$
$(13, -2)$	$(15, -27)$	$(9, -20)$	$(-10, -28)$	$(-20, 30)$
$(16, -8)$	$(15, -29)$	$(5, -7)$	$(-12, -4)$	$(-20, 28)$
$(16, -10)$	$(13, -29)$	$(2, -8)$	$(-14, 0)$	$(-19, 27)$
$(18, -15)$	$(14, -27)$	$(-3, -8)$	$(-13, 7)$	$(-19, 25)$
$(18, -17)$	$(14, -20)$	$(-7, -6)$	$(-16, 11)$	$(-12, 15)$
$(17, -17)$	$(9, -10)$	$(-9, -15)$	$(-18, 15)$	$(-7, 10)$
$(17, -15)$	$(10, -18)$	$(-8, -17)$	$(-21, 23)$	$(-5, 9)$
$(15, -10)$	$(11, -19)$	$(-9, -19)$	$(-25, 22)$	$(-3, 7)$
$(15, -8)$	$(10, -26)$	$(-9, -25)$	$(-26, 23)$	$(5, 5)$
$(13, -4)$	$(9, -27)$	$(-8, -27)$		

15 Thinking about multiplication

What is multiplication ?

Well, it's really only repeated addition.

About 25 years ago, small calculating machines were produced and these were sometimes bought by schools. To multiply 64 by 35, you put 64 on the levers of the machine, turned the handle 5 times, which meant it added 64 five times, then moved up one place and turned the handle 3 times.

Before that, we just had to use pencil and paper methods, unless we had a slide rule or log tables.

Nowadays, your calculator will do it as quickly as you can enter the numbers.

However, you can't always rely on having your calculator handy, so in case of emergency, you must be able to find the answer without it.

What is the cost of feeding your pet cat for a year ?
What is the weight of food it eats in a year ?

Mark uses his moped to travel to school. How can he estimate how many miles he will travel in a year ?

How could you estimate the number of vehicles which can be stored in this compound ?

How could you estimate the number of trees in a plantation such as this ?

Ways of multiplying

Cans of soft drinks are 64p each. There are 35 children on an outing. How much would it cost to buy each of them a drink ?

Work this out without using your calculator. Write down the steps in your working as clearly as you can so that you can explain how you did it. Compare your method with other people's and see how many different ways of working it out you can use, and which method seems easiest or best.

Here is a method which you may not have thought of:

64×35 is the same as 35×64, which is $35 \times 2 \times 2 \times 2 \times 2 \times 2 \times 2$.

```
     35
 ×    2
   ----
     70
 ×    2
   ----
    140
 ×    2
   ----
    280
 ×    2
   ----
    560
 ×    2
   ----
   1120
 ×    2
   ----
   2240     Cost is £22.40
```

There is no best method to do multiplication as it can depend on the numbers involved. Use whichever method you prefer as long as it gives the correct answer.

15 Multiplication

Long multiplication

To multiply by a number between 10 and 100

Examples

1   328 × 46

First multiply 328 by 6, then 328 by 40, and add the results together.

328 × 6 = 1968
328 × 4 = 1312 so 328 × 40 = 13120
Finally 328 × 46 = (328 × 6) + (328 × 40) = 1968 + 13120 = 15088

However, this looks much simpler set down like this:

```
      328                               328
   ×   46                  or        ×   46           } if you prefer to
     1968                             13120             multiply by 40
    13120  ← write down the 0          1968             before you multiply
    15088     because this comes       15088          } by 6.
              from multiplying by
              10, then multiply
              328 by 4
```

2   173 × 91

```
      173                               173
   ×   91                  or        ×   91
      173                             15570
    15570                               173
    15743                             15743
```

Normally you would use your calculator to do such questions but it is essential to know how to work out the answers yourself as you cannot always rely on having a calculator handy.

This method is called **long multiplication**. There are other methods of working, some of which are explained in the exercise. You can use any method you prefer, as long as it gives the correct answer.

Exercise 15.1

1. Practise the method of long multiplication by doing these questions. The check the answers on your calculator.

1	849 × 28	**5**	343 × 66	**8**	726 × 29
2	403 × 37	**6**	264 × 45	**9**	905 × 91
3	654 × 51	**7**	517 × 86	**10**	183 × 54
4	177 × 26				

2. Another way to work out the answers is to split both the numbers into separate parts and write the results down in a rectangular grid.

e.g. 243 × 75

Split 243 into 200 + 40 + 3, and 75 into 70 + 5

	200	40	3
70	14 000	2800	210
5	1000	200	15

Multiply the two numbers above and at the side for each of the six rectangles.

Write the numbers in the rectangles down in a neat column and add them together. Any order will do but it is probably easier if you put the larger numbers first.

```
14 000
 2800
 1000
  210
  200
   15
──────
18 225     So 243 × 75 = 18 225
```

Try some of the questions from question 1 again using the rectangle method, and if you prefer to use it then make up other questions for practice, and then check the answers on your calculator.

Note that a question such as 403 × 37 only needs four compartments in the rectangle.

	400	3
30		
7		

3.   From Doncaster to London is 159 miles by road. Peter makes the return journey once each month. How many miles in a year is this ?

4.   A train takes 392 passengers on an excursion. They have paid £18 each. How much have they paid altogether ?

5.   Boxes of drawing pins have 48 drawing pins in each. A secretary orders 12 dozen boxes. How many drawing pins will there be altogether ?

6.   The distance round a playing-field is 815 m. Latif goes round it 16 times on a sponsored run. How far has he run altogether ?

7.   There are 24 bottles in a crate of milk bottles. Edward has 125 full crates on his lorry. How many bottles are there ?

8.   A wire is wound round a reel 65 times, the distance round the reel being 124 cm. What is the total length of the wire ?

9.   If a household uses 25 kg of solid fuel each day in winter, how much should be bought to last from 1st November to 31st March (151 days) ?

10.   A glacier is moving at the rate of 32 cm per day. How far will it move in a year (365 days) ?

Exercise 15.2   Applications and Activities

Other methods for multiplication

1.   If you have to multiply by a number which has 1-figure factors, such as 48 which has factors 6 × 8, you can use another method.

e.g. 528 × 48 = 528 × 6 × 8

First multiply 528 by 6, and then the answer by 8.

```
    528
 ×    6
 _____
   3168
 ×    8
 _____
 25 344
```

Practise this method with these questions.

1 129×35 $(35 = 5 \times 7)$
2 256×36 $(36 = 6 \times 6 \text{ or } 4 \times 9)$
3 817×28
4 345×72
5 550×42

2.   If you have to multiply by 25, because 25 is one-quarter of 100, you can multiply by 100 and then divide by 4.

e.g. 385×25
         $= 385 \times 100 \div 4$
         $= 38\,500 \div 4$ $4)\overline{38\,500}$
         $= 9625$ $\overline{\quad 9625\quad}$

Multiply these numbers by 25.

1   244   **2**   128   **3**   451   **4**   670   **5**   529

3.   To multiply by 15.

First, multiply by 10, then multiply by 5 by finding half of the previous result. Add the two numbers together.

e.g. 596×15

         $596 \times 10 = 5960$
         $596 \times 5 = \underline{2980}$ (By dividing 5960 by 2)
         $596 \times 15 = \underline{8940}$

Multiply these numbers by 15.

1   134   **2**   325   **3**   810   **4**   509   **5**   618

4.   To multiply by 99.

Multiply by 100 and then subtract the original number, since $99 = 100 - 1$.

e.g. 186×99

         $186 \times 100 = 18\,600$
         subtract $\underline{\quad\quad 186}$

                             $\underline{18\,414}$

Multiply these numbers by 99.

1   528   **2**   481   **3**   370   **4**   239   **5**   112

5.   This is a method of multiplication used in the Middle Ages.

e.g. 947 × 52

The two numbers to be multiplied are written along the top and down the right side of a rectangular grid.

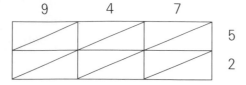

Each pair of numbers is multiplied separately, e.g. 9 × 5 = 45, so 45 is written in the 1st rectangle, but the rectangle is divided into two triangles for the tens number and the units number.
The other rectangles are filled in similarly.

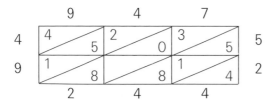

Next, the numbers are added down the diagonal columns, beginning with just 4 in the bottom right corner. (This is the units figure of the answer.) The next diagonal has 5 + 1 + 8 = 14, so write down another 4 and carry 1 forward to the next diagonal column. The results are written under the grid and they continue up the left side.

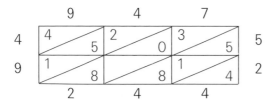

The answer is 49 244 (reading down the left side and along the bottom row).

Use this method to multiply
1   324 × 85
2   903 × 27   (Do not leave out the 0 column.)
3   285 × 42
4   654 × 31
5   279 × 56

6. 15 plots each of area $263\,m^2$ are sold from a total estate of $4000\,m^2$. How much land remains unsold ?

7. A box holds 12 model cars which each weigh 857 g. The box weighs 375 g. What is the total weight, in kg, correct to 1 decimal place ?

8. A rectangular piece of ground, 50 m long and 26 m wide, is to be surrounded by a fence. If the fencing costs £14 per metre, find the total cost.

9. **Multiplication practice**

    Write down 143.
    Then choose any 2-figure number to multiply it by.
    Multiply that result by 7.
    By investigation, can you discover the connection between the number you chose and the final answer ?

10. Copy and complete this number pattern

    $(0 \times 30 + 3 \times 9) \times 37 =$
    $(1 \times 30 + 3 \times 8) \times 37 =$
    $(2 \times 30 + 3 \times 7) \times 37 =$
    . . .

    up to the line beginning with 9×30.

PUZZLE

22. On graph paper label the x-axis from 0 to 18 and the y-axis from 0 to 13 using a scale of 1 cm to 1 unit on both axes.
    Plot these coordinates and join each point to the next, with a ruler, to make a closed shape. There are 5 shapes altogether. Cut them out, or copy them onto thick cardboard and cut those pieces out.
    Rearrange the pieces to make a square,
    1 without using the small square piece,
    2 using all 5 pieces.

    (1) (0, 0). (4, 0), (8, 4), (4, 8), (0, 4), (0, 0)
    (2) (6, 0), (14, 0), (14, 4), (18, 4), (14, 8), (6, 0)
    (3) (0, 5), (8, 13), (0, 13), (0, 5)
    (4) (5, 9), (13, 9), (9, 13), (5, 9)
    (5) (14, 9), (18, 9), (18, 13), (14, 13), (14, 9)

16 Thinking about equations

Equation

Look up the mathematical meaning of the word **equation** in a dictionary. It is derived from the Latin word aequus, meaning 'even'. Find other words beginning with 'equa' or 'equi' which are also related to this word, and write down their meanings.

Simple equations

Try this problem:

A group of people hired a minicoach for a day-out and the organiser worked out that it would cost them £7 each. On the day, 4 extra people turned up so it only cost each of them £5. How many people were there originally?

Have you solved it? Check your answer to make sure that it is correct.

Compare your method with those of your friends. How many different methods can you find to solve this problem?

You do not need to use algebraic equations, but here is one way to solve it, using an equation.

You are trying to find how many people there were originally, so begin by saying 'Let there be x people originally'.

Then, since they had to pay £7 each, the total cost would be £$7x$

When 4 extra people turned up, that meant there were $x + 4$ people.

They each paid £5, so the total cost was £$5(x + 4)$

These two expressions for the total cost are equal, so we can make an equation.

£$7x$ = £$5(x + 4)$

Now we just write down the **numbers** of £'s as they are also equal.

$7x = 5(x + 4)$

The first thing to do with this equation is to work out the brackets.

$7x = 5x + 20$

Now carry on solving the equation. When you have found x, that is the number of people there were originally.

Problems which are solved by simple equations can often be solved instead by other methods. However, you need to practise solving simple equations, so that you can use them when the algebra gets more advanced.

Here is a simple problem:

5 boys share 36p equally among themselves, putting the extra 1p into a charity box. How much do they each get?

Now if you let each boy get x pence, then you can write down an equation which is

$5x + 1 = 36$

and you can solve it to find x.

Keeping balanced, or else . . . ?

While the marker stays in the centre, the teams are pulling equally.

Inventing problems

Now can you do some questions the other way round ? Here are the equations. Invent some problems which they could apply to, and then find the solutions.

$$2x + 7 = 23$$
$$18 - x = x$$
$$4x + 1 = x + 21$$
$$7x - 2 = 26$$
$$\frac{x}{4} + 1 = 10$$

Here is an example of an equation in Chemistry
$$HCl + NaOH = NaCl + H_2O$$
This means
Hydrochloric acid + sodium hydroxide = sodium chloride (salt) + water.

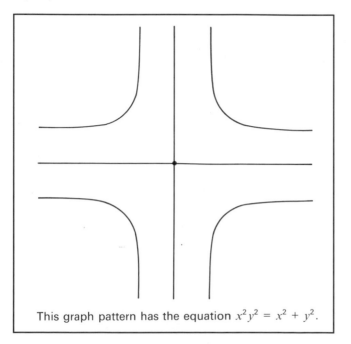

This graph pattern has the equation $x^2 y^2 = x^2 + y^2$.

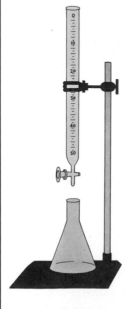

16 Equations

Introduction

$x + 3 = 11$ is an equation, which we can solve to find the value of x.

Imagine x is a box of unknown weight, on one side of a balanced weighing-scale together with a weight of 3 units. On the other side is a weight of 11 units.

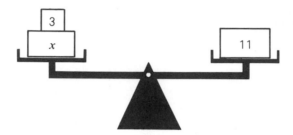

Now the scales will still be balanced if we take 3 units off **both sides**.

So $x = 8$ units.

This is the method of solving algebraic equations. We deal with both sides equally and the equation will still balance.
Set down the working as shown later (example 1).

Here is another example worked out on the weighing-scales.

$$13x - 20 = 6$$

On one side we have a box of unknown weight $13x$ with a piece of weight 20 units missing from it. This represents $13x - 20$. On the other side balancing it there is a weight of 6 units.

The first thing to do is to fill up the hole where the 20 units is missing so **add** 20 units to both sides.

Now we have the unknown weight $13x$ balanced by a weight of 26.
Make $13x$ into 13 separate boxes of weight x units each.

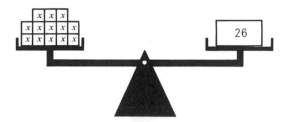

Now by dividing by 13 we leave just one weight of x units on. It will be balanced if we divide 26 by 13, leaving 2 units on the other side.

So $x = 2$ units.
The working is shown set down in example 5.

Here is one more example using the weighing-scales.
$$7x + 4 = 40 - 5x$$

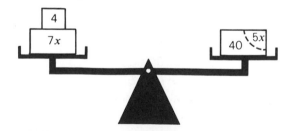

On one side of the scales we have an unknown weight $7x$ and also 4 units. This represents $7x + 4$. On the other side there is a weight of 40 units with a piece of weight $5x$ mising from it. This represents $40 - 5x$.

We can fill up the hole where the $5x$ units is missing, by adding $5x$ to both sides.

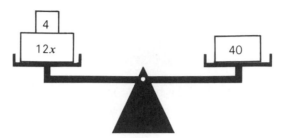

Now we can subtract 4 units from both sides. (It would not have affected the result if we had done this first.)

Next we can split the $12x$ weight into 12 weights of x units each, and then divide both sides by 12 to leave just one weight of x on one side, and 3 on the other.

So $x = 3$ units.
The working is shown set down in example 7.

Solving equations

The sides still remain equal if
1   equal numbers are added to both sides,
2   equal numbers are subtracted from both sides,
3   both sides are multiplied by the same number,
4   both sides are divided by the same number.

Examples

1 $x + 3 = 11$
   Subtract 3 from both sides
   $x = 8$

2 $x - 7 = 14$
   Add 7 to both sides
   $x = 21$

3 $5x = 15$
   Divide both sides by 5
   $x = 3$

4 $\frac{1}{3}x = 8$
   Multiply both sides by 3
   $x = 24$

5 $13x - 20 = 6$
   Add 20 to both sides
   $13x = 26$
   Divide both sides by 13
   $x = 2$

To check this equation, substitute $x = 2$ into the left-hand side of the equation.
Left-hand side (LHS) = $13x - 20 = (13 \times 2) - 20 = 26 - 20 = 6$
Right-hand side (RHS) = 6
The two sides are equal, both 6, so the equation checks.

6 $12x = 5x + 28$
   Subtract 5x from both sides
   $7x = 28$
   Divide both sides by 7
   $x = 4$

To check this equation, substitute $x = 4$ into both sides of the equation separately.
LHS = $12x = 12 \times 4 = 48$
RHS = $5x + 28 = (5 \times 4) + 28 = 20 + 28 = 48$
The two sides are equal, both 48, so the equation checks.

7 $7x + 4 = 40 - 5x$
Add $5x$ to both sides
$12x + 4 = 40$
Subtract 4 from both sides
$12x = 36$
Divide both sides by 12
$x = 3$

To check this equation, substitute $x = 3$ into both sides of the equation separately.
LHS = $7x + 4$ = $(7 \times 3) + 4 = 21 + 4 = 25$
RHS = $40 - 5x$ = $40 - (5 \times 3) = 40 - 15 = 25$
The two sides are equal, both 25, so the equation checks.

8   **Using equations to solve problems**

Rachel's father was 22 years old when Rachel was born. Now he is three times as old as Rachel. How old is Rachel now ?

Let Rachel be x years old now.
Then her father is $(22 + x)$ years old.
Father's age = $3 \times$ (Rachel's age).
So $22 + x = 3x$
Subtract x from both sides
$22 = 2x$
Divide both sides by 2
$11 = x$
Rachel is 11 years old (and her father is 33 years old).

You can check the solution in the problem.
If Rachel is 11 years old and her father was 22 years old when she was born, then her father will be 33 years old now. This is three times as old as Rachel, so the answer is correct.

9   Here is a Geometry question which can be solved by making an equation.

Write down an equation and solve it to find the value of x.

angle $a = 5x°$ (vertically opposite angles)
angle $a = 180° - x°$ (interior angles)
So $5x° = 180° - x°$
$5x = 180 - x$ (using the numbers and leaving out degrees)
Add x to both sides
$6x = 180$
Divide both sides by 6
$x = 30$

Exercise 16.1

Solve these equations and check the answers in your head.

1.
  1 $x + 12 = 17$
  2 $x - 4 = 8$
  3 $5x = 40$
  4 $\frac{1}{3}x = 5$
  5 $x - 6 = 0$
  6 $x + 8 = 20$
  7 $4x + 6 = 50$
  8 $3x - 1 = 5$
  9 $9x - 16 = 11$
  10 $5x + 2 = 37$

2.
  1 $4x = x + 30$
  2 $2x + 1 = 15$
  3 $2x + 9 = 5x$
  4 $6x + 12 = 12$
  5 $3x = 5 - 2x$
  6 $6x = 15 + x$
  7 $12 - x = 4$
  8 $15 - 2x = 13$
  9 $4x + 3x = 63$
  10 $20 = 21 - x$

Solve these equations and check your answers.

3.
  1 $3x + 1 = 2x + 7$
  2 $3x + 18 = 5x + 12$
  3 $2x + 7 = 5x - 11$
  4 $3x - 5 = x + 3$
  5 $4x - 4 = 3x + 5$
  6 $3x + 7 = x + 29$
  7 $10x + 3 = 4x + 45$
  8 $19 + 4x = 3 + 12x$
  9 $2x - 4 = 5x - 40$
  10 $10x + 1 = 7x + 25$

4.
  1 $7x - 11 = 13 - 5x$
  2 $20 - x = 2x - 7$
  3 $15 - x = 21 - 2x$
  4 $5 - x = 11 - 3x$
  5 $3x + 7 = 7 - x$
  6 $10x - 1 = 6x + 15$
  7 $13x - 20 = 8x$
  8 $3x - 12 = 0$
  9 $3x + 6 = 9x$
  10 $15x + 5 + 6x = 47$

5. Find the answers to these problems by making equations and solving them.

  1 I think of a number, multiply it by 4 and add 5. The result is 41. What was the original number ? (Let the original number be x.)

  2 I think of a number, multiply it by 3 and add 4. The result is 16 less than five times the original number. What was the original number ?

  3 Karen's mother was 20 years old when Karen was born, and now she is 5 times as old as Karen. How old is Karen now ? (Let Karen be x years old now.)

  4 Wayne bought 2 similar toy cars and a toy tractor. The tractor cost 50 pence more than a car and together the three toys cost £2.75 (275 pence). Find the cost of a car, and the tractor.
     (Let a car cost x pence. How much will the tractor cost ?)

  5 In a collecting-box there were x 5p coins and three times as many 2p coins. Together the collection totalled £2.86. How many of each kind of coin were there ?

Exercise 16.2   Applications and Activities

1. If $y = kx$ and $y = 27$ when $x = 3$, find the value of k. With this value of k, find the value of y when $x = 5$.

2. For what value of x is the value of the expression $4x - 3$ equal to the value of the expression $x + 12$?

3. A carpet-seller has a roll of carpet, x metres long, costing £10 per metre. What is its total cost ?
   He has a roll of more expensive carpet, which is 12 metres longer than the first roll. Find an expression for its length, in terms of x, and an expression for its cost, if it costs £15 per metre.
   The two rolls together are worth £930. Form an equation in x, and solve it to find x.
   How many metres were there in each roll ?

4. Use angle properties to write down an equation involving x and hence find the value of x in these figures.

   1   **2**   **3**

   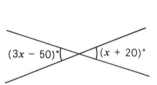   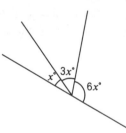   (figure 3)

   4   **5**

   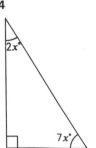   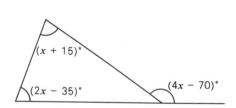

5. Mrs Collins and her two boys and Mrs Davies with her daughter go together to an adventure park. The total price for admission was £5.60, the three children each being charged half-price. If the cost for a child is x pence, what is the cost for an adult ? In terms of x, what was the total cost for the five people ?
   Write down an equation and solve it to find x.
   How much was the admission price for an adult ?

6. An exhibition organiser employs 30 temporary workers for a day's work.
    He pays x of them £25 each. What is the total amount paid to this group ?
    The rest of the workers are paid £20 each. How many workers are there in this
    group, and what is their total wage ? If altogether the wages total £630, form an
    equation in x, and solve it.
    How many workers were paid £25 for the day ?

7. Find the values of x, y and z, in that order.

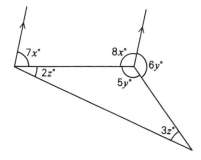

8. The angles of a triangle are $(3x + 12)°$, $(x + 19)°$ and $(2x - 7)°$. Find the value
    of x, and the sizes of the angles.
    What sort of triangle is it ?

PUZZLES

23. Arrange 6 similar coins like this, each coin
    touching those next to it.
    In 3 moves rearrange the coins into a circle.
    A move means moving 1 coin, and finishing
    the move with it touching at least 2 other
    coins.

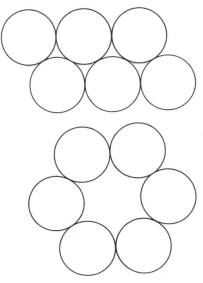

24. Mary and Joan joined the Guides. They gave their names as Mary Bell and Joan Bell, with
    the same address and the same date-of-birth. 'So you are twins,' said the leader. 'No,
    we're not,' they replied together. Can you explain this ? (They are not cousins, either.)

Miscellaneous Section B

Aural Practice

These aural excercises, B1 and B2, should be read to you, probably by your teacher or a friend, and you should write down the answers only, doing any working out in your head. You should do the 15 questions within 10 minutes.

Exercise B1

1. What is 75% of £12 ?

2. 350 marbles are shared out among some children. They get 50 each. How many children are there ?

3. I think of a number, multiply it by 5 and add 6. The answer is 41. What was the number ?

4. What sort of triangle has 3 equal sides ?

5. In the morning the temperature was $-3°C$, and later on it was 4°C. By how many degrees had the temperature risen ?

6. If Mrs Ross changes a £10 note into 10 pence pieces to use in the meter, how many 10 pence pieces will she get ?

7. If $a = 5$ and $b = 0$, what is the value of $2ab$?

8. Write correct to 2 significant figures the number 3.872.

9. For a recipe, Anna needs 250 g of sugar. What fraction of the sugar in a 1 kg bag is this ?

10. If the total amount of time represented on a pie chart is 24 hours, what angle is needed for a sector representing 8 hours ?

11. If 2 angles of a triangle are 40° and 30°, what is the size of the other angle ?

12. What is an expression for the change in pence if an article costing b pence is paid for with a £1 coin ?

13. Some children held a garden sale and raised £18 for charities. They sent $\frac{2}{3}$ of this to Barnado's. How much did they send ?

14. Mr Shaw is 4 years older than Mrs Shaw. Their ages added together make 48 years. How old is Mrs Shaw ?

15. A restaurant meal is £8 and Sadiq decides to give a 10% tip. How much is the tip ?

Exercise B2

1. What is 30 × 40 ?

2. How many minutes are there from quarter-past 2 to 3 o'clock ?

3. Write down the fraction 3 hundredths as a decimal.

4. What is the lowest number into which 2, 3 and 5 all divide exactly ?

5. What is x if $3x + 1 = 10$?

6. The temperature in a cold store was 5°C and it was reduced by 8 degrees. What was the temperature then ?

7. Write correct to 2 decimal places the number 2.891.

8. Of the members of a club, 56% are over 18 years old and the rest are under 18. What percentage are under 18 ?

9. If the angle at the centre of a pie chart is 45°, what fraction of the whole amount is represented ?

10. If £5 is equally divided among 4 children, how much would they each get ?

11. Malik is x years old. In 9 years time he will be 21. What is the value of x ?

12. Bus fares increase by 20%. What is the new fare if the old fare is 40 pence ?

13. Simplify the algebraic expression $x \times x \times x$.

14. In dropping a drawing pin onto a table, it came to rest point upwards 70 times out of 100. What is an estimate of the probability that the next time it is dropped it will land point upwards ?

15. If a triangle has one angle of 80° and the other 2 angles are equal, how big are they ?

Exercise B3   Revision

1. When boxes are stacked in piles of 5 there are 2 left over but they can be stacked exactly in piles of 6 or 8. How many are there, if there are less than 100 ?

2. In the diagram, $\angle DBC$ is cut in half by BE.
What is the value of x ?

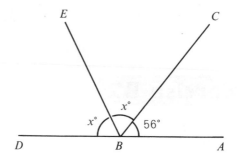

3. Write these fractions in their simplest forms.

1 $\frac{32}{48}$ **2** $\frac{60}{84}$ **3** $\frac{27}{45}$ **4** $\frac{49}{77}$ **5** $\frac{30}{54}$

4. The items A, B, C are shown in a pie chart. What should be the size of the angle in sector A ?

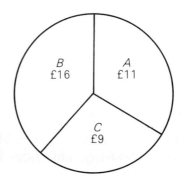

5. If $x = \frac{1}{6}(3a + 2b + c)$, find the value of x if $a = 11$, $b = 8$ and $c = 5$.

6. A medicine spoon holds 5 ml. How many spoonfuls are there in a bottle containing $\frac{1}{4}$ litre of medicine ?

7. A man buys a television set which costs £360. He pays an initial payment of $\frac{1}{4}$ of the cost and arranges to pay the rest in 20 equal monthly instalments. How much is the monthly instalment ?

8. Find the values of the following, without using your calculator.

1 $8 - 0.4$ **4** $0.8 + 0.4$
2 8×0.4 **5** $8000 \div 40$
3 $0.8 \div 4$

9. A salesman is paid a commission of 8% on the value of goods he sells. When he sells goods to the value of £750, how much commission does he get ?

10. Solve these equations.

1 $a - 8 = 22$ **4** $3d + 15 = d + 25$
2 $3b + 17 = 26$ **5** $5e - 8 = 10 - e$
3 $9c = 63$

11. A watch loses 8 seconds every hour. It is correct at 9.00 am on Monday. What time does it show at 3.00 pm the next day ?

12. Calculate the size of angle a.

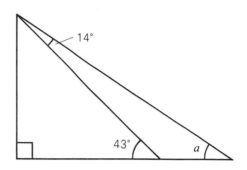

13. Which of the numbers 19, 29, 39, 49, 59 are prime numbers ?

14. John had a bag which contained a large number of discs, each with a number from 1 to 5 written on. He took a disc out at random, recorded its number, and then replaced it. His results after 500 goes showed a disc with a number 3 on coming out 200 times. What is an estimate of the probability that the next disc taken out will have a number 3 on it ?

15. Mrs Barker buys 5 kg of potatoes at x pence per kg and 3 cauliflowers at x pence each. Find an expression for the total cost, and also an expression for the change she should get, in pence, if she pays with a £5 note.

16. On graph paper, draw axes with x from -5 to 5 and y from 0 to 10, using equal scales on both axes.
    Plot the points A (5, 0) and B (0, 10) and draw the line AB. Plot the point C $(5, 2\frac{1}{2})$ and draw the line OC, where O is the origin. Let the point where the lines AB and OC cross be D. What are the coordinates of D ? What is the size of $\angle ODB$?
    Find a point E such that the line OE is equal in length and parallel to DB. Join OE and BE. What are the coordinates of E ? What kind of figure is $ODBE$?

17. In the diagram, equal lines are marked.
    Find the sizes of angles a, b, c, d.

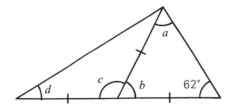

18. (Try to answer this question without using your calculator.)
    There were 325 children in a P.E. display. For each child's costume 72 cm of ribbon was needed. How many metres of ribbon should be bought ?

19. A farmer had 800 kg of potatoes but $\frac{1}{4}$ of them were bad and had to be thrown away. He kept $\frac{1}{5}$ of the remainder to feed to his pigs and sold the rest. What quantity did he sell ?

20. If the temperature one morning is $-3°C$, and it rises by 8 degrees during the day and then falls by 12 degrees at night, what is the night's temperature ?

Exercise B4   Activities

1. **Roman Numerals**

These are still in use as numbers, although not for calculations. Find the numbers from one to twelve on a clock or watch. Here the number four will be shown as IIII, but the more usual way is IV. Note that number one is the capital letter I, not figure 1.

In old books you will find the chapters labelled in Roman numerals. Larger numbers can be found as dates on foundation stones, old gravestones or memorial tablets. Parts of questions in some textbooks are numbered using small-lettered numbers in the Roman numeral system, e.g. (i), (ii), etc.

Look for examples of Roman numerals and make a list of those you find. From these you can discover how the system works.
What are the letters used for 1, 10, 100, 1000 ?
What are the letters used for 5, 50, 500 ?
Note the connections between

1	10	100	1000
2	20	200	2000
3	30	300	3000
4	40	400	
5	50	500	
6	60	600	
etc.			

To change a number such as 1946 into Roman numerals you deal with each figure in turn. Change 1000, then 900, then 40, then 6.

Change these numbers into Roman numerals:
1 27 **2** 84 **3** 1990 **4** 475 **5** 1839

Change these Roman numerals into ordinary numbers:
6 MMCMII **7** XLIII **8** CDIV **9** MCMXCV **10** CCLIX

2. A traffic survey

Do a survey on a main road to see what sorts of traffic use it, with categories such as car, bus or coach, lorry, light van. Make a table of results and represent them on a pie chart. To make it simpler to calculate the angles in the pie chart you could collect data from 90, 120, 180 or perhaps 360 vehicles. Write down the day and the time when you did your survey.

Perhaps you could repeat your survey at a different time of day, or do it on a weekday and then at a weekend, or do one on a different road, so that you can compare two pie charts to see if they are similar or how they differ. Comment on your results.
(Do not do this survey unless your teacher and your parents approve of your plans, and be careful to stand in a safe place.)

3. A right-angled triangle

Draw a right-angled triangle *ABC*, drawing the right angle at *A* accurately, using your protractor or set-square.
Find, by measurement, the mid-point *M* of *BC*.
With compasses, centre at *M*, and radius to reach *B* (or *C*), draw a circle.
Repeat for a different-sized right-angled triangle.
What do you notice about the circles ?

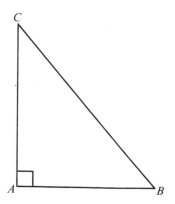

4.   **A million**

This is such a big number that it is hard to imagine, so it may help if you find out some facts using this number. Here are some ideas to begin with.
Think of others and add them to your list. Put the facts in a booklet or on a poster, and illustrate them with drawings, pictures or photographs.

Write a million in figures.
Write a million as a power of 10.
How much is a million pence worth ?
How high would a column of a million penny coins be ?
If a million pennies are laid side by side along a line, each one touching the next, how long would the line be ?
How much would a million penny coins weigh ?

What distance is a million mm ?
If you had a million squares of width 1 cm and you put them together to make a large square, how long would a side of the large square be ?

1 cm

If you had a million cubes of edge 1 cm and you put them together to make a large cube, how long would an edge of the large cube be ?

1 cm

What weight is a million grams ?

How long would it take you to count to a million ?
How long ago was a million seconds ?
How long ago was a million minutes ?
How long ago was a million hours ?
How long ago was a million days ?

How many people live in London, or other large cities ? How many people live in your nearest town ? Wembley Stadium holds 90 000 people. How many such stadiums would be needed to hold a million people ?

If you have the number sequence 1, 3, 9, 27, . . . how many terms are there before you get to more than a million ?

Wembley Stadium

5. **Number patterns with a circle**

You will draw these on plain paper, using a sharp pencil.

To begin with you need a circle with a number of equally-spaced points round the circumference. We are using 45 points. Draw a circle just larger than your protractor, then you can use your protractor to mark dots on the circle. (For 45 points you need a dot every 8°, since 360 ÷ 45 = 8.)

Number the points clockwise from 1 to 45, writing the numbers outside the circle. The first pattern uses the 2 times table.

Draw straight lines, using your ruler, from 1 to 2, 2 to 4, 3 to 6, 4 to 8, etc. When you get to 23 you need point 46, so number round the circle again, carrying on from 45, but you will only use the even numbers so you only need to label every alternate point. The last few lines you draw are 42 to 84, 43 to 86, 44 to 88. You can't join 45 to 90 because they are at the same point. Did you notice that one line was used twice ? Although you have used straight lines, can you see the curve in your drawing ?

The curves in this group are called **epicycloids** and this one is a **cardioid**. Can you think what the word cardioid is related to and why it is used for this curve ?

Now try the pattern for the 3 times table. You will have to number round the circle 3 times although after 45 you will only use the multiples of 3. The curve is called a **nephroid**.

You can continue with the 4 times table and other tables, although for these you would get a better drawing if you start with 72 points on the circle.

To draw hypocycloids

You still need a circle with 45 points but you also need to draw round it a circle with a radius approximately 2 to 2½ times larger, with the same centre point. So you will need a large piece of paper. Since the pattern is going to extend outside the inside circle the numbers should be feint, small and neat, and perhaps by now you can manage without writing many of them down.

This time for the 2 times table you join 1 to −2, 2 to −4, 3 to −6, and so on, so you must extend your numbering, going anticlockwise from 1 to 0 then −1, −2, etc., and round twice to −90. Extend your straight lines both ways until they meet the larger circle.

You can also try the 3 times table, with 1 to −3, 2 to −6, etc., then the 4 times table, which is more interesting than the 3 times table. You might try other tables as well.

You can make the epicycloids as curve stitching or string art, but the hypocycloids are not suitable since the interesting parts are outside the circle of points.

6. **Curve stitching and String Art**

Curve stitching is done with embroidery thread onto cardboard. Here is a
basic pattern to get you started. Draw any lines and mark points on the wrong
side of the cardboard so that only the thread shows on the right side.
Draw 2 lines *AB*, *AC* 9 cm long, meeting at *A* at an angle of about 50°.
Mark 8 points along *AB* 1 cm apart and number them from 1 to 8 starting 1 cm
from *A*. Mark 8 points along *CA* 1 cm apart and number them from 1′ to 8′
starting 1 cm from *C*.
3-strand embroidery thread is suitable to use. Choose a colour which shows up
against the background of the cardboard.
Begin by making a knot then go through point 1 from the wrong side to the
right side. Prick the hole at 1′ so that you can find it from the right side and go
through hole 1′ from right side to wrong side. Go on the wrong side to 2′
(because that is nearer than 2), go through 2′ and then through 2. Then go
through 3 and 3′, and so on until you have used all the numbers. Fasten off the
thread by looping under some on the wrong side, and tying it. On the right side
the threads will make the outline of a curve called a parabola.

A design using an equilateral triangle

Draw an equilateral triangle, on the wrong side.
Start with the basic pattern on sides (1) and (2).
Then, in the same colour or a different colour, do the
pattern again along sides (2) and (3).
Perhaps you will then want to do the same again
using sides (3) and (1). If you are using a 3rd
colour, some of the lines would be better pushed
under the previous ones. Think out how to do this.

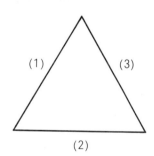

A design using 2 lines crossing at right angles

Start with the basic pattern on sides *AM* and *CM*.
Then with the same colour repeat the pattern along
sides *BM* and *DM*.
Now you may like to change colours and fill in the
other 2 quarters.

These examples should have given you enough ideas
to invent your own patterns.

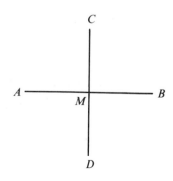

String Art is based on the same idea but it is done on a board with nails and thread. Paint the board or cover it with cloth, to contrast with the colour of the thread. Use nails $\frac{3}{4}$ inch long, with large heads so that the thread will not slip off. Draw the basic pattern on paper, put it over the board and then knock nails in positions 1 to 8 and 1' to 8'. Remember which is which and then tear off the paper.

Start by knotting the thread round nail 1, leaving a small end to tuck in later.

Take the thread to 1' and go round the nail, then go to 2' and round the nail, then to 2, 3, 3', 4' and so on. Fasten off round nail 8 and try to tuck the end out of sight.

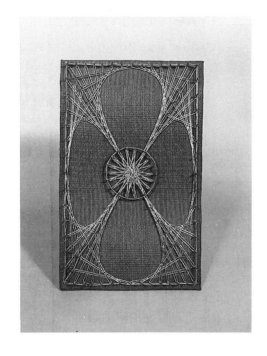

Now try to use the patterns for an equilateral triangle, and for 2 lines crossing at right angles, and then invent your own patterns.

You could discuss with your teacher the idea of having a competition for curve stitching or string art, perhaps for all the 1st year classes. You could plan the details of the competition, e.g. the rules for size, and closing date. You could have two sections, one for 'geometrical designs' and one for 'pictures'. When you have got all the entries in, and they have been judged, you could put them on display.

7. **Angle bisectors**

Draw a triangle ABC of any shape and bisect its three angles. (See page 126 for ways to bisect an angle.)

Repeat for a different-shaped triangle.

What do you notice about the angle bisectors, if you make them long enough?

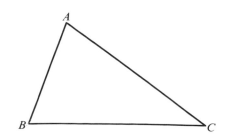

8. **VAT**

When you buy goods or pay for services there is a tax added which is called Value Added Tax (VAT). At present, the rate of tax is 15%, but this may be changed in the future. Certain goods are zero-rated or exempt from VAT.
Most shop prices have the VAT already added on, but in a few cases you have to work it out for yourself.
e.g. A builder says that a repair job will cost £120 + VAT. What is the total cost ?

> The VAT is 15% of £120.
> This is £(0.15 × 120) = £18
> The total cost is £120 + £18 = £138.
> The other way to work out the total cost is to work out £(1.15 × 120).
> As long as the rate stays at 15%, there is another way to calculate the VAT, which you can do without using your calculator.
> Since 10% is $\frac{1}{10}$, 10% of £120 is $\frac{1}{10}$ of £120 = £12
> Since 5% is half of 10%, 5% of £120 = $\frac{1}{2}$ of £12 = £6
> So 15% of £120 = £12 + £6 = £18.

Find the VAT on these items, and the total cost.

1   A TV repair costs £24 + VAT
2   A self-catering holiday cottage costs £350 + VAT
3   The phone bill is £50.24 + VAT
4   A computer system costs £1020 + VAT
5   Goods bought at a builders' supply warehouse cost £5.60 + VAT.

Copy and complete this ready reckoner showing how much VAT is added on, and the total cost. Use your ready reckoner to find
6   the total cost of a plumber's bill initially costing £63,
7   the amount of tax included in the price of a piece of jewellery which including VAT costs £92.

Initial cost £	VAT £	Total cost £	Initial cost £	VAT £	Total cost £
1			20		
2			30		
3			40		
4			50		
5			60		
6			70		
7			80		
8			90		
9			100		
10			1000		

9.   **A fraction fountain**

On a sheet of graph paper make a
rectangle 12 cm wide (60 small
squares) and 11 cm long, using the
thick lines as edges. Then draw
lines across to make 11 strips 12 cm
across and 1 cm in depth.

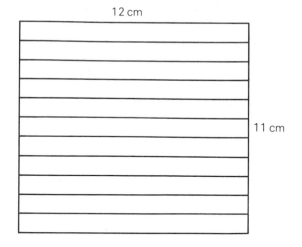

Divide the top strip in half with a
vertical line, as shown. Label this
middle line $\frac{1}{2}$.

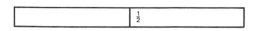

Divide the next strip into 3 equal parts.

Continue in this way, until the last strip is divided into 12 equal parts.
Be very careful with 7ths, 9ths and 11ths.
Using your calculator, $\frac{1}{7}$ of 60 = 60 ÷ 7 = 8.57 . . . so the 1st vertical line is just
over $8\frac{1}{2}$ small squares from the edge. For the next one you want $\frac{2}{7}$ of 60 which is
60 × 2 ÷ 7 = 17.14 . . . , just over 17 small squares from the edge, and so on.

When the diagram is complete, put your ruler along the left hand edge and then
move it along towards the right edge, keeping it parallel to the edges.
The first fraction bar you come to is $\frac{1}{12}$. This is the smallest fraction on the
diagram. Then the next two in order are $\frac{1}{11}$ and $\frac{1}{10}$. Write down the next few. $\frac{2}{12}$
and $\frac{1}{6}$ are in the same vertical position. They have equal value. The higher one, $\frac{1}{6}$,
is the fraction in its simplest form.

Use your diagram to answer these questions.
Which is larger, $\frac{3}{7}$ or $\frac{4}{9}$?
Which fractions have the same value as $\frac{1}{3}$?
What is $\frac{8}{12}$ in its simplest form ?
What is half of $\frac{6}{7}$?
What is $\frac{7}{10} - \frac{3}{10}$, in its simplest form ?

To draw the 'fountain'

Use crayons or felt-tips. Choose a colour, e.g. red.

Put a red blob on the top of the vertical bar of each fraction with numerator 1, i.e. $\frac{1}{2}$, $\frac{1}{3}$, $\frac{1}{4}$, etc., and join these blobs with a smooth red curve, drawn freehand.

To match this curve, keep to the same colour and put a blob on top of the vertical bar of each fraction where the numerator is 1 less than the denominator, i.e. $\frac{1}{2}$ (again), $\frac{2}{3}$, $\frac{3}{4}$, . . . , and draw another curve through these points.

Change to another colour and draw another 2 curves, one with blobs where the fraction has numerator 2, beginning with $\frac{2}{3}$, and the other where the numerator is 2 less than the denominator, beginning with $\frac{1}{3}$.

Continue in a similar way, until the last 2 curves will go through $\frac{10}{11}$, $\frac{10}{12}$ and $\frac{1}{11}$, $\frac{2}{12}$.

10.   Arranging triangles

Draw two right-angled triangles of the same size on thin card, and cut them out. Place them together so that they meet completely along one edge. They can be turned over. What different shapes can be made ?

Repeat using two equilateral triangles, then two isosceles right-angled triangles, and then two isosceles triangles which are not right-angled.

11.   A bar chart program

Here is a computer program which draws a bar chart. It is written to run on a BBC computer.

It has 5 bars labelled from A to E. Every time you enter one of these letters its bar is increased by one unit. Afterwards, the frequency totals are shown.

```
 10 REM BAR1: BAR CHART PROGRAM
 20 DIM F(5)
 30 MODE 1
 40 VDU 24, 0;132;1279;1023;
 50 VDU 28,0,31,39,28
 60 COLOUR 129:COLOUR 2
 70 GCOL 0,130:CLS:CLG
 80 GCOL 0,0
 90 VDU 29, 180;180;
100 MOVE -120,0:DRAW +1160,0
110 MOVE 0,620:DRAW 0,-512
```

```
120 VDU 5:MOVE 0,-10
130 PRINT "    A    B    C    D    E"
140 FOR K=110 TO 510 STEP 100
150 BH$=STR$ ((K-10)/10)
160 MOVE -5,K:DRAW 5,K
170 MOVE -80,K+10:PRINT BH$
180 NEXT K
190 MOVE 350,600
200 PRINT "BAR CHART"
210 MOVE -150,560:PRINT"freq"
220 VDU 4
230 B$="AaBbCcDdEe"
240 PRINT "Enter A B C D E or * to end"
250 X$=GET$
260 PRINT X$;
270 IF X$="*" THEN 350
280 X1=INSTR(B$,X$)
290 IF X1=0 THEN 340
300 X1=INT((X1+1)/2)
310 F(X1)=F(X1)+1
320 X2=X1*128+1:FX=F(X1)*10
330 PROCREC(X2,FX-10,90,10)
340 GOTO 250
350 VDU 28,0,31,39,0
360 CLS
370 PRINT
380 PRINT "      SUMMARY OF DATA"
390 PRINT
400 PRINT "  LETTER      FREQUENCY"
410 PRINT
420 FOR P=1 TO 5
430 PRINT "      ";CHR$(64+P),F(P)
440 NEXT P
450 END
460 DEF PROCREC(X,Y,L,W)
470 MOVE X,Y
480 MOVE X+L,Y
490 PLOT 85,X+L,Y+W
500 MOVE X,Y+W
510 PLOT 85,X,Y
520 ENDPROC
```

12. **Random numbers**

In probability experiments, as well as for
games, we often need a collection of random
numbers. We can use a computer to generate
these. (They are not really random numbers
when we get them from a computer. It is really
a sequence of numbers obtained by a rule,
and the sequence is a very long one so that
the numbers appear to be random. By giving
the instruction 'randomize timer' the starting
number along the sequence will be varied so
we do not get the same numbers every time.)

This computer program will give whole numbers from 1 to 6 so it can be used to
simulate dice throws.

```
10   REM PROG: DICE. To simulate tossing dice.
20   CLS
30   RANDOMIZE TIMER
40   PRINT: PRINT
50   PRINT "This program simulates the tossing of a single
     die"
60   PRINT
70   INPUT "Enter number of tosses: ";N
80   FOR I = 1 to N
90   LET X= INT(RND*6+1): PRINT" ";X;
100  NEXT I
110  PRINT
120  END
```

You can use the readings for the dice experiments in chapter 13. By altering
the program you might be able to use the computer to help you with the
calculations in the experiments.

Another investigation you could do is:
How many throws are made before you get a six ?

Alter the program to print numbers until a six appears, and then it could count
the number of throws. Repeat this several times.
Group the results for the number of throws and plot them in a histogram.
(Classes might be 1 to 6, 7 to 12, 13 to 18, etc.)

You could also alter the original program to give whole numbers 1 and 2 only.
By printing H for 1 and T for 2 you have the simulated results for tossing coins.
You could get the computer to work out the frequency of heads after every
20 tosses. You could also investigate 'runs' of heads or tails.

13. **Using computer programs**

As well as writing your own programs for the computer, there are many commercial programs available for the type of machine you will be using. Your school will probably have some of these, and with them you will be able to do your own activities.

A spreadsheet program is a program which is useful for calculations involving columns or rows of numbers. You just enter the figures in it and it will do the calculations for you. It is easy to see how useful such programs are for business purposes.

You can use such a program to investigate the effect of changes. For instance, a small percentage increase on an amount can make a big increase over a few years.

The data in a spreadsheet can be represented on a bar chart or pie chart, or if it is suitable, on a histogram. The computer will draw these for you. You can compare the effect of the different types of diagram and decide which is the most suitable for your purpose. The diagrams, too, are helpful in showing the effect of changes in the data.

PUZZLES

25. The church choirmaster had lost the number cards used to put up the hymn number on the board in the church, but after searching around he found these 5 cards, so although there are 300 hymns in the hymnbook he must choose one whose number can be made from some of these cards.
How many hymns has he got to choose from ?

26. The five boys, Alec, Benjamin, Christopher, Darren and Eddie took part in a race.

Alec said 'I was not last.'
Benjamin said 'Darren was not first.'
Christopher said 'Eddie was third.'
Darren said 'Benjamin was second.'
Eddie said 'Alec ran slower than Benjamin.'

If the remarks of those who were 1st and 2nd were false, and the rest true, and no-one tied, what was the order ?

17 Thinking about British units

Units of weight and measurement

Write down in a column all the letters of the alphabet, and try to think of the name of a unit of weight or measurement for each one.

Perhaps you will be stuck on two or three letters but you should be able to find words for most of them, and two or three words for some of them.

Then group these words into metric measures and British measures, with another group for those which do not come into either category, such as units of time.

Look again at British measures. Which are measures of length, which are weights and which are measures of capacity?

What length, weight and capacity measures are used here ?

A road sign mixing British and metric units

Numbers and measures

The metric system is based on a scale of ten, but the British measures were developed in a very unscientific way, so there is a variety of numbers used in converting from one unit to another. For instance, there are 12 inches in a foot.

Can you say where these numbers are used ?

3   4   8   14   16   20   28
112   1760   2240   5280

Paul must keep his weight stable if he is to box as a lightweight. At present he weighs 9 st 11 lb.

Using British units

Although we are gradually using the metric measurements more and more, we still use the British measurements in some situations.
Name some items, bought by weight, which will be weighed in British units, and say which units will be used.
In what other situations do we tend to talk of weights in British units?
Name some liquids which will be measured in British units, and say which units will be used.
Name some lengths which we tend to talk of in British units and say which units will be used.
If you know of any items which are still sold by measures of length in British units, say what they are.

Time for a change?

Do you think that we should keep using British units or some of them, or should we change over completely to the metric system?

17 British Units

The Metric System originated in France at the time of the French Revolution. Since it is based on 10 and powers of 10 it is a very useful system for scientific work.

The British system of units for weights and measures is much older. It is still partly in use although it is not so convenient for use with calculators, not being based on 10.

Length

We use inch, foot, yard, mile.

```
  12 inches = 1 foot
    3 feet = 1 yard
1760 yards = 1 mile
```

The old symbol for inches was ", and for feet was ', so 7' 6" means 7 feet 6 inches. Other units which used to be used are rod, pole, perch (each $5\frac{1}{2}$ yards), chain (22 yards) and furlong (220 yards).

The approximate comparisons with the metric system which are useful are:

```
1 inch . . . 2½ cm
1 foot . . . 30 cm
1 yard . . . 0.9 m
1 mile . . . 1.6 km
5 miles . . . 8 km
```

```
1 cm . . . 0.4 inches
1 m  . . . 40 inches = 4 ins longer than 1 yard
1 km . . . ⅝ mile
8 km . . . 5 miles
```

Weight

We use ounces, pounds, stones, hundredweights and tons.

```
16 ounces          = 1 pound
14 pounds          = 1 stone
112 pounds         = 1 hundredweight
8 stones           = 1 hundredweight
2240 pounds        = 1 ton
20 hundredweights  = 1 ton
```

The symbol for ounces is oz, for pounds is *lb* (from Latin, libra for pound), for stones st, for hundredweight cwt (from the Roman C for a hundred).
Another unit which used to be used is a quarter ($\frac{1}{4}$ of a hundredweight = 28 pounds).

The approximate comparisons with the metric system which are useful are:

1 lb . . . 450 g (nearly $\frac{1}{2}$ kg) 1 ton . . . 1 tonne	1 kg . . . 2.2 lb (just over 2 lb) 1 tonne . . . 1 ton

Capacity

We use pint, gallon.

8 pints = 1 gallon

Other units which used to be used are a gill ($\frac{1}{4}$ pint), although this unit is sometimes used for $\frac{1}{2}$ pint, e.g. when asking for a gill of beer; also fluid ounces. There are 20 fluid ounces in 1 pint.

The approximate comparisons with the metric system which are useful are

1 pint . . . just over $\frac{1}{2}$ litre 1 gallon . . . $4\frac{1}{2}$ litres	1 litre . . . $1\frac{3}{4}$ pints 1 litre . . . 0.22 gallon

It is useful to know that

1 pint of water weighs $1\frac{1}{4}$ lb
1 gallon of water weighs 10 lb

More exact comparisons with the Metric System

Probably you do not need to learn these figures. It will be sufficient for you to know the approximate comparisons which have already been given.
If you need these more accurate figures you can look them up here, or you will find them in many diaries and reference books.

To change to the metric system

Length

1 inch = 2.54 cm
1 foot = 30.48 cm
1 yard = 91.44 cm = 0.9144 m
1 mile = 1.609 km

Weight

1 oz = 28.35 g
1 lb = 453.6 g
1 ton = 1016 kg = 1.016 tonne

Capacity

1 pint   = 0.568 litre
1 gallon = 4.546 litre

To change from the metric system

Length

1 cm = 0.394 in
1 m = 39.37 in = 1.094 yd
1 km = 1094 yd = 0.621 mile

Weight

1 kg   = 2.205 lb
1 tonne = 0.984 ton

Capacity

1 litre = 1.76 pints = 0.220 gallons

Examples

1 How many cm are there in 12 inches ?

1 inch is equivalent to 2.54 cm
12 inches are equivalent to 12×2.54 cm = 30.48 cm. To the nearest mm this is 30.5 cm.

2 How many miles are equal to 50 km, (i) approximately, (ii) more exactly ?

Approximately,   1 km = $\frac{5}{8}$ mile
$\qquad\qquad\qquad$ 50 km = $50 \times \frac{5}{8}$ mile = $\frac{250}{8}$ mile = 30 or 31 miles.

More exactly,   1 km = 0.621 mile
$\qquad\qquad\qquad$ 50 km = 50×0.621 miles = 31.05 miles.

Use of a calculator

As with calculations with time, be careful if using your calculator when dealing with mixed units not based on 10, such as lb and oz, gallons and pints, feet and inches. You will have to deal with the different units separately.

Examples

1 One parcel weighs 14 lb 9 oz and another weighs 10 lb 12 oz. What is the total weight ?

14 lb 9 oz	First, do the ounces part. 9 + 12 = 21.
10 lb 12 oz	Since 16 oz = 1 lb, this is 1 lb 5 oz.
25 lb 5 oz	Write down 5 oz and carry forward 1 lb, making 25 lb altogether.

   (It is usual to have only 2 units in our measurements, which is why stones are not used in this question, where there are already lbs and oz.)

2 6 gall 2 pints − 1 gall 7 pints.

   6 gall 2 pints   First do the pints. You can't take 7 from 2 so change 1 gall into 8
   1 gall 7 pints   pints and take 7 from 10, answer 3.
   4 gall 3 pints   Then either do 6 gall − 2 gall or 5 gall − 1 gall, depending on the way you usually do subtraction, leaving 4 gall.

3 The space between two gateposts is 3 ft 5 in. This space is to be blocked with 6 strands of wire. What total length of wire is needed ?

   3 ft 5 in × 6

3 ft 5 in	Do the inches first. 6 × 5 = 30.
× 6	Now there are 12 inches in 1 foot so 30 in = 2 ft 6 in. Carry 2 ft
20 ft 6 in	forward.
	For the feet, 6 × 3 = 18 and 18 + 2 = 20.

4 A sackful of apples weighing 23 lb 7 oz is to be divided among 5 people. How much should they each get ?

5)23 lb 7 oz	5's into 23 goes 4 so they will each get 4 lb.
4 lb 11 oz	There is a remainder of 3 lb.
	This is 3 × 16 oz = 48 oz. Add this to the 7 oz making 55 oz.
	5's into 55 goes 11 so they will also get 11 oz.

Temperature

The temperature scale used nowadays is the Celsius scale (which used to be called the Centigrade scale).

In this scale:
0° is the temperature at which water freezes,
100° is the temperature at which water boils.

In Britain, we still often use the Fahrenheit scale.

In this scale:
32° is the temperature at which water freezes,
212° is the temperature at which water boils.

To change from Fahrenheit to Celsius

Write down the temperature in deg F

↓

Subtract 32

↓

Multiply by 5

↓

Divide by 9

↓

This is the temperature in deg C

Or use the formula
$C = \frac{5}{9}(F - 32)$
where F is the temperature in deg F
C is the temperature in deg C

To change from Celsius to Fahrenheit

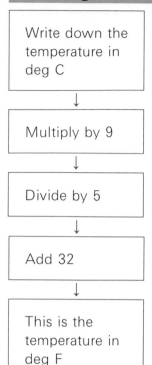

Write down the temperature in deg C

↓

Multiply by 9

↓

Divide by 5

↓

Add 32

↓

This is the temperature in deg F

Or use the formula
$$F = \tfrac{9}{5}C + 32$$

You can draw a conversion graph to use, as described on page 316.

Examples

1   Change 30°C into deg F.

Using the flow chart:
Write down 30
Multiply by 9, . . . 270
Divide by 5, . . .   54
Add 32,   . . .   86
The temperature is 86°F

2   Change 40°F into deg C.

Using the formula $C = \tfrac{5}{9}(F - 32)$
$$= \tfrac{5}{9}(40 - 32) = \tfrac{5}{9} \times 8 = \tfrac{40}{9} = 4.4 \text{ to 1 decimal place.}$$
The temperature is 4.4°C.

Exercise 17.1

1. Change the following:

    1 6′ 3″ into inches   **6** 96 inches into feet
    2 8 st 3 lb into lb   **7** 48 oz into lb
    3 2 gall 1 pint into pints   **8** 20 pints into gallons
    4 2 lb 4 oz into oz   **9** 5280 yards into miles
    5 $\frac{1}{4}$ mile into yards   **10** 90 feet into yards

2. Use the flow chart or the formula on page 236 to change these temperatures into °C.

    1 41°F   **2** 77°F   **3** 203°F

    Change these temperatures into °F.

    4 15°C   **5** 40°C   **6** 80°C

3. Read the measurements given on these scales:

    1 Weighing scale   **2** Measuring jug in pints
           in stones and lb

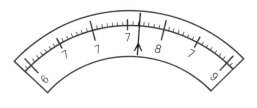
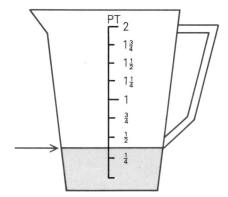

    3 Ruler in inches and sixteenths

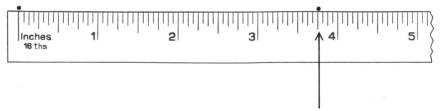

4. Find approximate metric equivalents for these British weights and measures.

    1 24 miles   **2** 6 lbs   **3** 80 inches   **4** 2 gallons   **5** 3 tons

5.   Find approximate British equivalents for these metric weights and measures.

    1   20 cm   **2**   12 litres   **3**   10 kg   **4**   80 kg   **5**   900 g

6.   Using your calculator and the lists on page 234 find more accurate equivalents for the weights and measures in questions 4 and 5, giving them correct to 3 significant figures.

7.   **1**   Express 9 inches as a fraction of 1 yard
    2   Express 5 oz as a fraction of 1 lb 9 oz
    3   Express 3 pints as a fraction of 1 gallon
    4   Express 880 yards as a fraction of 1 mile
    5   Express 2′ 3″ as a fraction of 2 yards

8.   Find these quantities:

    1 $\frac{2}{3}$ of 2 ft   **4** $\frac{1}{6}$ of 1 yard
    2 $\frac{3}{8}$ of 1 lb 8 oz   **5** $\frac{1}{4}$ of 2 stone
    3 $\frac{5}{8}$ of 2 gallons

9.   Work out the answers to these calculations.

    1   2 lb 7 oz + 1 lb 6 oz + 5 lb 4 oz   **4**   4 lb 5 oz ÷ 3
    2   2 ft 2 in − 1 ft 7 in   **5**   (4 ft 9 in + 3 ft 7 in) ÷ 5
    3   2 gall 3 pints × 4

Exercise 17.2   Applications and Activities

1.   The luggage allowance when travelling by a certain airline is 15 kg. What is this in lbs ?

2.   This sign shows the price for 4-star petrol. Find the cost per gallon, taking 1 gallon = 4.546 litres, giving the answer to the nearest penny.

3.   The distance from Liverpool to Panama along a shipping route is 4570 miles. Taking 1 mile as 1.609 km, find this distance in km, to the nearest 10 km.

4.   Paul was told by his trainer to run 10 km every morning. What distance is this, in miles, to the nearest $\frac{1}{10}$ mile ?

5.   A brick is 9″ by $4\frac{1}{2}$″ by $2\frac{3}{4}$″. What are these measurements in cm, to the nearest mm ? (1 inch = 2.54 cm.)

6.

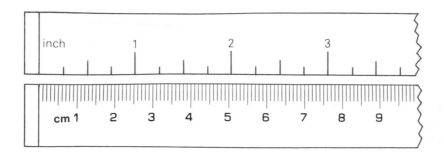

The two rulers show measurements in inches and in centimetres. The top ruler has inches and is divided into quarter inches. The other ruler has centimetres and is divided into millimetres.

1   What measurement in cm is equivalent to $1\frac{3}{4}$ inches ?
2   What measurement in inches is equivalent to 8.9 cm ?

7.   A piece of wire 4 ft long is bent to make the outline of an equilateral triangle. What is the length, in inches, of each side of the triangle ?

8.   An empty tank weighs 65 lb. When full the tank holds 18 gallons of water. What is the total weight of the tank when it is half-full of water ?
(1 gallon of water weighs 10 lb.)

9.   A candle is 1 ft long. It is lit at 7.30 pm and it burns at the rate of 1 inch every hour. How long will it be at midnight ?

10.   A dress needs $3\frac{3}{4}$ yards of material. How much material is left from a 5-yard length ?

11.   A car will travel 36 miles on 1 gallon of petrol. How far will the car travel on $3\frac{1}{2}$ gallons ?

12.   Paula is 6 st 6 lb and Rebecca is 4 st 10 lb. How much heavier is Paula than Rebecca ?
If they stand on the scale together, what weight will be shown ?

13.   How many pieces of wood 1' 3" long can be cut from a plank 10' long ?

14.   A cake weighed 8 lb 3 oz. A man guessed 9 lb 8 oz and his daughter guessed 6 lb 15 oz. Which was the better guess ?

15.   Jafar's temperature was 101.3°F. How much was this above the normal temperature of 98.4°F ? In a few hours his temperature was taken again and it was 99.8°F. How much had it fallen ?

16. The diagram shows a thermometer marked in deg C and
    deg F.

    1 What temperature does the thermometer show, in °F,
    and in °C ?
    2 What would be the temperature in °C if it was 90°F ?
    3 The classroom should be heated to 16°C. What is
    this temperature in °F ?
    4 A holiday guide gives these temperatures as the
    average daily maximum temperatures on the Costa
    Blanca. Change these readings into °F, giving them
    to the nearest degree.

May	24°C
June	27°C
July	31°C
Aug	31°C
Sept	29°C

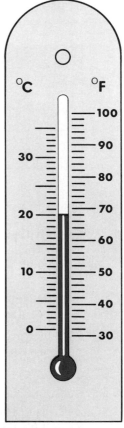

17. On an old weighing scale, the standard weights which were available were 1 oz,
    2 oz, 4 oz, 8 oz, 1 lb and 2 lb. There was one of each.
    Which weights would you use to weigh
    1 14 oz   **2** 2 lb 6 oz   **3** 3 lb 9 oz ?

18. A quick way used to measure a yard of string or cloth is to stretch out an arm
    and measure from the finger and thumb to the tip of the nose.
    Try this with several friends. Measure your results in inches. Ask some adults
    also. Comment on your measurements.

19. **History of British measurement**

    It is interesting to find out about the measures which were used long ago in
    Britain. Did you know that 1 inch was the length of 3 barleycorns placed end to
    end, and 1 furlong ($\frac{1}{8}$ of a mile) derives its name from a furrow-length ?
    Why was a **foot** so called ?
    How is a mile connected with the Romans ?
    Why was it necessary to have a standard system of weights and measures ?
    Try to find information in reference books, and write about this.

20.   These amounts are given in an old book as the average amounts a person eats in one day. Using the up-to-date prices in a local shop, find the cost of this food.

bread	10 oz	jam	$1\frac{1}{2}$ oz
cheese	$1\frac{1}{2}$ oz	butter	$\frac{1}{2}$ oz
bacon	$1\frac{1}{3}$ oz	tea	$\frac{1}{3}$ oz
potatoes	$\frac{1}{2}$ lb	sugar	2 oz
meat	4 oz	milk	$\frac{1}{3}$ pint

Do you agree with the amounts in this list ? Work out the average amounts eaten in your family nowadays, and find their cost ?

21.   **British Coinage**

Talk to an older person to find out about coinage before it was changed to decimal currency. On what date did this happen ? It wasn't so long ago. Before decimalisation, we used shillings. You may still find a shilling or a two-shilling coin in your change as they are still in use. How many shillings were there in £1 ? What was a two-shilling coin called ? How much was half-a-crown worth ? There were 240 'old' pence in £1. This had some advantages as 240 can be divided exactly by many numbers. List all the factors of 240. In comparison, we now have 100 pence in £1. List all the factors of 100.

Children spent much more time than you do on learning how to do money sums. There were no calculators in those days ! Here are some sums to try, if you are interested.

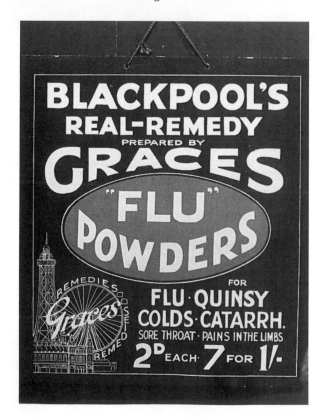

1   What change was left from £1 note after paying the butcher 7s 2d and the grocer 5s 11d ?

2   The charge for hire of a deck-chair at the seaside was 3d. How many chairs had been used when the total takings amounted to £5 16s 9d ?

3   On one particular Saturday, 58 832 people watched a 1st Division football match. If the average price of admission was 2s 6d, how much was paid altogether ?

4   Find the cost of 10 gramophone records at 5s 6d each and 1 box of gramophone needles at 2s 3d per box.

5   A shopkeeper bought 100 lettuces for 15s 0d and sold them at 4d each. What profit did he make ?

PUZZLES

27.   A chess set consists of 16 black pieces and 16 white pieces. All the pieces are put in a bag and 2 pieces are taken out at a time.
If they are the same colour they are put in a pile on the table, if they are different colours they are put away in their box.
What is the probability that there will be equal numbers of black and white pieces on the table after all the pieces have been removed from the bag ?

28.   Copy the diagram and arrange the 13 letters **A C C E G I L N Q R S T U** in suitable positions in it, so that
the circle contains the letters **C I R C L E**,
the triangle contains the letters **T R I A N G L E**,
and the square contains the letters **S Q U A R E**.

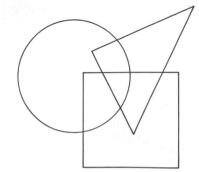

29.   A man rode every day to work, on his bicycle. But one day he had a puncture exactly a mile before he reached the factory, and as he did not have a repair outfit with him, and there wasn't one at the factory either, he had to wheel his bicycle the rest of the way to work, and all the way home. How many miles did the man walk *further* than he rode ?

30.   There was a water-lily in a pond. Each day it doubled its size and on the tenth day it completely filled the pond. On which day did it half-fill the pond ?

18 Thinking about frequency distributions

Frequency distributions and histograms

Here are three histograms. The labelling of the axes is not shown.

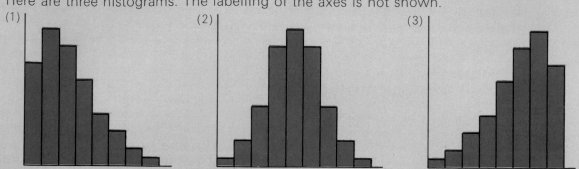

We often draw a histogram because we can deduce things from its general shape.
Describe the differences in the shapes above.

(1) is said to be a positive skew distribution, (2) is a normal distribution and (3) is a negative skew distribution. (The term 'normal distribution' has a very exact meaning but at present we will use it for a graph of this general shape.)

These histograms represent the following distributions,

(a) heights of all 13 year-old girls in a school,

(b) ages of cars in a survey, from 0 to 8 years,

(c) marks in a test, out of 10, for a class which is good at Maths.

Say which you think is which.

What shape of histogram would result from the times taken by the runners in the London Marathon (a run of 26 miles) ?

You can measure the heights of your friends.

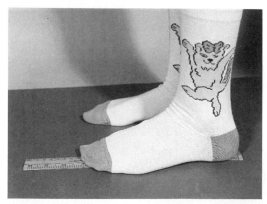

Investigate the lengths of feet of a group of friends.

Sketching histograms

Sketch the general shape of the histograms which you think you would get from these data:
(d) Numbers of the population in age groups 0–10, 10–20, 20–30, etc.
(e) Length of time torch batteries will last for, if the average time is about 5 hours.
(f) Goals scored in the matches of the 4 divisions of the football league, on one Saturday.
(g) Times of pupils' arrival at school, in classes 20–15 min early, 15–10 min early, etc.
(h) Distances of pupils' homes from the school.

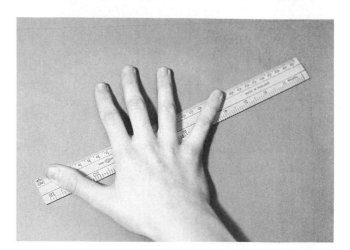

Handspans are another simple set of measurements you can collect.

Find the distribution of times taken by pupils travelling to school.

18 Frequency Distributions

Continuous data

Some statistical results are obtained by **counting**, usually in whole numbers, e.g. number of pupils in a school, number of cars waiting at traffic lights, number of marks gained in an exam. Counting goes up in jumps, 1, 2, 3, etc. However, results of length, weight, capacity, temperature and time are obtained by measurement. These are called **continuous data**. Measurement goes up continuously, not in jumps.

Frequency distributions and histograms were used in Chapter 7, but in this chapter we are going to use frequency distributions of continuous data, and draw their histograms.

Example

Here is a record of the weights of 100 young men.

Weight in kg	Tally	frequency
30 to just under 40	II	2
40 to just under 50	JHT JHT	10
50 to just under 60	JHT JHT JHT JHT IIII	24
60 to just under 70	JHT JHT JHT JHT JHT JHT JHT	35
70 to just under 80	JHT JHT JHT IIII	19
80 to just under 90	JHT I	6
90 to just under 100	II II	4
		100

We can draw a histogram of the results.

Histogram to show the distribution of weights of 100 young men

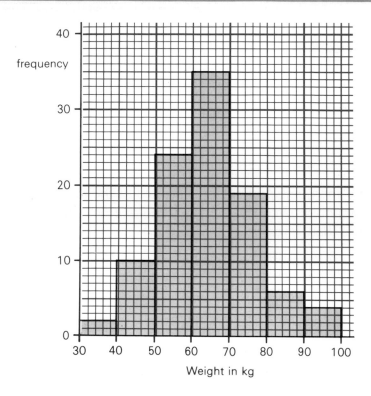

Weight in kg

Notes

1   The weights are grouped into 7 classes, with an equal range of 10 kg in each class, so the 7 blocks in the histograms have equal widths.
   (At this stage it is desirable to have an equal range in each class because otherwise the histogram is more complicated to draw.)

2   Since there is no gap between measurements, there is no space between the blocks.

3   We have labelled the edges of the blocks, because this is simpler than labelling the blocks themselves.

4   The class with the greatest frequency is called the **modal class**. Here the modal class is the class of weights 60 kg to just under 70 kg.

5   Notice the shape of the graph. The bars in the centre are higher than those at the beginning and end. This sort of shape often occurs from this kind of data, because more measurements are usually average and so in the centre, rather than the measurements being evenly spread over the whole range.

Exercise 18.1

1. 24 girls measured their heights and the results are shown. (Heights are in completed cm.) Make a tally table, grouping these heights into classes 115–under 125, 125–under 135, 135–under 145, 145–under 155, 155–under 165. Draw a histogram to show this distribution.

154	152	116	162	160	134	144	136
145	143	142	151	137	127	157	134
163	144	149	158	146	132	137	140

2. This is a list of the number of completed years of the reigns of Kings and Queens of England, beginning with William the Conqueror in 1066. (0 means the person reigned for less than 1 year.)

21	13	35	19	35	10	17	56	35	20	50
22	13	9	39	22	0	2	24	38	6	0
5	44	22	24	36	3	13	6	12	13	33
59	10	7	63	9	25	0	15			

    Add the figure for Elizabeth II which was 38 years up to February, 1990.

    Tally the data in years 0 to 9, 10 to 19, etc. and draw a histogram to represent the distribution.

3. The histogram shows the times taken by a group of boys to run a race.

    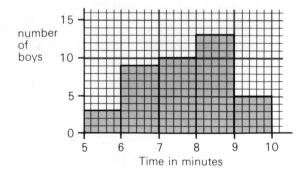

    Copy and complete this frequency distribution table, and find how many boys there were altogether.

Time in minutes	f
5 to just under 6	3
6 to just under 7	
. . .	

4.   A group of girls were going horse-riding and they had to state their weights. Here
     they are, in completed kg.

42	44	46	34	41	48	33	28	42	32
39	38	25	51	49	38	50	36	31	42
43	44	39	41						

     Make a tally table grouping these weights in the classes 25–under 30,
     30–under 35, etc.
     Draw a histogram to show the distribution.

5.   Here are the times taken in a 10-mile road race.

	Number of runners
50 min but less than 1 hour	57
1 hr but less than 1 hr 10 min	221
1 hr 10 min but less than 1 hr 20 min	276
1 hr 20 min but less than 1 hr 30 min	163
1 hr 30 min but less than 1 hr 40 min	51
1 hr 40 min but less than 1 hr 50 min	16
1 hr 50 min but less than 2 hr	8
2 hr but less than 2 hr 10 min	5
2 hr 10 min but less than 2 hr 20 min	3

     How many runners took part ?
     How many of them took 2 hours or longer ?
     Draw a histogram of the results. (A suitable scale on the vertical axis, if it will fit
     on your graph paper, would be 2 cm to represent 40 runners.)
     Comment on the shape of the graph.

6.   The weights of a group of children are given in this histogram.

     1   How many children are
             there altogether ?
     2   What is the modal class ?
     3   How many children are
             there in the modal class ?
     4   What fraction of the
             children weigh 12 kg or
             more ?

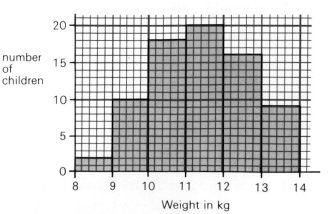

7.   This table shows the ages, in completed years, of children in a Youth club.

Draw a histogram to show the distribution of ages.
If it was decided to divide the activities of the club
into a Junior and a Senior section, what ages would
you suggest for membership of each section ?
Give your reasons.

Age	Number of children
8	22
9	30
10	38
11	23
12	8
13	5
	126

8.   60 teenagers were asked to say for how long they had watched television on the
previous day, which was a Tuesday in term time. The replies were:

1	0	3	2	2	0	2	1	3	$3\frac{1}{2}$
2	4	$2\frac{1}{2}$	$2\frac{1}{2}$	1	1	$1\frac{1}{2}$	$\frac{1}{2}$	1	2
2	1	$3\frac{1}{2}$	1	1	$\frac{1}{2}$	2	$\frac{1}{2}$	$2\frac{1}{2}$	$2\frac{1}{2}$
0	$1\frac{1}{2}$	2	$1\frac{1}{2}$	1	1	1	$1\frac{1}{2}$	$2\frac{1}{2}$	$1\frac{1}{2}$
2	3	$\frac{1}{2}$	$\frac{1}{2}$	$3\frac{1}{2}$	$2\frac{1}{2}$	2	1	$1\frac{1}{2}$	$\frac{1}{2}$
$\frac{1}{2}$	1	4	1	$1\frac{1}{2}$	2	$3\frac{1}{2}$	0	$\frac{1}{2}$	$1\frac{1}{2}$

The times are in completed half-hours, so that 0 means less than $\frac{1}{2}$ hour, $\frac{1}{2}$ means
at least $\frac{1}{2}$ hour but less than 1 hour, and so on.
List this information in a table and draw a histogram to show the distribution of
times.
If you were asked a similar question, what would your likely answer be ?
Some people think that teenagers watch too much television. Judging by these
figures, what are your views ?

Exercise 18.2   Applications and Activities

1.   50 leaves from an evergreen shrub were measured and these are the results in cm.

7.2	6.5	6.7	7.3	6.4	7.0	6.0	6.5	6.2	6.7
5.8	5.1	6.9	5.8	5.9	5.5	5.1	6.0	5.9	5.0
5.8	5.9	5.9	5.3	4.6	5.9	5.7	6.9	7.4	6.7
7.2	6.9	7.7	7.8	5.5	5.3	5.6	5.4	5.0	6.1
6.0	6.7	7.0	6.6	5.9	5.9	7.0	7.2	7.4	6.2

Group these lengths into classes 4.5–under 5.0, 5.0–under 5.5, etc. and show
them in a frequency table. Draw a histogram to show the distribution of lengths.

2. At the beginning of the century, in 1901, a census was taken of the population.
    (A census is a Government survey held every 10 years. A form is sent to every
    household and it asks questions about everyone living there, as well as questions
    about the type of housing. Other forms are sent to hospitals, hotels, prisons, etc.
    so that the census includes everyone in the country.)
    These were the details of the population of the U.K. in 1901. (The population
    numbers are given to the nearest 100 000.)

Age (years)	Number of people
0–under 10	8 500 000
10–under 20	7 800 000
20–under 30	7 000 000
30–under 40	5 300 000
40–under 50	4 000 000
50–under 60	2 800 000
60–under 70	1 800 000
70–under 80	800 000
80 and over	200 000

Draw a histogram to show this information. Assume the last age-group goes to
under 90, although a few people may have been older. On the vertical scale take
2 cm to represent 1 000 000 people if it will fit on, then every 2 mm line will
represent 100 000 people.
If you can obtain the figures for the latest census, or the latest population
estimates for the U.K., draw a histogram to represent these, compare the two
histograms, and comment on them.
Give some reasons why you think the Government holds a census every 10 years.

3. 50 potatoes, bought from the greengrocer, were weighed on the kitchen scales.
    These weights are given to the completed 25 g, so 25 means 25 g but less than
    50 g.
    List this information in a table.
    Make a second table grouping these weights in the classes 0–under 50, 50–under
    100, etc., and draw a histogram of this distribution. Comment on the shape of the
    histogram.
    Weights in grams:

100	275	175	250	225	150	75	100	75	300
100	125	225	225	75	75	200	75	250	100
125	175	50	50	25	25	50	75	175	150
75	125	75	75	50	25	175	125	75	50
75	125	25	50	225	200	75	100	25	150

4.   Sarah and Claire made a survey of the ages of cars, by recording the registration
      letter of 200 cars. The results were as shown. A few cars without a registration
      letter had to be left out of the survey.

```
D  F  B  F  D  E  W  C  X  F  F  V  E  F  C  F  E
E  A  X  A  E  D  Y  B  F  E  F  C  C  D  C  C  W
B  D  B  F  V  X  D  A  Y  E  D  F  B  Y  C  D  F
Y  D  C  V  Y  C  T  C  W  D  E  B  X  Y  C  A  C
F  C  Y  V  E  E  Y  E  E  T  F  D  A  F  D  B  E
Y  D  F  T  D  C  Y  C  C  W  B  Y  A  E  D  F  E
Y  E  F  B  E  V  E  X  B  A  T  B  F  X  W  B  Y
W  F  F  X  F  F  B  W  Y  C  F  V  B  C  Y  F  D
F  E  C  D  A  F  D  Y  B  F  D  X  B  A  S  A  D
F  V  V  W  E  B  S  D  C  D  D  C  T  F  F  E  F
A  W  C  A  C  W  B  F  V  C  F  F  C  F  V  A  A
E  F  B  D  D  X  F  Y  Y  F  C  B  T
```

      List these results in a table with entries (in order), F E D C B A Y X W V T S.
      The survey was done (in Mid Wales) in the last week of July, 1989, so cars with
      letter F were less than 1 year old, those with letter E were 1 year but less than
      2 years old, and so on. Those with letter S were the oldest, 11 years but less than
      12 years old. Add these ages to your table.
      Make a new table with ages 0–under 2, 2–under 4, etc. Draw a histogram of this
      distribution.
      Can you make any comments about the histogram ?

5.   There are many investigations you can do, collecting the data yourself. Read
      the instructions on page 94 about collecting information. Here are some
      extra instructions for making a frequency distribution using continuous data.

   1   **Accuracy of measurements**

       You will have to decide how accurately you are going to make your
       measurements. It will depend on the particular data you are collecting.
       For instance, if you are measuring people's heights it will be sufficient to
       measure in whole centimetres.

   2   **Recording the measurements**

       You will have to decide how to record your measurements. Instead of
       recording to the **nearest** kg, cm, minute, etc., it will make the boundaries
       of the histogram simpler if you record to the **completed** unit. (That is what
       we have done in this chapter.)

3   **Grouping the data into classes**

After you have got a list of measurements you must look at the complete set of data and decide on suitable classes. It is useful to have about 7 equal classes but in a particular situation you may find it more convenient to have a few less or more. For example, if you have a range of lengths from 4 cm to just under 20 cm, that is a range of 16 cm. If you put a 2 cm range in each class you would get 8 classes, which would be 4 cm to under 6 cm, 6 cm to under 8 cm, 8 cm to under 10 cm, etc.

4   **To draw the histogram**

Look at the frequency distribution table. Count how many classes of data you have and decide how wide you can make each one. If there are 7 classes then you can probably fit them on your graph paper if you make them each 2 cm wide. Draw the horizontal axis. Label the edges of the blocks for the classes and give the axis a title, e.g. time in minutes.
You will choose a suitable scale for the vertical axis by looking at the class with most items in, (the modal class). Give the vertical axis a title, e.g. number of items, or just label it 'frequency'.
Draw the histogram, and give it a title.

Here are some suggestions for investigations, but you should think of others.

Surveys at school

Times taken to travel to school.
Distances travelled to school.
Times of arrival at school.
Times spent on homework.
Heights.
Width of hand-spans.
Times taken to do various tasks.

Traffic surveys

Ages of cars.
Times between successive cars on a fairly quiet road.

Distribution of results when people make estimations

Length of a line.
Size of an angle.
Weight of an object.
Guess of 1 minute's time.

19 Thinking about symmetry

Making 'butterflies'

Fold a small piece of paper in half.
Open it up and put a blob of wet paint on one half or on the fold line.
Then fold it again and press hard so that the wet paint is transferred to the other half.
Open it again.

Making doyleys

cut off

centre
of square

centre
of square

Fold a square piece of paper in half, then in half again, and then cornerways into half
again. Cut the edge to make a curve and then cut bits out of all three edges. Open it
out.

Letters of the alphabet

Which capital letters in the alphabet have a horizontal axis of symmetry, a vertical axis
of symmetry, other axes of symmetry or two axes of symmetry ?
Which letters have a point of symmetry ?
Find some words which have a vertical axis of symmetry, e.g. **MUM**, a horizontal axis
of symmetry, e.g. **BED**, a point of symmetry e.g. **NON**, or words which have a vertical

M
axis of symmetry when written vertically e.g. A
T

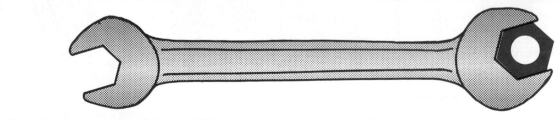

Describe the symmetry of the nut. Why are nuts made symmetrical ?

Symmetry around you

Look around you in the room. What examples can you see of symmetrical objects ?
List or sketch other examples of symmetrical objects seen in daily life, and say what kind of symmetry they have. Some will be objects found in nature, such as birds, animals, flowers, etc, and others will be man-made objects. Why have the different man-made objects been made symmetrically ? There may be different reasons for different objects.
Look for examples of symmetry in art, and in patterns on such things as wallpaper and carpets.

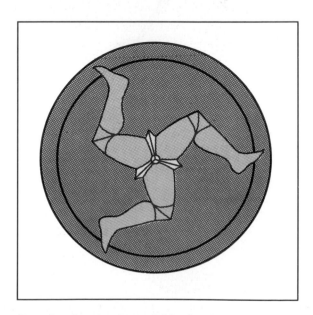

Compare these three cards and describe their symmetries, ignoring the numbers and letters.

Describe the symmetry of this circular symbol.

19 Symmetry and Congruence

Symmetry

These diagrams show **axes of symmetry**, marked by dotted lines.

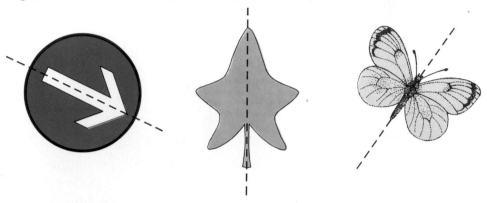

If an object is 3-dimensional, its 2-dimensional picture may show an axis of symmetry when it actually has a plane of symmetry.

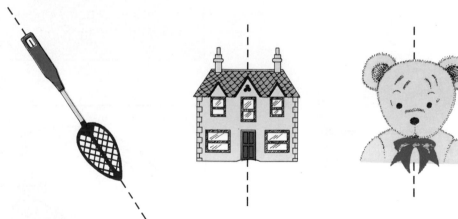

Axes of symmetry for a circle

The diagram shows a diameter of a circle, and it is an axis of symmetry.

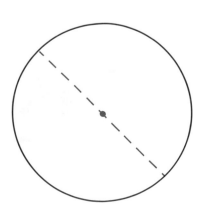

A circle has an **infinite number** of diameters. (This means that if we try to count them we never get to the end of the counting.) They are all axes of symmetry, so a circle has an infinite number of axes of symmetry.

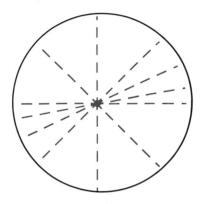

This glass, which has a circular shape, has an infinite number of planes of symmetry.

These diagrams show **points of symmetry**, marked by ●.
If the object is turned through 180°, its shape is unchanged. (Look at it upside down.)

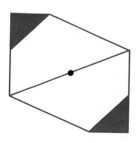  

Some figures have axes and points of symmetry.

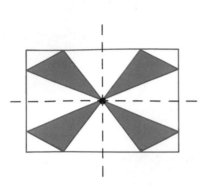

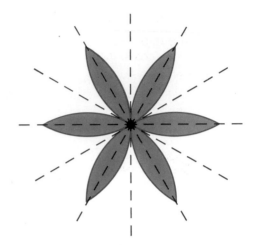

Rotational symmetry

This equilateral triangle has rotational symmetry of order 3.
If it is turned through 120°, and then 120° again, it is unchanged.
The • is the centre of rotational symmetry.

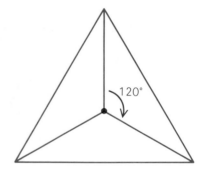

This tile has rotational symmetry of order 4.
It can be turned through 90°, four times and it is unchanged.
The • is the centre of rotational symmetry.

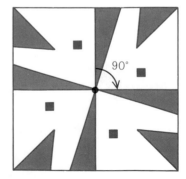

Note We will use the term 'point of symmetry' if the shape is unchanged when it is turned through 180°.

We will use the term 'centre of rotational symmetry' when the shape has rotational symmetry.

If a shape has an **even** order of rotational symmetry, the centre of rotational symmetry is also the point of symmetry.

If a shape has an **odd** order of rotational symmetry, the centre of rotational symmetry is **not** a point of symmetry.

Exercise 19.1

1. Sketch these capital letters and mark in any axes and points of symmetry.

C N T X

2. Sketch these figures and mark in any axes of symmetry.

3. Sketch these figures and mark in the points of symmetry.

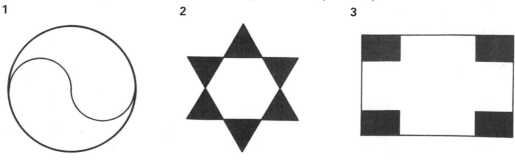

4. These figures have rotational symmetry about the centre point marked •.
    Say whether it is of order 2, 3, 4 or 5.

1   **2**   **3**

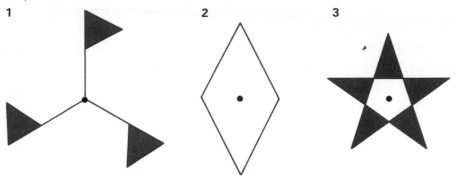

5. These solid figures have planes of symmetry. How many do they have ?

1   **2**

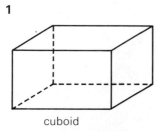

cuboid

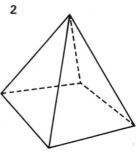

pyramid on
square base

3

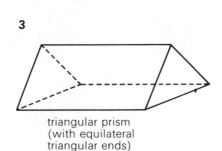

triangular prism
(with equilateral
triangular ends)

6. An isosceles triangle has one axis of symmetry. Sketch these triangles or draw
    them on tracing paper and mark on your diagrams the axes of symmetry.

1   **2**   **3**

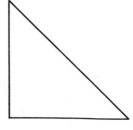
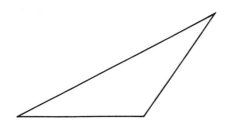

7.   An equilateral triangle has 3 axes of symmetry. Sketch these triangles or draw them on tracing paper and mark on the diagrams the axes of symmetry. They also have rotational symmetry of order 3. On the diagrams mark the centres about which there is rotational symmetry.

1

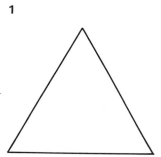

2

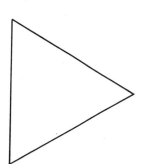

8.   Sketch these figures and mark in all axes of symmetry.

1

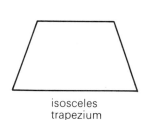

isosceles
trapezium

2

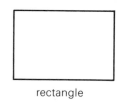

rectangle

3

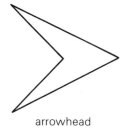

arrowhead

4

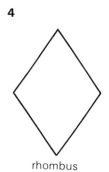

rhombus

5

square

9.   Say which of the figures in question 8 have a point of symmetry.

10.   For each of these diagrams, state how many axes of symmetry there are.
       Which of the diagrams have a point of symmetry ?

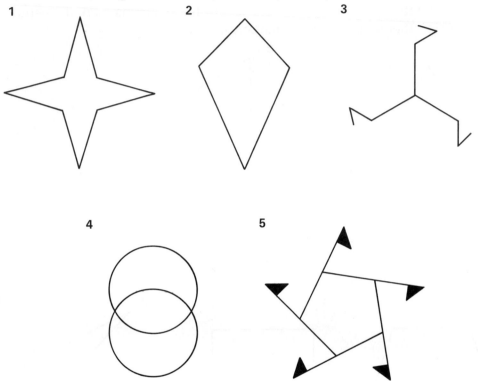

11.   Say which of the figures of question 10 have rotational symmetry, and state the
       order of rotational symmetry.

12.   Begin with 5 squares joined together as shown. On separate diagrams sketch
       the figure and add 1 extra square so that the complete figure has:

       1   an axis of symmetry,
       2   a different axis of symmetry,
       3   a point of symmetry.

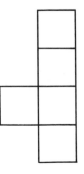

13.   On separate diagrams, copy and complete the shading so that the diagram has

     1   a vertical axis of symmetry,

     2   a horizontal axis of symmetry,

     3   a point of symmetry,

     4   an axis of symmetry along one diagonal of the figure,

     5   an axis of symmetry along the other diagonal of the figure,

     6   2 axes of symmetry along both diagonals. In this diagram, how many axes of symmetry are there altogether ?

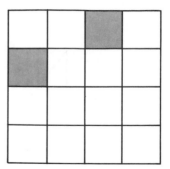

Congruence

Congruent figures are the same shape and the same size.

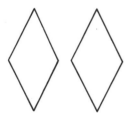 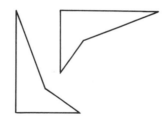 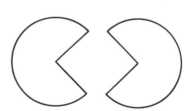

Congruent triangles

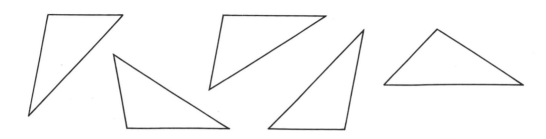

(Some may have to be turned over to fit.)

In these diagrams, the dotted line is an axis of symmetry so the triangles are congruent.

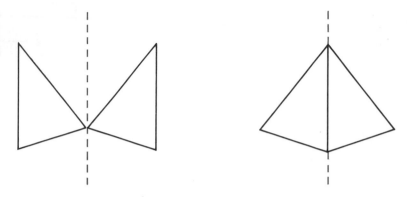

In these diagrams, C is a point of symmetry so the triangles are congruent.

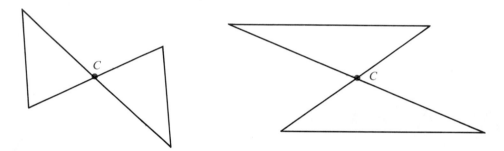

Exercise 19.2

1.   Name the pairs of congruent figures in the diagram.

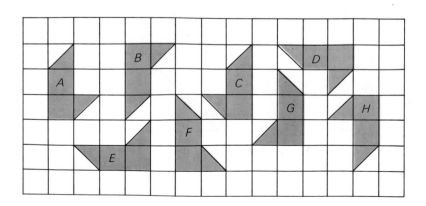

2.   Name the pairs of congruent triangles in the diagram.

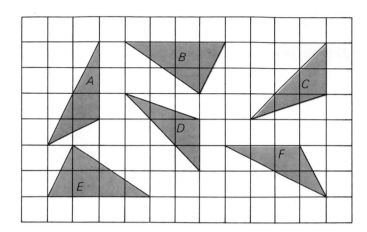

3.   In this figure, AC is an axis of symmetry. Name three pairs
      of congruent triangles.

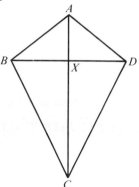

4.   In this figure C, is a point of symmetry. Name four
      pairs of congruent triangles.

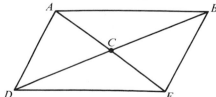

Drawing triangles accurately

Follow the instructions in these examples and draw the triangles yourself.

1. To draw a triangle, given 1 side and 2 angles

Example

Draw a triangle ABC with $AB = 10$ cm, $\angle A = 66°$ and $\angle B = 51°$.

Draw AB, 10 cm long.
Measure an angle of 66° at A and an angle of 51° at B.
Continue these lines until they meet at C.

If instead of being given the size of $\angle B$, you had been told that $\angle C = 63°$, you could have calculated the size of $\angle B$, (how ?), and then you could continue as above.

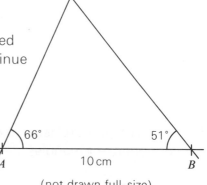

(not drawn full-size)

2. To draw a triangle, given 2 sides and the angle included between these sides

Example

Draw a triangle ABC with $AB = 10$ cm, $\angle A = 66°$ and $AC = 8$ cm.

Draw AB, 10 cm long.
Measure an angle of 66° at A and measure off a distance of 8 cm along this angle line, to give the point C.
Join BC.

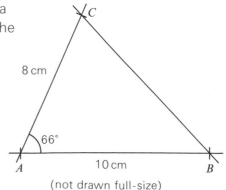

(not drawn full-size)

3. To draw a triangle, given two sides and a non-included angle

Example

Draw a triangle ABC with AB = 6 cm, $\angle A$ = 37° and BC = 7 cm.

Draw AB, 6 cm long.
Measure an angle of 37° at A and extend this angle
line onwards.
With compasses, centre B, radius 7 cm, draw an arc
to meet this extended line at C.
Join BC.

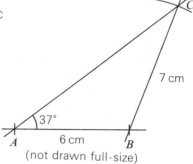

(not drawn full-size)

(In some cases there could be two points where the arc meets the line, so there
would be two possible triangles of different shapes satisfying the given data.)

4. To draw a triangle given 3 sides

Example

Draw a triangle ABC with AB = 10 cm, BC = 8 cm and AC = 7 cm.

Draw AB, 10 cm long.
With compasses, centre A, radius 7 cm, draw an arc.
With centre B, radius 8 cm, draw an arc to cut the
first arc at C.
Join AC and CB.

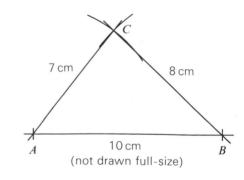

(not drawn full-size)

Exercise 19.3

In questions 1 to 4, using geometrical instruments, construct the triangles full-size.

1.
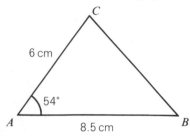

Measure the length of BC and the sizes of $\angle B$ and $\angle C$.

2.
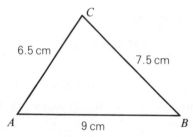

Measure the angles A, B and C.

3.
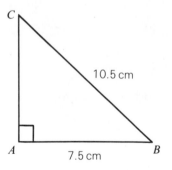

Measure the length of AC and the sizes of $\angle B$ and $\angle C$.

4.
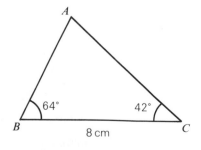

Measure the lengths of AB and AC. Calculate the size of $\angle A$ and check this by measuring it.

5. **To draw an angle of 60°, using ruler and compasses**

Example

To make an angle of 60° at *P*, on the line *PS*.

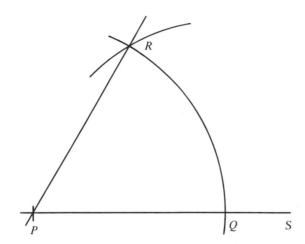

With centre *P* draw a large arc, to cut *PS* at *Q*.
With centre *Q* and the same radius, draw an arc to cut the other arc at *R*.
Join *PR*.
Then angle *QPṘ* = 60°.

If you joined *QR*, what sort of triangle would triangle *PQR* be ? Explain why this shows that ∠*QPR* = 60°.
How could you use this angle to draw an angle of 30°, using ruler and compasses ?

6. **To find the mid-point of a line AB or the perpendicular bisector of AB**

The dotted line is an axis of symmetry of the line *AB*. It passes through the mid-point of *AB*, and it is at right angles to *AB*. It is called the **perpendicular bisector** of *AB*.

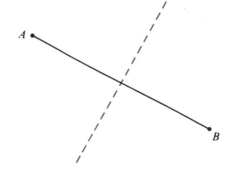

1   **By measurement.** Find the length of *AB*, divide this by 2 and measure this
    distance from *A* to get the mid-point.
    If you need the perpendicular bisector also, use your protractor to draw a line
    through this mid-point at right-angles to *AB*.

2   **By paper folding.** You need to use thin paper such as tracing paper. Fold
    the paper so that *B* lies on top of *A* and make a firm crease. This crease is the
    perpendicular bisector of *AB* and cuts *AB* at its mid-point.

3   **Using ruler and compasses.**
    With centre *A* and a radius more than
    half of *AB*, draw two arcs.

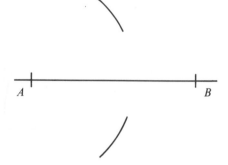

With centre *B* and the same radius,
draw two arcs to cut the first two arcs
at *X* and *Y*.
Join *XY*, cutting *AB* at *Z*.
Then *Z* is the mid-point of *AB*, and
XZY is the perpendicular bisector of
AB.

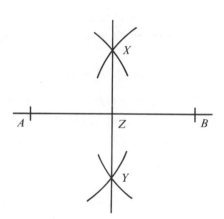

Exercise 19.4   Applications and Activities

1.   Copy and complete the figure so that *PQ*
     is a line of symmetry.

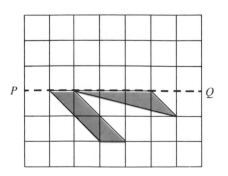

2. Here is one quarter of a symmetrical
    pattern. Copy it and complete the other
    three quarters to match, so that the
    dotted lines are axes of symmetry.

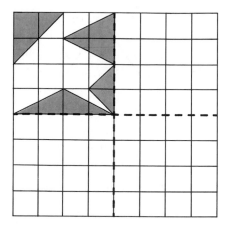

3. In each diagram the dotted line is an axis of symmetry. Decide which angles are
    equal and then calculate the marked angles.

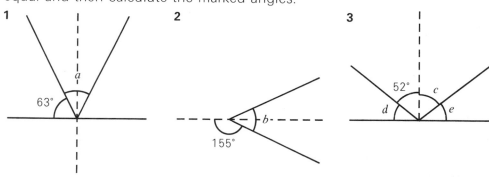

4. On graph paper or squared paper draw the x-axis from -6 to 10 and the y-axis
    from -6 to 8 using equal scales on both axes. Draw triangles labelled A to F by
    plotting and joining the 3 points given in each case.

    Triangle A $(1, 6)$, $(2, 8)$, $(4, 6)$
    Triangle B $(7, 4)$, $(9, 2)$, $(9, 6)$
    Triangle C $(7, -5)$, $(9, -3)$, $(10, -6)$
    Triangle D $(2, -1)$, $(4, 1)$, $(6, -1)$
    Triangle E $(-4, -2)$, $(-3, -5)$, $(-1, -3)$
    Triangle F $(-6, 2)$, $(-6, 5)$, $(-4, 3)$

    Which pairs of triangles are congruent ?

5. The triangles *ABC* and *DEF* are
    congruent with *BC* = *DE*,
    $\angle A = \angle F$ and $\angle C = \angle E$.
    Which side in triangle *DEF*
    is equal to *AC* ?

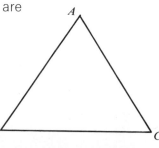

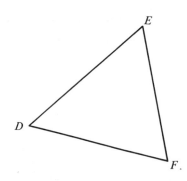

6.

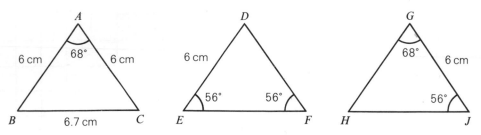

Calculate the sizes of the unmarked angles. What are the lengths of *DF* and *GH* ? Are the triangles congruent ?

7.

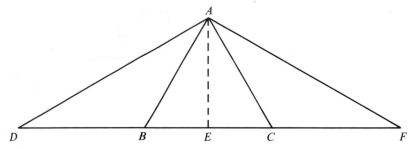

ABC is an equilateral triangle and *DBECF* is a straight line. *DB* = *BC* and *AE* is an axis of symmetry of the figure.

   1   Name 3 pairs of congruent triangles.
   2   Name all the lines equal in length to *DB*.
   3   Calculate the size of ∠*DBA*.
   4   If *DB* = 6 cm, what is the length of *DE* ?

8.   Construct triangle *ABC* with the measurements given. *D* is the mid-point of *AB*. Mark *D* on your diagram. Through *D* draw a line parallel to *BC*. Let this line cut *AC* at *E*.
Measure *AE* and *EC*.
Comment on your results.

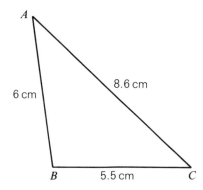

9.   Construct triangle *ABC* with the measurements given.
Measure ∠*A*.
Draw the bisector of ∠*A*, meeting *BC* at *D*.
Measure *BD* and *DC*. Comment on your results.

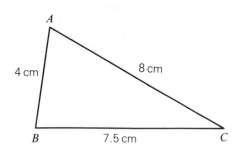

10. Construct a triangle ABC with $AB = 6$ cm, $BC = 7$ cm and $\angle B = 95°$.
     Measure $\angle A$ and $\angle C$ and the length of AC.

11. Construct a triangle ABC with $AB = 8$ cm, $\angle A = 46°$ and $\angle B = 64°$.
     Join D, the mid-point of AC, to E, the mid-point of BC. Join BD.
     Measure the angles ABD and BDE. Comment on your results.

12. Construct a triangle ABC with $AB = 6$ cm, $\angle A = 90°$ and $BC = 10$ cm.
     Measure AC. Calculate the perimeter of the triangle.

13. Draw a triangle ABC of any shape and find the perpendicular bisectors of its
     3 sides.
     Repeat for a different triangle.
     What do you notice about the perpendicular bisectors ? (You may have to make
     them slightly longer.)

14. Draw a triangle ABC of any shape and find the mid-points of its 3 sides.
     Join each mid-point to the opposite angle of the triangle. These lines are called
     medians of the triangle. Can you discover anything about them ?

15. Draw the parallelogram $ABCD$
     with the measurements given.
     (First, draw AB, $\angle A$ and AD.
     Then through D draw a line
     parallel to AB, and through B
     draw a line parallel to AD. These
     lines meet at C.)

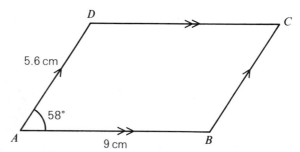

     Measure the lengths of BC and CD. Do you notice anything about these lengths ?

     AC and BD are diagonals of the parallelogram.
     Join AC and decide whether the 2 triangles formed are congruent.
     Join BD, letting it cross AC at E.
     Has the diagram got a point of symmetry ?
     Investigate the measurements on the diagonals and discover something about
     them.
     Which triangles are congruent ?

16. Repeat question 15 using this
     rhombus $ABCD$.
     (A parallelogram with 2 adjacent
     sides equal is called a rhombus.)

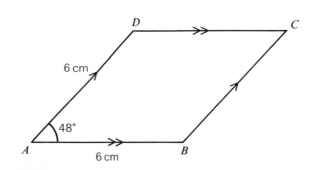

17.   Is the Union Jack a symmetrical design ?
       If you have a chart of the national flags of several countries, you can study the
       symmetry of the designs. You can list those which have 1 axis of symmetry or
       2 axes of symmetry, and which have points of symmetry.
       You can also look separately at the symmetry of some of the symbols on the
       flags, which include crosses, stars, crescents, the sun, crowns, etc.

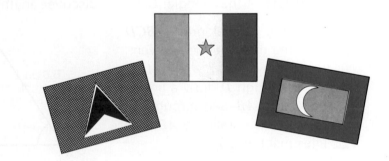

18.   **Drawing symmetrical patterns**

       Begin with a symmetrical figure such as an equilateral triangle, square or circle.
       In this equilateral triangle the mid-points and quarter-way points were marked.
       By joining these a pattern is formed.

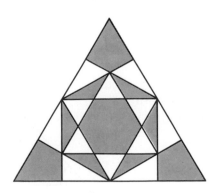

This is a similar idea, starting with a square with each side marked by points $\frac{1}{3}$ and $\frac{2}{3}$ of the way along.

You can use a piece of squared paper divided into 4 quarters. Draw a design in the 1st quarter and then balance this in the other 3 quarters.

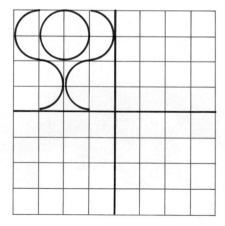

Here are some symmetrical patterns originally drawn on isometric paper.

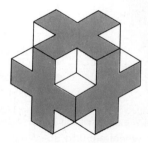

20 Thinking about probability

Questions about probability

In chapter 13 you did some probability experiments. In chapter 20 you are going to calculate probabilities.

Here are some questions to remind you about probability.

What does a probability of 0 mean ? Give an example.

What does a probability of 1 mean ? Give an example.

If we say that someone has a fifty–fifty change of success, what is the probability of success as a fraction ? Give some examples of events which have a 50–50 chance of success.

If you throw 1 die, what is the probability of scoring a six ?

If you throw 2 dice, what scores are possible for the sum of the two numbers on the dice ? What is the probability of scoring a sum of 12 ? (You have got some results from exercise 13.1. Does your answer agree with them, and if not, why not ?)

The numbers on a roulette wheel are 0 to 36. What is the probability of a particular number winning ?

There are various competitions which involve different chances of winning.

In gambling games, sometimes you can calculate the probability of winning.

Backgammon is played with two dice. Why are games with two dice more interesting than games using one die ?

Random selection

Suppose someone has to be picked at random from your class, to represent you on a committee. What does 'at random' mean ? Think of fair ways of choosing someone. Using these ways, has everyone in the class an equal chance of being chosen ? What is the probability that you will be chosen ? If yours is a class of boys and girls, what is the probability that a boy will be chosen ? What is the probability that a girl will be chosen ? (It is certain that either a boy or a girl will be chosen so what could you say about the last two answers ?) Which is more likely, that a boy will be chosen or a girl will be chosen ?

Using probability

Explain how these people can make use of probability:

A toyshop retailer, ordering stock
A weather forecaster
The education authority
A doctor doing research on a new cure
A firm selling holiday insurance
A person doing the football pools

20 Probability

Probability or chance is the likelihood of an event happening.

We measure probability on a number scale from 0 to 1.

A probability of 0 means that there is no chance of the event happening.
e.g. What is the chance of you visiting the planet Jupiter ?

A probability of 1 means that it is certain that the event will happen.
e.g. If you drop a marble, what is the chance of it falling downwards ?

A probability of $\frac{1}{2}$ means that there is a 50–50 chance of the event happening. In the long run, $\frac{1}{2}$ of the trials will give successful results.
e.g. If you toss a coin properly, the chance of it showing heads is $\frac{1}{2}$.

A probability of $\frac{2}{3}$ means that there is a more than even chance of the event happening. In the long run, $\frac{2}{3}$ of the trials will give successful results.
e.g. If you throw a die properly, the probability of it showing a number less than 5 is $\frac{2}{3}$.

The nearer the value of the probability is to 1, the more chance there is of a successful outcome.

In chapter 13 you found the value of probability by experiment. In some cases we can find the value by calculation, and that is what we are doing in this chapter.

Equally likely outcomes

We can calculate the value of the probability of a certain result in an experiment or trial if there are several outcomes which are equally likely.
For example, in throwing a die, there are six outcomes, the numbers 1, 2, 3, 4, 5, 6; and these are equally likely to occur. If we want to work out the probability of getting a four, then one of the six equally likely outcomes is a successful one, so the probability is 1 out of 6, that is, $\frac{1}{6}$. If we want to work out the probability of getting a number greater than four, then two of the six equally likely outcomes (5 or 6) are successful ones, so the probability is 2 out of 6, that is, $\frac{2}{6}$ or $\frac{1}{3}$.

Formula for probability

Probability of a successful outcome $= \dfrac{s}{n}$

where n is the total number of equally likely outcomes,
and s is the number of successful outcomes.

The result can be expressed as a fraction in its lowest terms, as a decimal or as a percentage.

Example 1

Find the probability of a tossed coin showing heads.

There are 2 equally likely outcomes, heads or tails, and of these 1 outcome, heads, is successful.

Probability of heads $= \dfrac{s}{n} = \dfrac{1}{2}$

Example 2

Find the probability of a number picked at random from the numbers 1 to 20 being divisible by 3.

There are twenty equally likely outcomes of which six (3, 6, 9, 12, 15, 18) are successful.

Probability of picking a number divisible by 3 $= \dfrac{s}{n} = \dfrac{6}{20} = \dfrac{3}{10}$

Example 3

In a pack of 52 cards one card is drawn at random. What is the probability that it is

1 a diamond,   **3** a Jack or a diamond,

2 a Jack,   **4** the Jack of diamonds ?

1 There are 13 diamonds.

P(diamond) $= \dfrac{s}{n} = \dfrac{13}{52} = \dfrac{1}{4}$

(We are using the notation P(diamond) to mean 'the probability of a diamond',)

2   There are 4 Jacks.

$$P(\text{Jack}) = \frac{s}{n} = \frac{4}{52} = \frac{1}{13}$$

3   There are 13 diamonds including the Jack and 3 other Jacks making 16 successful outcomes altogether.

$$P(\text{Jack or diamond}) = \frac{s}{n} = \frac{16}{52} = \frac{4}{13}$$

4   There is 1 Jack of diamonds.

$$P(\text{Jack of diamonds}) = \frac{s}{n} = \frac{1}{52}$$

Exercise 20.1

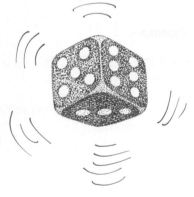

1.   A fair die is thrown once. What is the probability of getting
   1   a six,
   2   an odd number ?
   3   In a game, the die is thrown 300 times. Approximately how many times would it score a six ?

2.   12 discs, numbered from 1 to 12, are placed in a bag and one is drawn out without looking at it.
   What is the probability of getting a disc with
   1   a number which divides by 3,
   2   a square number,
   3   a number greater than 9,
   4   a number which includes the figure 1 ?

3.   In a tombola game, $\frac{9}{10}$ of the counters are blank. The rest have a number on them and they win a prize. If you take a counter out of the drum at random what is the probability that you win a prize ?

4.   In a fairground game a pointer is spun and
     you win the amount shown in the sector
     where it stops. Assuming that the pointer is
     equally likely to come to rest in any sector,
     what is the probability that

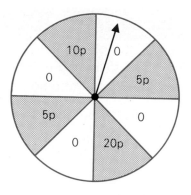

     1   you win 20p,
     2   you win 5p,
     3   you do not win any money ?
     4   If the pointer is spun 1000 times during
             an afternoon, approximately how many
             times would 20p be won ?

5.   30 tickets are sold in a raffle. Anil buys one ticket and Bimla buys two tickets.
     What is the probability that one of them wins the 1st prize ?

6.   A card is drawn from a full pack of 52 playing cards. What is the probability that
     1   it is a seven,
     2   it is a club,
     3   it is the seven of clubs ?

7.   The 11 letters of the word PROBABILITY are written on separate cards and the
     cards are mixed up. One card is drawn at random. What is the probability that
     on it is
     1   the letter T,
     2   the letter B,
     3   a vowel,
     4   a letter from the first half of the alphabet ?

8.   A bag contains 8 red beads and 12 blue beads. Julie takes one bead from the
     bag, without looking. What is the probability that it is red ?

9.   In a pencil case there are 3 red crayons, 4 blue ones, 2 green ones and 1 yellow
     one. If you take a crayon out without looking, what is the probability that it is
     1   red,   **2**   not green ?

10. 5   8   9   12   15   16   17   20   25
     These numbers are written on discs which are placed in a bag. One disc is
     drawn out at random. What is the probability that the number on it is
     1   an odd number,
     2   a number which divides exactly by 5,
     3   a square number,
     4   a prime number ?

Exercise 20.2   Applications and Activities

1. The following numbers were written on pieces of paper, put into a box and drawn out at random.

   6,   9,   17,   23,   25,   29,   37,   39,   41,   48,   49,   64.

   What is the probability that a number drawn out
   1 is even,
   2 is a square number,
   3 is a prime number ?
   4 If an odd number is drawn out and not replaced, what is the probability of drawing out a second odd number ?

2. A pack of 52 cards is split into two piles with the Aces, Kings, Queens and Jacks in the first pile and the rest of the cards in the second pile.

   1 If a card is drawn at random from the first pile what is the probability that it is the Queen of Hearts ?
   2 If a card is drawn at random from the second pile what is the probability that it is a seven ?

3. The members of a school club belong to three forms, 1R, 1S and 1T.

	1R	1S	1T
girls	16	14	10
boys	9	7	14

   The chart shows the number of members in each form. If from this club one member is chosen at random, what is the probability that it is
   1 a boy,
   2 a member of 1S,
   3 a girl from 1R ?
   4 If a girl from the club has to be chosen at random, what is the probability that she is from 1T ?

4. What is the probability that if a person is chosen at random, his/her birthday this year is on a Saturday ? If 100 people were chosen, approximately how many would you expect to have a birthday on a Saturday ?

   Ask as many people as you can on what day of the week their birthday falls this year. (Have a calendar available.) Record the results and represent them in a bar chart. Compare these results with the theoretical ones.

5.   Seven boys were planning what to do on a half day's holiday. Their choices were
      swimming, playing football or going to the fairground.
      They wrote these three choices, swim, football, fairground, on slips of paper, put
      them in a box and drew one out without looking.
      What was the probability that 'swim' was the one drawn out ?
      In fact, 'fairground' was drawn out, and this led to some argument.
      So the boys all wrote their own choice on a new slip of paper, and again one slip
      was drawn out.
      Their choices were: Hugh, swim; Alec, football; Ken, fairground; Timothy, swim;
      Peter, football; David, swim; Michael, swim.
      What was the probability that going swimming was chosen then ?
      Which do you think was the fairer method of choosing what to do ?

6.   In a game played with two dice, the dice are thrown together and the score is the
      difference of the numbers.

1st die

Score		1	2	3	4	5	6
	1			2			
	2			1			
2nd die	3			0			
	4			1			
	5	4	3	2	1	0	1
	6			3			

      Copy and complete the table showing the scores. 1 row and 1 column have
      already been filled in.
      All the results in the 36 spaces are equally likely.

      1   How many of the spaces show a score of 0 ?
      2   What is the probability of score of 0 ?
      3   What is the highest possible score ?
      4   What is the probability of getting this score ?
      5   If these dice are thrown 200 times, how many times approximately would
            you get a score of 1 ?

      You could use the previously-recorded results of dice throwing, in twos, to get
      some experimental results, and compare these with your answers.

7. A coin tossing experiment

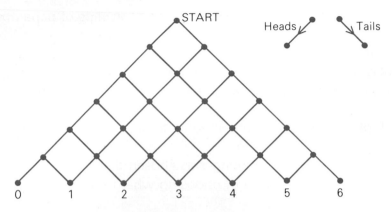

Begin with a counter on START.

Toss a coin. (You can use your previously-recorded results of coin tossing.)

If you get a head, go left, as far as the next blob.

If you get a tail, go right, as far as the next blob.

Toss again, and repeat.

After 6 tosses you will get to one of the 7 destinations labelled 0 to 6. Record which one.

Repeat about 300 times.

Which destination occurred most often ?

Show your results on a histogram, with the blocks numbered from 0 to 6. What shape is it ?

Why have the destinations been labelled 0 to 6 ?

Can you investigate the pattern in your results ? You may want to begin by considering a simpler diagram first, like this.

8. Random numbers

We often talk about choosing things 'at random'. In Statistics this means that every item in the group has an equal chance of being chosen. You could imagine this as a raffle. Give every item a name or number, put these into a hat, mix them up and then pick one out without looking.

What is the probability that a single-figure number (from 0 to 9) picked at random will be a 7 ? If there were 200 random single-figure numbers, approximately how many times would we expect each number to occur ?

One way of getting a collection of random numbers is to use the phone book, using the units figure of each number in turn. (Occasionally a firm may have several consecutive numbers listed. In this case, only use the first one.) Collect 200 single-figure numbers and record them. Represent your results in a histogram. Compare them with the theoretical results.

Can you think of other sources for getting a list of random numbers ? You may prefer to use your own ideas instead of getting the numbers from the phone book.

Is it suitable just to **ask** people for a number, to make a collection of random numbers ?

Ask as many people as you can, but ask them quietly, so that other people you intend to ask do not hear other answers. Try to use the same words each time, such as 'For an experiment, I would like you to tell me any number between 0 and 9.' Do not go into details about being able to include 0 or 9, unless the person asks you. Otherwise you are emphasizing these two numbers by mentioning them specially. Do not comment on the answer, just say 'Thank you.' Record the answers as before, and represent them in a histogram. Compare them with the previous results and comment on your findings.

PUZZLES

31. A man filled two buckets with water. One was left in the garage all night, where the temperature was 15°C. The other was left in the garden where the temperature was 15°F. The man's small son came along and dropped a penny into each bucket. Which penny reached the bottom of its bucket more quickly ?

32. **1** What is the next term in the sequence 1, 2, 4, 8, 16 ?
    2 A circle is divided into regions, as shown. How many regions are there for the hexagon ?

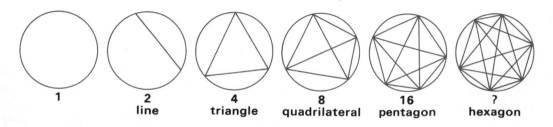

1	2	4	8	16	?
	line	triangle	quadrilateral	pentagon	hexagon

33. In an enclosure at the Zoo I can see 160 giraffe legs and 80 ostrich legs. How many animals are there in the enclosure ?

21 Thinking about scale drawing

Maps

Name some people who have to use maps in their work.

List some occasions when you have referred to a map recently, and say what sort of region the map showed, from as large a region as the whole world, to a continent, a country, a region of the country, a town or a smaller area still.

Look in a newspaper and see if any maps are printed there. You could cut these out and stick them on a poster. Have you seen any maps recently shown on television programmes? If so, what were they showing?

List some of the uses we can make of maps.

If you have some maps available, look at the scales marked on them, e.g.

a map in an atlas, of Europe,
a map in an atlas, of England and Wales,
a road map of a region in England or Wales,
an OS (Ordnance Survey) map of a region in England or Wales,
an OS map on a larger scale, suitable for walkers, etc.,
a street map of a town.

Why do you think different types of maps have different scales?

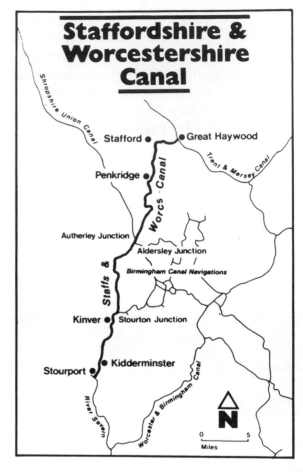

Maps and plans are useful for someone planning a canal holiday.

MORNING STAR CLASS (5/7 Berths)
(3 Doubles & 1 Single)
Boat—MORNING STAR (1990)
Length—50ft Beam—6ft 10ins Draught—1ft 9ins

DESCRIPTION — No. of cabins—Three

Forward cabin—Stools provide additional seating around the dinette which converts to form a double berth.

Centre cabin—A single two tier bunk bed is provided with the lower berth being convertible to a double if required. The cabin includes shelves and an airing cupboard with additional storage below the lower bunk.

Rear cabin—A permanent double berth with interior sprung mattress is provided. The cabin includes shelves and hanging space with additional storage below the berth.

Galley—The galley is fitted with a full size four ring gas cooker with grill and oven, 4 cu ft fridge, sink unit with inset S/S bowl and drainer, plastic coated laminated worktops, cupboards and shelves.

Shower/toilet—A flushing pump-out toilet and shower/bath are located in a separate compartment together with a wash hand basin, mirror and shaver socket.

Water system—Hot & cold running water is provided to the galley sink, wash hand basin and shower/bath from a 200 gall water tank below the forward deck. The hot water is supplied from a central heating boiler via an indirect hot water cylinder.

Electrical system—A dual 12v battery system provides power for the engine as well as for cabin fluorescent lighting, reading lights, water pumps, 12v DC 2 amp 3 pin sockets, 240v AC shaver socket and stereo radio/cassette player.

Heating—Full central heating is provided from a gas fired central heating boiler via radiators forward and rear.

Headroom—A minimum of 6ft 3ins is provided for both cabins and berths.

Lining—The boats are fully insulated with polystyrene behind tongue and groove varnished panelling with faced ply fixtures edged in hardwood with brass fittings.

Access—Double doors provide access to the forward cabin, with doors and hatches at the side and rear for access to the centre and rear cabins.

Engine—A three cylinder Lister diesel engine is housed beneath the rear deck flooring.

MORNING STAR

Plans

Name some people who have to use plans in their work.

Explain how plans can be used in these situations:

someone making a model airplane,

someone doing dressmaking,

a teacher wishing to fit as many tables as possible into the school dining-hall, but leaving room for comfortable movement,

a family which is moving into a new house, which is too far away to be visited in advance of moving in,

a person wishing to book a seat at a theatre.

Think of other situations where you would find it helpful to use a plan.

Networks

The most famous problem connected with a network is 'The Bridges of Königsberg'.

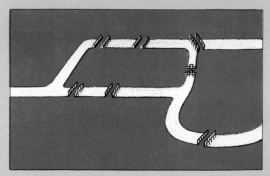

There were 7 bridges over the various parts of the river. The townspeople suspected that the 7 bridges could not be crossed in one continuous walk without recrossing the route somewhere. In 1735, Euler, one of the world's great mathematicians, was asked to give a proof of this, which he did. Now if there was an 8th bridge, just out of view on the left side of the picture, would it be possible to cross the 8 bridges in one continuous walk ?

21 Scale Drawing

Here is a plan of a room, drawn to a scale of 1 cm to represent 1 m.

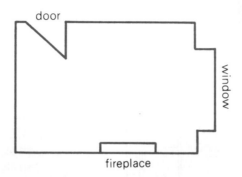

door

window

fireplace

If you measure the length of the room (from the left-hand side to the window) you will find that it is 5.2 cm. Since 1 cm represents 1 m, this represents 5.2 m.
Measure the width of the room on the plan, and say what the actual width is.

This scale can be written as
1 cm represents 1 m, or 1 cm ≡ 1 m, using the sign ≡ for 'represents'.
It can also be written as a fraction.   Scale $\frac{1}{100}$.
It can also be written as a **ratio**.   Scale 1 : 100   (read as 1 to 100).

If a scale 1 cm ≡ 2 m is used, this means that 1 cm represents 200 cm, so it can be written as $\frac{1}{200}$ or 1 : 200.

If a scale 1 cm ≡ 5 km is used, this means that 1 cm represents 500 000 cm, so it can be written as $\frac{1}{500\,000}$ or 1 : 500 000.

Examples

1   A plan has a scale of 5 cm to represent 1 m. What is this scale in ratio form ?

5 cm represents 100 cm.
1 cm represents 20 cm.
The scale is $\frac{1}{20}$ or 1 : 20.

2   A map has a scale of $\frac{1}{5000}$ or 1 : 5000. What is the actual distance in metres between two points which are 6.4 cm apart on the map ?

1 cm represents 5000 cm.
6.4 cm represents 6.4 × 5000 cm = 32 000 cm = 320 m.
The points are 320 m apart.

3 Two villages are 4.6 km apart. On a map the distance between them is 18.4 cm. What is the scale of the map ?

18.4 cm represents 4.6 km = 4600 m = 460 000 cm.
1 cm represents $\frac{460\,000}{18.4}$ cm = 25 000 cm.
The scale is $\frac{1}{25\,000}$ or 1 : 25 000.

4 A plan of some buildings is being drawn using a scale of 1 : 400. A warehouse is 27.6 m long. How long should the corresponding length on the plan be ?

400 cm is represented by 1 cm.
4 m is represented by 1 cm.
1 m is represented by $\frac{1}{4}$ cm (or 0.25 cm)
27.6 m is represented by $\frac{27.6}{4}$ cm (or 27.6 × 0.25 cm) = 6.9 cm
The length on the plan should be 6.9 cm.

5 The diagram shows a sketch of one end of a garage.
Draw an accurate scale drawing using a scale of 1 : 50.
Find the length of the sloping roof.

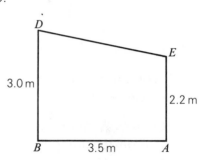

1 : 50 means that 1 cm will represent 50 cm,
so 2 cm will represent 1 m.
1 m is represented by 2 cm.
3.5 m is represented by 3.5 × 2 cm = 7 cm.
2.2 m is represented by 4.4 cm.
3.0 m is represented by 6 cm.

Begin by drawing the line AB, 7 cm long.

Make accurate right angles at A and B and draw the lines AE (4.4 cm long) and BD (6 cm long). Join DE.
Measure DE to the nearest mm. (It should be approximately 7.2 cm.)
Then 1 cm will represent 50 cm, so 7.2 cm represents 7.2 × 50 cm = 3.6 m.
The sloping roof is 3.6 m long.

Compass Directions

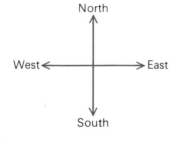

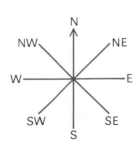

Example

Here are 8 places on a map, denoted by the letters A to H.

Give the approximate direction from the 1st place to the 2nd place.

1 From C to D.   (This direction is North-East.)
2 From A to B.
3 From E to A.
4 From F to G.
5 From C to F.

If you are at the place given and travel in the stated direction, which place will you arrive at ?

6 From E, going South.   (You will arrive at F.)
7 From D, going North-West.
8 From H, going West.
9 From A, going North-East.
10 From G, going South-West.

Exercise 21.1

1. On a scale of 1 : 200, how long is a path whose length on the plan is 3.5 cm ? How long is a line on the plan representing a length of 12.4 m ?

2. On a scale of 1 : 5000, how long is a street whose length on the plan is 7.2 cm ? How long should lines be drawn on the plan to represent a field which is 200 m long and 120 m wide ?

3. This island is drawn on a map with a scale 1 : 50 000. Measure on the map to find how far it is, in km, between *A* and *B*,
    1 in a direct line,
    2 going via *C*.

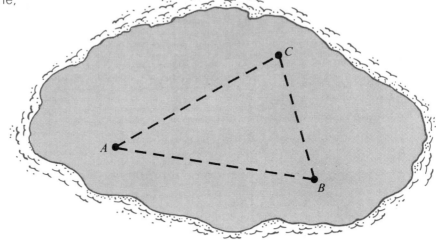

4. *A*, *B*, *C* are 3 points on level ground. From *A*, *B* is 2000 m due East and *C* is 1200 m due North. Draw an accurate scale drawing showing the positions of *A*, *B* and *C* using a scale of 1 : 20 000. Find the distance from *B* to *C* on your drawing. What is the actual distance on the ground from *B* to *C* ?

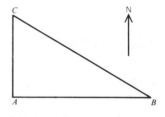

5. A model is made of a liner. If the liner was 270 m long, and 30 m wide, what are the corresponding measurements on the model if the scale is 1 : 400 ?

6. Here is a scale drawing of a holiday chalet, drawn to a scale of 1 : 250.
    By taking measurements on the drawing, find the length and width of the chalet, and the measurements of the two bedrooms.

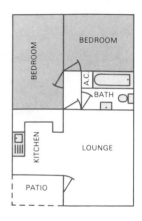

7.   A model plane is 25 cm long, and the
      actual plane is 30 m long. What is the
      scale of the model ?

8.   This is a scale drawing of the front of a storehouse.
      By taking measurements on the drawing find, in
      metres to the nearest 0.1 m,
      1   the width of the storehouse,
      2   the height of the storehouse at the sides,
      3   the height of the highest point,
      4   the length of one of the sloping roofs.

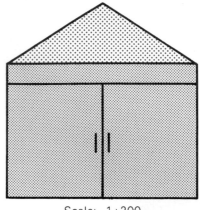

Scale:- 1 : 200

Networks

A network consists of a set of lines connecting a set of points.

Example

A messenger has to deliver magazines to 7 houses, *A, B, C, D, E, F* and *G*.
He sets out and finishes at the shop. The network
of possible routes is shown here. What is his
shortest route ?

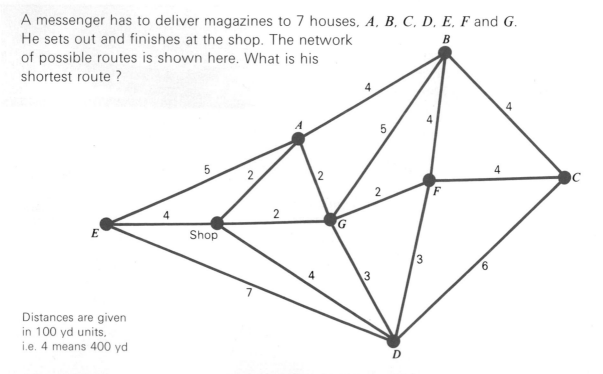

Distances are given
in 100 yd units,
i.e. 4 means 400 yd

There does not seem to be any better way to do this than by trying several routes. If he went round the outside paths in the order *A, B, C, D, E*, then the distances (in units) are

The longest distance here is from *D* to *E* so perhaps it might be shorter to start by going to one of these places first and finishing from the other.

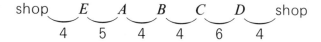

Now *F* and *G* have to be fitted in.
To go to *F* between *C* and *D* just takes an extra 1 unit. This seems the best diversion for *F*.
To visit *G* after *D* and then return to the shop takes an extra 1 unit. This seems the best diversion for *G*.
So the route is

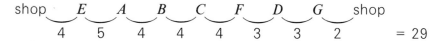

We could do the same route in reverse order.
The total distance is 2900 yd.
Is this the shortest route ? We think it is.
We will mark it on the plan.

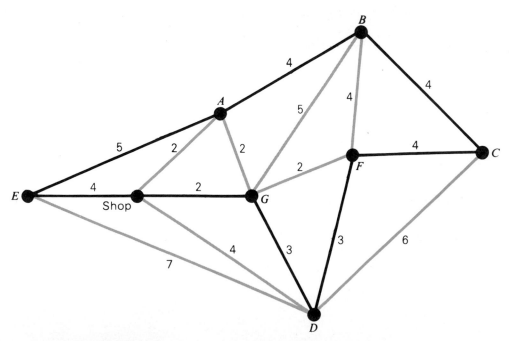

Exercise 21.2

1.   Use the same network as in the previous example.
      On one particular week the person at *E* is on holiday so the messenger does not
      have to deliver there. In addition, there are roadworks which mean that he cannot
      go along the road between *G* and the shop. Which is the shortest route now ?

2.   This map shows the network of local bus services. All the routes start from and
      return to the bus station.

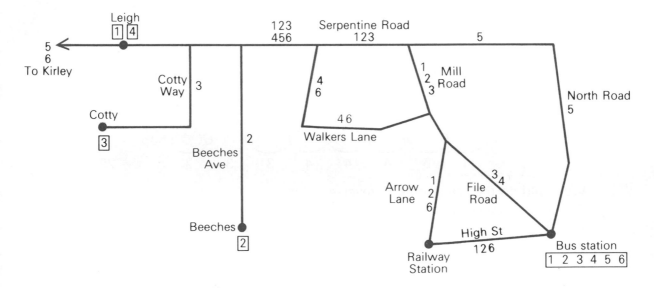

      Which number of bus must I get
      1   from Mill Road to Beeches,
      2   from Leigh to the Railway station,
      3   from the bus station to Cotty,
      4   from North Road to Leigh,
      5   from File Road to Mill Road ?

Exercise 21.3   Applications and Activities

1.   It is planned to use the shaded area on the map for a plantation of young trees. The area will be completely enclosed by a wire fence. Measure the distance round the shaded area on the map. Use your result to calculate the length of fencing around the plantation.

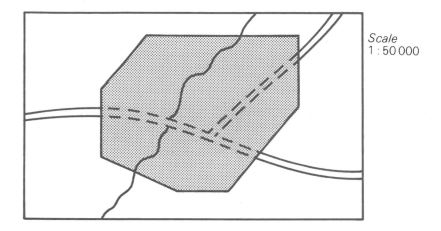

Scale
1 : 50 000

2.   The sketch shows the plan for the front of a dolls' house. The dolls' house is to be 60 cm wide. What is the scale of the drawing ?
By measurement on the drawing find the height of the dolls' house to the top point.

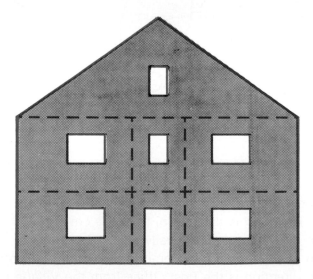

3.   Here is a map of the district around Wishby.
   1   By measurement and calculation, find the direct distance from Wishby to
            Tolver, in kilometres.
   2   Find the distance by road from Wishby to Tolver. (One way to measure
            the length along the road is to use a length of cotton and then measure the
            cotton along your ruler.)
   3   Which town is due South of Shalton ?
   4   Which town is due North-West of Wishby ?
   5   In which direction is Shalton from Harly ?
   6   In which direction is Irby from Morton ?
   7   In which direction is Wayton from Melby ?
   8   In which direction is Dulton from Bilton ?

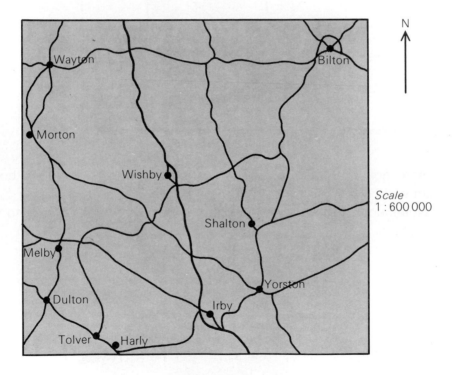

Scale
1 : 600 000

4.   Here is a map of Eastly village.
   1   In which direction is the school from the cross-roads ?
   2   In which directions does the railway run ?
   3   In which direction is the swimming pool from the football ground ?
   4   In which direction is the Post Office from the Village Hall ?
   5   In which direction is the Hotel from the lake ?

Assuming that you are in the village, give someone clear directions to get to various places, e.g. Go along here, take the second turning on the right, then keep straight on. It's on the left-hand side. (You can already be facing the way you want them to go.)

6   From the hotel, direct someone to the railway station.

7   From the school, direct someone to the football ground.

8   From the railway bridge north of the village, direct someone to the garage.

9   From the road between the lake and the tennis courts, direct someone to the swimming pool.

10 From the health centre, direct someone to the Post Office.

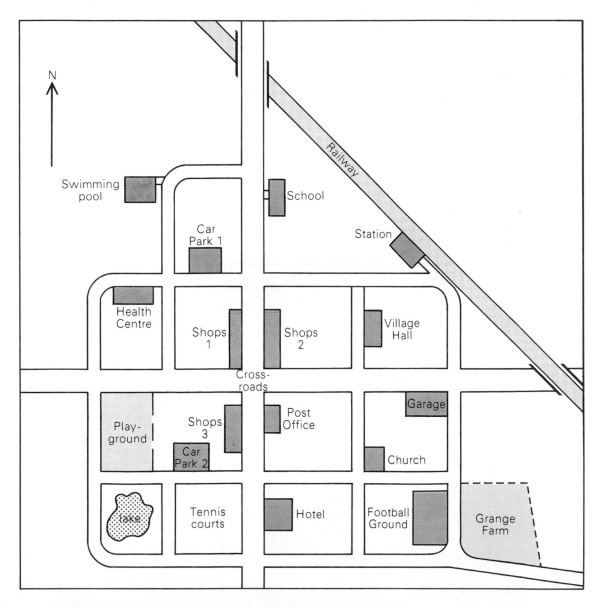

5.   This is a sketch of a plan for two Maths classrooms and a storeroom. Draw an accurate plan using a scale of 1 : 250. The measurements of the classrooms are 15 m by 12.5 m, the storeroom is 10 m by 10 m, and the corridor is 2.5 m wide.

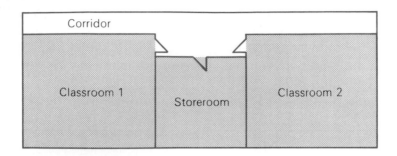

6.   A boat is just off the cape at *A* and it wants to reach the harbour at *B*. In what direction must the boat sail, and how far away is *B* ?
      After reaching *B*, the boat then sails to a bay at *C*. In what direction does the boat sail, and how far away is *C* ?
      How far is it from *C* for the boat to sail directly back to point *A* ?

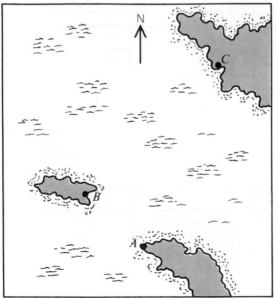

Scale. 1 : 1 000 000

7.   Here is a picture of a cottage. Make scale drawings, on cardboard, choosing a suitable scale, of the 4 sides joined together, and the 2 roof pieces joined together. Put tabs on the edges to be glued, score the fold lines, and make a model of the cottage. (The roof overhangs the sides slightly. Add a piece of suitable size for the chimney.)

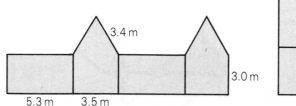   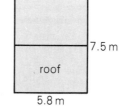

8.   Use the map of the district around Wishby, of question 3 on page 296.

A salesman has to visit the 11 towns shown on the map, by car. He lives in Bilton so he will start and finish his journey there. Plan a suitable route for him to follow.
When you have decided on the best route, put tracing paper over the map and mark the 11 towns and the route joining them on your tracing paper.

9.   Use the map of Eastly village, of question 6 on page 297.
   1   The postman comes into the village by van to deliver parcels. On one morning he has parcels to deliver to the Church, garage, Grange Farm, Health Centre, hotel, railway station, shops (2), shops (3), swimming pool, school and Village Hall. He enters the town from the West and leaves the same way, but just before leaving he calls at the Post Office to collect any parcels to be taken to town. Plan a suitable route for the postman to take. The village roads are not too busy so he can approach places from either direction and walk across the roads when necessary.
   Put tracing paper over the map to mark your route on.

   2   The local policeman does a patrol of the village on his motorcycle. He wants to go along every part of every road in the village. He comes into the village from the East, and leaves by the road going South. Plan a suitable route for him to take, keeping to a minimum the places where he travels along the same stretch of road more than once.
   Put tracing paper over the map to mark your route on.

10.   A good example of a network map is a map of the London Underground.

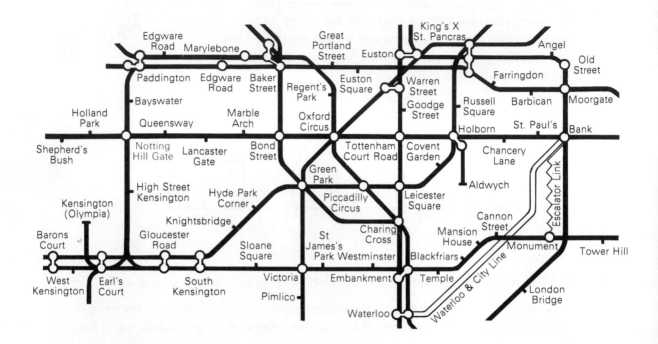

Try to find a proper map, because it will be in colour and you can give a more complete answer. You will probably have one if you live near London. If you have not, you often find them published in diaries or Guide books of London.

Example

How would you get from Holland Park to South Kensington ?

First, find these two places. Holland Park is on the West of the above map, on the line running through the middle of the map. South Kensington is roughly South-East of it.

From Holland Park you would go 1 stop to Notting Hill Gate. This station is marked by a circle because it is a station where you can change to other lines. Change lines and go 3 stops to South Kensington. This makes 4 stops altogether with 1 change.
If you have a proper map, you would also know that you start on the Central Line, and then change to the Circle Line.

How would you get by the most direct way
  1   from Bond Street to Temple,
  2   from Oxford Circus to Charing Cross,
  3   from Euston to Victoria,
  4   from Goodge Street to Hyde Park Corner,
  5   from Barbican to St Paul's,
  6   from Baker Street to Piccadilly Circus,
  7   from Great Portland Street to Russell Square,
  8   from Pimlico to Marble Arch,
  9   from Bayswater to Sloane Square,
  10   from Tower Hill to Waterloo ?

PUZZLES

34. Find the missing figures in this multiplication sum.

```
        8 . . . 6
              3 .
      _____
        8 . . . 6
    2 . 3 1 . 8 0
    _____
    2 5 1 . . 3 6
```

35. A farmer has five half-sized haystacks in the corner of a field and two three-quarter-sized haystacks in another corner. If he puts them all together, how many haystacks will he have ?

36. A secretary typed 4 letters to 4 different people and addressed the 4 envelopes. Then she told the office junior to put them in the envelopes. If the junior inserts the letters at random, what is the probability that exactly 3 letters will go into the right envelopes ?

37. Michael had some marbles which he arranged in a triangular shape.

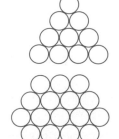

When he won 9 more he arranged them in a hexagonal shape.

He then played again and won more. Then he found that he had exactly the right number to arrange them either in a triangular or a hexagonal shape, although he still had less than 100.
How many more had he won ?

22 Thinking about division

Methods of division

A coach holds 54 passengers. There are 918 people going on a school outing. How many coaches would be needed ?
Don't use your calculator to do this question. We must have an emergency method for times when the calculator is not handy.
So work it out, writing down the steps in your working so that you can explain how you did it. (Having worked it out, how can you check that your answer is correct ?)
Now compare your method with other people's and see how many different ways of working it out you can use, and which method seems best.

Using division

Think of a different situation where division might be needed. Make up a question, work it out and write down the answer.

An old question

Here is a question from a textbook written in 1900. Can you find the answer ?

'In a procession the route was 7 miles long, and there were on an average 15 rows of spectators on each side; each person occupied 15 inches of frontage. Calculate the number of spectators.'

How many cakes can be made from 1 bag of flour ?

How many cups of tea can be made from the water in an urn which holds 20 litres ?

If you had £40 to spend on a children's party, and the costs were £2.50 per child, how many children could you invite ?

Anil's parents were repaid £27.04 for his travel costs to school. If each journey cost 26p, how many journeys had he made during the term ?

22 Division

You should know how to divide without using a calculator, as there will be times when you do not have a calculator available.

e.g. You buy 4 similar cakes and they cost £1.48. Your friend wants to buy one from you. What does it cost ?

You must divide £1.48 by 4. This is 148 pence ÷ 4.
Set it down like this.   4)148
                             ‾‾37‾

They cost 37 pence each.

The working is:
4's into 1 won't go.
4's into 14 goes 3 times. Put 3 in the answer under the 4 of 14.
Three 4's are 12, 12 from 14 leaves 2, so the next figure has 2 in front, i.e. it is 28.
In the next place, 4's into 28 goes 7. Put 7 in the answer under the 8.
Seven 4's are 28 so there is no remainder. The exact answer is 37 pence.

If you cannot do some of the working in your head you can set it down like this:

```
      3 7  Answer
   4)1 4 8
     1 2
     ‾‾‾
       2 8
       2 8
       ‾‾‾
         0
```

Notice that because the working goes underneath, the answer goes **above** the question.

This is the same method to use when dividing by larger numbers and it is called **Long Division**.

Examples

1   14 similar machines together weigh 826 kg. What is the weight of one ?

You must divide 826 by 14.

First, 14 into 8 won't go.   5 9 Answer
14's into 82 goes 5 times. Put 5 in the answer above the 2 of 82.   1 4)8 2 6
Multiply 14 by 5 (=70) and write this under the 82.   7 0
Subtract 70 from 82 leaving 12.   1 2 6
Bring down the next figure, 6, making 126.   1 2 6
14's into 126 goes 9 times. Put 9 in the answer above the 6.   0
Multiply 14 by 9 (=126) and write this under the 126.
Subtracting leaves 0 so there is no remainder. The answer is 59.
Each machine weighs 59 kg.

The difficult part of such a question is deciding how many times 14 goes into 82, and into 126. You can do it the long way by working out the 14 times table until you get far enough:
$14 \times 1 = 14$, $14 \times 2 = 28$, $14 \times 3 = 42$, etc.
You could make a rough guess instead.
$14 \times 10 = 140$ so half of that, $14 \times 5 = \frac{1}{2}$ of $140 = 70$. Then $14 \times 6 = 70 + 14 = 84$, so 14 goes into 82 five times.

2 $988 \div 19$.

19)988   First, think of 19 as nearly 20.
                               How many 20's in 98. Nearly 5.
                               Check whether 19×5 is less than 98. Yes, it is, so the first part
                               of the answer is a five.

      5
19)988 $19 \times 5 = 95$. Put the 5 above the 8 of 98, and 95 below 98,
     95   subtract 95 from 98 and put the 3 below. Bring down the
     38   next 8.

     52 Answer
19)988   How many 19's in 38 ? (How many 20's ?)
     95   There are nearly 2 20's, and there are exactly 2 19's.
     38                        $19 \times 2 = 38$. Write 2 in the answer above the 8 of 38.
     38
      0   Write 38 below 38 and subtract, leaving 0 so there is no
                               remainder. The answer is 52.

If the numbers do not divide exactly, it may be appropriate to leave a remainder, or alternatively you can continue the division using decimal places.

e.g. One morning a school ordered 919 bottles of milk. The milk comes in crates of 24 bottles. How many crates were brought ?

Do a division question, and find the remainder.

```
       38
   24)919
       72
      199
      192
        7 Answer 38, remainder 7.
```

In this case it is not appropriate to give an answer using decimals. The milkman will leave 38 full crates, and also 7 extra bottles, which he may also leave in a crate.

Consider this question:
On a holiday, the total distance travelled by a car was 919 miles and the car used 24 gallons of petrol. How far, on average, did the car run on a gallon of petrol ?

Here it is more appropriate to give the answer as a decimal, and 1 decimal place should be adequate. So work to 2 decimal places so that you can correct the answer up to 1 decimal place.
Remember to put the decimal point in the answer. There is no need to show it in the working.

```
       38.29
   24)919.00
       72
      199
      192
        7 0
        4 8
        2 20          Answer so far 38.29 . . .
        2 16          Answer correct to 1 decimal place = 38.3
           4
```

On average, the car ran 38.3 miles on 1 gallon of petrol.

There are other methods of working, some of which are given in the exercises. You can use any method you prefer as long as it gives the correct answer.

Exercise 22.1

1. Try these questions to practise long division.

    1 $819 \div 21$ **5** $954 \div 18$ **8** $949 \div 73$
    2 $986 \div 17$ **6** $987 \div 47$ **9** $682 \div 31$
    3 $1120 \div 35$ **7** $972 \div 54$ **10** $992 \div 16$
    4 $936 \div 13$

2. Work out the answers to these questions and also give the remainder.

    1 $980 \div 75$ **4** $900 \div 27$
    2 $857 \div 61$ **5** $602 \div 17$
    3 $988 \div 34$

3. Work out the answers to these questions, giving them correct to 1 decimal place.

    1 $759 \div 22$ **4** $801 \div 26$
    2 $638 \div 17$ **5** $376 \div 15$
    3 $523 \div 41$

4. 624 children went on a school outing. There were 48 children on a coach. How many coaches were needed ?

5. People paid 15p each to visit an exhibition. The total takings were £9.30. How many people visited the exhibition ?

6. A length of ribbon was 896 cm long and it was cut into 32 strips. How long was each strip ?

7. A length of wire 13.5 m long had to be cut into pieces of length 25 cm. How many pieces could be made ?

8. A group of boys went looking for conkers and collected 490. When they shared them out they got 35 each. How many boys were there ?

9. The product of two numbers is 832 and one of the numbers is 26. Find the other.

10. How many containers, each holding 13 litres of liquid, can be filled from a tank containing 500 litres, and how much liquid will be left over ?

Exercise 22.2   Applications and Activities

1.   You may prefer to do division using rectangles. The answer is the sum of the numbers at the side of the rectangle.

e.g. 312 ÷ 13

$$
\begin{array}{r|r}
 & 13 \\
\hline
10 & 130 \\
\hline
10 & 130 \\
\hline
4 & 52 \\
\hline
\end{array}
\qquad
\begin{array}{r}
312 \\
130 \\
\hline
182 \\
130 \\
\hline
52 \\
52 \\
\hline
0
\end{array}
$$

24 Answer

13 × 10 = 130. Subtract 130 twice, leaving 52.

13 × 4 = 52

952 ÷ 34

$$
\begin{array}{r|r}
 & 34 \\
\hline
10 & 340 \\
\hline
10 & 340 \\
\hline
5 & 170 \\
\hline
2 & 68 \\
\hline
1 & 34 \\
\hline
\end{array}
\qquad
\begin{array}{r}
952 \\
340 \\
\hline
512 \\
340 \\
\hline
272 \\
170 \\
\hline
102 \\
68 \\
\hline
34 \\
34 \\
\hline
0
\end{array}
$$

28 Answer

34 × 10 = 340. Subtract 340 twice, leaving 272.

34 × 5 = ½ of 340 = 170. Subtract 170, leaving 102.

34 × 2 = 68. Subtract 68, leaving 34.

34 × 1 = 34

Try some of the questions from Exercise 22.1 again using the rectangle method, and if you prefer to use it make up other questions for practice, and then check the answers on your calculator.

2.   If you have to divide by a number which has 1-figure factors, such as 48 which has factors 6 × 8, you can use another method.

e.g. 912 ÷ 48 = (912 ÷ 6) ÷ 8

First divide 912 by 6, and then divide the answer by 8.

6)912
8)152
    19 Answer

Practise this method with these questions.

1   832 ÷ 32   (32 = 4 × 8)
2   684 ÷ 36
3   621 ÷ 27
4   882 ÷ 49
5   765 ÷ 45

3.   If you have to divide by 25, because 25 is one-quarter of 100, you can multiply by 4 and then divide by 100.

e.g. 675 ÷ 25 = (675 × 4) ÷ 100
                     = 2700 ÷ 100
                     = 27

      123 ÷ 25 = (123 × 4) ÷ 100
                     = 492 ÷ 100
                     = 4.92

Divide these numbers by 25, giving the answers correct to 2 decimal places if they do not divide exactly.

1   525   **2**   375   **3**   411   **4**   836   **5**   912

4.   £843 is divided among 15 people. One person gets £6 more than each of the others. How much do they each get ?

5.   Find the least number which must be added to 800 so that the sum will divide exactly by 52.

6.   A bag of 50 pence coins weighs 950 g. How much are the contents worth, if the bag weighs 5 g and two 50 pence coins together weigh 27 g ?

7.   How many fence posts will be needed for a length of 910 m, if the posts are placed 14 m apart ?

8.   A sheet of A4 paper is 210 mm wide and 297 mm long. The paper is to be ruled into squares. If each square is 15 mm wide, how many squares are there along the top row ? How many rows of squares are there ? What are the measurements of the small strip of paper left at the bottom of the sheet ?

9.   Copy and complete this number pattern

(10 × 20 + 21) ÷ 13 =
(20 × 30 + 21) ÷ 23 =
(30 × 40 + 21) ÷ 33 =
. . .

up to the line which begins with 90 × 100.

23 Thinking about conversion graphs

Converting from feet to metres

Mrs Kay works for an estate agent. When she visits a house which is for sale, she must take the measurements of the rooms. She uses her measuring-tape which gives the measurements in feet and inches. When she gets back to the office she types out a description of the house. But nowadays some of the buyers may prefer to know the metric measurements so she has to give these as well. Rather than keep working them out, she has drawn a conversion graph to refer to.

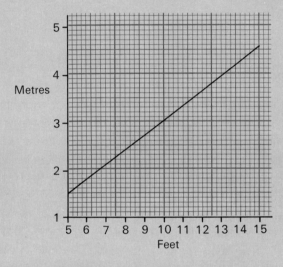

Lounge 13′ 9″ (. . . m) by 11′ 9″ (. . . m) with a modern tiled fireplace.
Dining Room 11′ 3″ (. . . m) by 9′ 3″ (. . . m) with a patio door to the rear garden.
Kitchen 12′ 3″ (. . . m) by 9′ 6″ (. . . m) with a single drainer sink unit with cupboards and drawers below and a range of wall and floor cupboards with laminated working surfaces.

Use the graph to find the metric measurements to go in the description. (Remember than 3″ is $\frac{1}{4}$ of a foot.)
How could Mrs Kay find out the metric measurements without using a conversion graph ?
Do you think the graph is useful to her ?

You will need to change your money into foreign currency if you are travelling abroad.

When you write to your pen-friend, how much does it cost to send the letter ? Is it more expensive for your pen-friend to send a letter to you ?

Using conversion graphs

Can you think of some situations where you would find a conversion graph useful ?

Using conversion graphs in Europe

If you were going on holiday to a European country, are there any conversion graphs which it might be useful to have with you ? If so, what would they show ?

Using conversion graphs at work

Name some people who might find conversion graphs useful in their jobs, and say what the graphs would show.

Do motorists prefer to see prices in pence per gallon or pence per litre ?

The temperature is 45°C. What is this in °F ?

23 Conversion Graphs

If we want to convert measurements from one kind of scale to another, then we can draw a graph to show the connection between the different scales.

Example

Draw a graph to convert gallons into litres, given that 1 gallon is equivalent to 4.55 litres, to use for any number of gallons up to 30.

Draw the 'gallons' axis horizontally, from 0 to 30.
A suitable scale would be 1 cm to represent 2 gallons.

Find the number of litres in 10 gallons, then in 30 gallons.
$4.55 \times 10 = 45.5$
$4.55 \times 30 = 45.5 \times 3 = 136.5$

The 'litres' scale must go up to 136.5 litres.
Draw the 'litres' axis vertically, from 0 to 140. A suitable scale would be 2 cm to represent 20 litres.

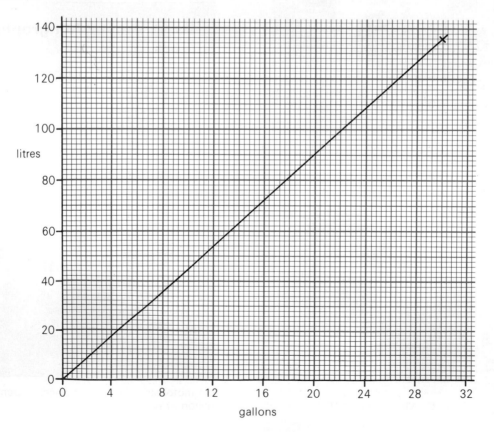

Plot these points:

0 gallons = 0 litres, so plot a point at (0, 0).

30 gallons = 136.5 litres, so plot a point at (30, 136.5).

A third point would be useful as a check in case you have plotted the second point wrongly, since then all three points should lie on a straight line.

10 gallons = 45.5 litres, so plot a point at (10, 45.5).

Join the points with a straight line.

You can use this graph to convert gallons into litres or litres into gallons.

1   Convert 25 gallons into litres.

2   Convert 75 litres into gallons.

For **1**, draw a dotted line up from the horizontal axis where the reading is 25 gallons, to the graph. Then draw a dotted line sideways from this point on the graph to the vertical axis, where its value can be read. (It is 114 litres.)

For **2**, start with a dotted line sideways from the vertical axis where the reading is 75 litres, to the graph. Then draw a dotted line downwards from this point on the graph to the horizontal axis, where its value can be read. (It is 16.4 gallons. On this scale each 2 mm line represents 0.4 gallons.)

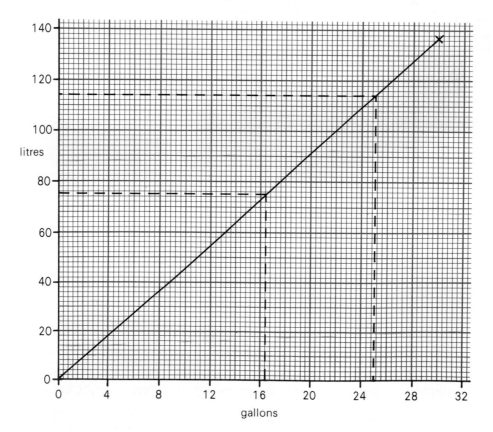

Foreign Currency

Different countries have their own system of money, so when you travel abroad you must change some money. You can change your money at banks, at some travel agencies and at a few other places. They will make a small charge for changing your money.

The rate of exchange varies slightly from day to day and may change considerably at times, depending on the financial situations in Britain and the other countries concerned. Some places may offer better rates than others for changing your money. Here are some of the rates quoted on one particular day. These amounts are equivalent to £1.

TOURIST RATES	
Australia	2.03 dollars
Austria	21.00 schillings
Belgium	63.00 francs
Canada	1.8150 dollars
Cyprus	0.78 pounds
Denmark	11.73 kroner
Finland	6.83 markkaa
France	10.13 francs
Germany	3.00 marks
Greece	259.00 drachmae
Holland	3.39 guilders
Iceland	87.00 kronur
Ireland	1.1275 punts
Israel	3.00 shekels
Italy	2165 lire
Japan	223 yen
Malta	0.5425 pounds
New Zealand	2.65 dollars
Norway	11.00 kroner
Portugal	251.00 escudos
South Africa	4.25 rand
Spain	187.00 pesetas
Sweden	10.30 kronor
Switzerland	2.58550 francs
Turkey	3.300 lire
United States	1.5600 dollars
Yugoslavia	34,700 dinars

A conversion graph is a useful way to find the values of different amounts in different currencies.

Example

Draw a graph to convert between British and Belgian currency at a time when the rate of exchange was £1 = 62 Belgian francs, for amounts from £0 to £10.

On the horizontal axis, for £'s, label from 0 to 10. A suitable scale would be 2 cm to represent £2.

Since £1 = 62 francs,
       £10 = 620 francs.
The vertical axis must go up to 620 francs.
Draw the 'francs' axis vertically, from 0 to 700, using 2 cm to represent 100 francs.

Plot these points:
£0 = 0 francs, so plot a point at (0, 0).
£10 = 620 francs, so plot a point at (10, 620).
A third point would be useful as a check.
£5 = $\frac{1}{2}$ of £10 = 310 francs, so plot a point at (5, 310).

Join the points with a straight line.

Use your graph to find
1   how many francs are equivalent to £2.20,
2   how much 500 francs is worth in £'s, to the nearest 20 p.

Exercise 23.1

1.   Draw a graph to convert miles into kilometres, given that 1 mile = 1.61 km, for a range from 0 to 100 miles.

     (Draw the 'miles' axis horizontally from 0 to 100 and the 'kilometres' axis vertically from 0 to 180. A suitable scale on both axes would be 2 cm to represent 20 units.)

     Use your graph to find
     1   how many kilometres are equivalent to 35 miles,
     2   how many miles are equivalent to 100 km.

2.   Draw a graph to convert ounces into grams, given that 1 lb = 16 oz = 450 g, for a range from 0 to 16 ounces.

     Draw the 'ounces' axis horizontally from 0 to 16 and the 'grams' axis vertically from 0 to 450.
     A suitable scale on the 'ounces' axis would be 2 cm to represent 2 oz and on the 'grams' axis, 2 cm to represent 50 g.

Use your graph to find
1   how many grams (to the nearest 5 g) are equivalent to 2 oz,
2   how many ounces (to the nearest 0.1 oz) are equivalent to 100 g.

3.   Draw a graph to convert £'s into Portuguese escudos at a time when the rate
      of exchange was £1 = 250 escudos.

      Draw the £ axis horizontally from 0 to 16 and the escudos axis vertically from
      0 to 4000.
      A suitable scale would be 2 cm to represent £2 and 2 cm to represent
      500 escudos.

      Use your graph to find the following:
      1   How many escudos would you get if you changed £15 ?
      2   What is the cost of a picture, to the nearest 20 p, if it is for sale marked
           at 1600 escudos ?

Exercise 23.2   Applications and Activities

1.   Draw a graph to convert temperatures from the Celsius scale (°C) to the
      Fahrenheit scale (°F).

      Draw the °C axis horizontally and label from 0 to 100, using a scale of 2 cm to
      represent 20 units. Draw the °F axis vertically and label from 0 to 220, using a
      scale of 2 cm to represent 20 units if your graph paper is large enough.

      When the temperature is 0°C, it is 32°F, so plot a point at (0, 32). This is the
      temperature at which water freezes.
      (Note that this graph does not pass through (0, 0).)

      When the temperature is 100°C, it is 212°F, so plot a point at (100, 212). This is
      the temperature at which water boils.
      Join these two points with a straight line.
      1   It is recommended that elderly people keep their rooms heated, in winter, to
           20°C. What is this temperature in °F ?
      2   A person's 'normal' temperature is marked on a thermometer as 98.4°F. What
           would this be on the Celsius scale ?

2.   Find a list in a newspaper showing the up-to-date rates of exchange for various countries. Choose a country which you would like to visit, and make a conversion graph to change £'s into that country's currency.
(Decide on the range of £'s to be shown on your graph, perhaps up to £10 will be suitable. Choose suitable scales for both axes, and draw the graph.)
Make a list of a few things which you might expect to buy while on holiday, and give the up-to-date prices charged in the UK. Use your graph to convert these prices into the currency of the foreign country. How will this information be useful to you when you are on holiday ?

PUZZLES

38.   Agnes Thompson was born in the 19th century, in a year that reads the same when turned upside down. She died in a year with the same property. What are the dates of her birth and death, and how old was she when she died, if she had had a birthday that year ?

39.   In a hospital ward there is a system of light signals to tell doctors that they are wanted. For example, if the Red only is lit, Dr Snow is wanted. If the Red and Blue are lit, Dr Corless is needed. How many doctors can be given a signal using all possible combinations of colours ?

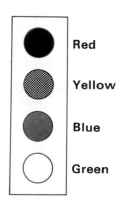

40.   If it costs 50p to break a link and £1 to weld it again, what is the least cost of joining these 5 segments of 3 links each together in one long chain ?

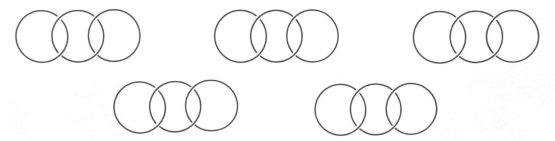

41.   If you wrote down all the numbers from 1 to 100, how many times would you write the figure 7 ?

24 Thinking about trial and improvement

What are trial and improvement methods ?

We use this technique so often in our lives, without realising it.

For example, if the potatoes are being boiled on the gas cooker, and the water is boiling too fiercely, then you will turn the gas down. If you turn it down too much, the water will go off the boil and so the potatoes will not get cooked, so you must turn it up a bit, and then if the water starts bubbling too much you must turn it down slightly again, and you carry on until you have got the water just boiling gently. You also decide when the potatoes are cooked enough by trial and improvement. You stick a fork into them to see if they are soft enough, and if they are not, you repeat this at short intervals until you think they are just right.

If you have a bath, you use the water from the hot tap, which is too hot, and from the cold tap, which is too cold, and you turn each until you are satisfied that the temperature is just right.

To blow up a balloon, you blow quite strongly at first, but as it gets larger you take more care, or you will burst it. You continue by short puffs until you are satisfied that it is as large as it will safely go.

Think of other situations where people use trial and improvement methods. You will probably find that in some of these situations you are quite an expert.

Can you tune a guitar ?

Can you get a green colour by mixing two other colours ?

methods

A puzzle

Now trial and improvement is a good method to use in some mathematical situations, especially where other methods rely on advanced algebra which you may not have learned yet.

Here is an old puzzle which is easier to solve by trial and improvement than by using algebra.

'Two farmers' wives were taking their apples to sell at the market. They both had the same number of apples to sell, but those Mrs Barnes had were large ones and she was going to sell them at 2 for a penny, whereas Mrs Parker was going to sell hers at 3 for a penny, since they were smaller.

When they arrived at the market, they set up their stalls side-by-side, but Mrs Barnes had some other errands to do so she asked Mrs Parker if she would look after both stalls for a time, and she agreed. However, as soon as Mrs Barnes had gone, Mrs Parker mixed all the apples on the two stalls together, and sold them at 5 for twopence, and at that price she soon sold them all.

When Mrs Barnes returned, the two ladies counted out their money, but they were sevenpence short of what they expected to have. After some argument they divided the money equally. So how much did Mrs Barnes lose by not looking after her own stall ?'

When you pump up your bike tyre, how do you get it to the right pressure ?

24 Trial and Improvement Methods

Example 1

Two girls each write down a whole number. When they add the numbers together the sum is 80, and when they multiply the numbers the product is 1564. Find the numbers.

Now, this kind of question can be solved using algebra, when you know more methods in algebra. But now you can solve the problem by trying certain pairs of numbers.

First, think of two numbers which add up to 80 and investigate their products. Begin with multiples of 10.

Smaller number	Larger number	Product
10	70	700
20	60	1200
30	50	1500
40	40	1600

This table of results suggests that the product grows larger as the numbers get nearer to each other. We could test this if we were not sure by adding multiples of 5 to the table.

Smaller number	Larger number	Product
5	75	375
10	70	700
15	65	975
20	60	1200
25	55	1375
30	50	1500
35	45	1575
40	40	1600

Yes, this theory seems to work.

Since the product we want is 1564, it comes from pairs between 30,50 with product 1500, and 35,45 with product 1575.

We can make a new table for these numbers.

Smaller number	Larger number	Product
30	50	1500
31	49	1519
32	48	1536
33	47	1551
34	46	1564
35	45	1575

and we have found the solution. The numbers were 34 and 46.

Now this is not the only way to do this question.
You may have decided to consider the unit figures.
Suppose we begin by investigating unit figures whose sum ends in 0, for the 0 in 80, so they could be 0 and 0, 1 and 9, 2 and 8, 3 and 7, 4 and 6 or 5 and 5.
Their product has to end in 4, from 1564, so the only pair involved is 4 and 6.

So you might try

Smaller number	Larger number	Product
4	76	304
6	74	444
14	66	924
16	64	1024
24	56	1344
26	54	1404
34	46	1564
36	44	1584

and you have found the solution.

Example 2

Suppose the $\boxed{\sqrt[x]{y}}$ button on your calculator is not working properly, or there is not that key on your calculator, and you need to find the cube root of 500, correct to 2 decimal places.

First make a list of cube numbers.

Number	Cube
1	$1^3 = 1 \times 1 \times 1 = 1$
2	$2^3 = 2 \times 2 \times 2 = 8$
3	27
4	64
5	125
6	216
7	343
8	512

You can stop at 8, because the cube root of 343 is 7, the cube root of 512 is 8, and so the cube root of 500 is somewhere between 7 and 8, and it seems to be nearer 8 than 7 because 500 is nearly up to 512.

So find the value of 7.7^3 (or 7.8^3 would do).
$7.7^3 = 7.7 \times 7.7 \times 7.7 = 456.5$; too small.
$7.8^3 = 474.6$; still too small.
$7.9^3 = 493.0$; still too small.
You already know that 8^3 is too big, so the number lies between 7.9 and 8.0.

$7.95^3 = 502.5$; too big.
Now you know that the number lies between 7.9 and 7.95.

$7.93^3 = 498.7$; too small.
$7.94^3 = 500.6$; too big.
So the number lies between 7.93 and 7.94.

Then try $7.935^3 = 499.6$, too small.
So the answer lies between 7.935 and 7.94, and therefore to 2 decimal places it is 7.94.

(Finally, borrow a calculator with a $\boxed{\sqrt[x]{y}}$ key which works. Press 500 $\boxed{\sqrt[x]{y}}$ 3 $\boxed{=}$ and it gives 7.93700526 so we can see that our answer is the correct one, to 2 decimal places.)

Try to find the cube roots of other numbers using this method.

Exercise 24.1

1. The sum of the squares of three consecutive numbers is 3074. Find the numbers.

2. Two positive whole numbers have a product of 682. One number is 9 larger than the other one. Find the numbers.

3. Tony and Karen are playing a number game. Tony thinks of a number less than 100 and gives these clues:
    1   It is a multiple of 9.
    2   It is 1 less than a square number.
    What is Tony's number ?

    Karen thinks of a number and here are her clues:
    1   The two figures have a sum of 11.
    2   When divided by 4 there is a remainder of 3.
    3   If the figures are reversed in order, the number divides exactly by 19.
    What is Karen's number ?

4. Ravi thinks of a number.
    He finds the cube of the number and from this subtracts twice the original number. His answer is 1704.
    What is the number ?

Exercise 24.2   Applications and Activities

1. When a stone is thrown vertically downwards from the top of a cliff, with a certain initial speed, the distance d metres it falls in t seconds is given by the formula $d = 10t + 5t^2$.
    The cliff is 80 m high above the beach. How long does the stone take to hit the beach ? Give the answer correct to 0.1 second.

2. Robin wants to find a point B so that the distance AB is 500 m.
    The expression for the distance AB, in metres, is $\sqrt{40\,000 + x^2}$.
    What distance does he need for the length of B from C ? Give the answer to the nearest metre.

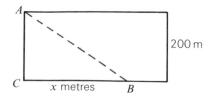

3.   Joanne ties her pet goat by a rope to a stake in the
     corner A of the paddock, so that the goat can graze
     an area as shown.
     She wants it to be able to graze an amount
     between $\frac{1}{4}$ and $\frac{1}{2}$ of the area of the paddock.
     If the length of the rope is x metres, the shaded
     area, in m^2, is found from the formula
     Area $= 0.785x^2$.
     What are the least and greatest lengths of rope she
     can use ? Give the answers correct to the nearest
     metre.
     (The area of the whole paddock is 2500 m^2.)

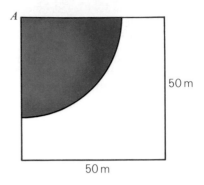

4.   If a stone is thrown vertically upwards with a speed of 24 m/s, then after a time
     t seconds it will be at a height h metres above the starting level, where
     $h = 24t - 4.9t^2$.
     Find its height at times 1, 2, 3, 4 seconds after being thrown.
     By a trial method, find the greatest height the stone reaches, correct to the
     nearest 0.1 m.

5.   A metal tank to hold 200 litres of water is to be made in the shape of a box with
     a square base and rectangular sides. There is no lid.
     If the length of an edge of the base is x cm, the amount of metal needed weighs

     $$\left(\frac{x^2}{100} + \frac{8000}{x} \right) \text{ kg.}$$

     Find how much metal is needed, correct to the nearest kg, if $x = 20, 40, 60, 80,$
     100.
     It is decided to choose the measurements so as to use the least amount of metal.
     By a trial method, find the least weight of metal which can be used, correct to the
     nearest kg.

PUZZLES

42. This square pattern is made with 24 matches. Remove 8 of the matches to leave two complete squares.

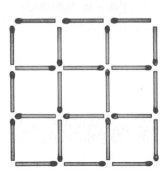

43. How many times, between 1 am and 1 pm, are the hands of a clock pointing in the same direction ?

44. You have 3 flasks which hold exactly 8 litres, 5 litres and 3 litres, and the 8 litre one is filled with an expensive liquid. You want to divide this exactly in half, leaving 4 litres in the big flask and 4 litres in the 5 litre one. By pouring from flask to flask and without wasting any liquid, show how you could do this, in as few pourings as possible.

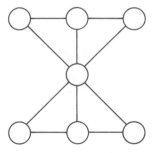

45. Put numbers 1 to 7 in the circles so that each row of three adds up to 12.

46. If there were 7 crows on a wall and the farmer shot one of them, how many would be left on the wall ?

47. The diameter of an L.P. record is 30 cm. The unused centre has a diameter of 10 cm and there is an unused outer edge of width $\frac{1}{2}$ cm around the recording. If there are 100 grooves to 1 cm, approximately how far does the needle move during the playing of the record ?

48. Nine girls were queueing outside the cinema to see a film. Jane was in front of Vicki but behind Mary. Elizabeth was in front of Sarah, and Carol was behind Anna. Sarah was two places in front of Jane. Debbie was six places behind Mary. Louise was three places behind Vicki.
If there were only six seats left, who would be able to see the film ?

Miscellaneous Section C

Aural Practice

These aural exercises, C1 and C2, should be read to you, probably by your teacher or a friend, and you should write down the answers only, doing any working out in your head. You should do the 15 questions within 10 minutes.

Exercise C1

1. What is the cost of a turkey of weight 11 lb if the price is 80 pence per pound ?

2. What sort of triangle has 2 equal sides ?

3. What is 3.5 multiplied by 100 ?

4. What is the probability of throwing a 5 with an ordinary die ?

5. A boat sailed 5 miles North and then 8 miles South. How far is it from its starting point and in which direction ?

6. Write down the fraction $\frac{4}{5}$ as a decimal.

7. Simplify the algebraic expression $6x - 5x$.

8. A running track was 500 m all round. How many times did Lucy run round if she ran 2 km ?

9. If a scale on a drawing is 1 : 5, how long is a line which represents 20 cm ?

10. Write correct to 1 decimal place the number 18.86.

11. If 2 angles of a triangle are 45° and 25°, what is the size of the exterior angle opposite these angles ?

12. If 1 gallon is approximately $4\frac{1}{2}$ litres, and I get 4 gallons of petrol, how many litres is this ?

13. If I toss a coin properly 6 times and it turns up heads 4 times, what is the probability that next time I toss it, it will show tails ?

14. If a scale is 1 : 100, what does 1 cm on the drawing represent ?

15. A radio is priced by a shopkeeper at £20 + VAT. If the rate of VAT is 15%, how much is added to the £20 ?

Exercise C2

1. How many axes of symmetry has an equilateral triangle ?

2. A milkman started out with 480 pints of milk and returned with 64 pints. How many pints had he delivered ?

3. Three children share 24 sweets equally. Then Tara eats 3 of hers. How many has she left ?

4. If the temperature in a fridge is 2°C and it has to be reduced to −5°C, by how many degrees must it drop ?

5. A car does about 30 miles to a gallon of petrol. How many gallons of petrol, approximately, would be needed for a journey of 150 miles ?

6. After washing, a roll of cloth shrinks by 10%. If at first it is 50 m long, how long will it be after washing ?

7. One lap on a race course is 3.54 miles. Write down this number correct to 1 decimal place.

8. What is an expression for each length of ribbon, in cm, if 1 metre of ribbon is cut into q equal parts ?

9. What time is shown on a 24-hour clock if it is 5.35 pm ?

10. If the length of a fence is 20 m and it is represented on a plan by a line of 20 cm, what is the scale of the plan, in ratio form ?

11. Edward thinks of a number, adds 10 and then divides by 4. The answer is 9. What number did he think of ?

12. If I turn up the top card of a well-shuffled pack of 52 cards, what is the probability that it will be a 7 ?

13. What is the value of $y^2 - 2y$ when $y = 10$?

14. If the angle at the centre of a sector in a pie chart is 36°, and this represents an amount of £5, what amount is represented by the whole circle ?

15. Taking 5 miles to be equal to 8 km, what is 40 miles in km ?

Exercise C3   Revision

1.   Use your calculator to express these fractions as decimals, giving the answers correct to 2 decimal places.

   1 $\frac{4}{13}$ (Divide 4 by 13)   **4** $\frac{7}{16}$

   2 $\frac{5}{7}$ **5** $\frac{8}{9}$

   3 $\frac{6}{11}$

2.   Raffle tickets are numbered from 1 to 50. What is the probability that the winning ticket will include a figure 3 ?

3.   (Try to answer this question without using your calculator.)
      The total cost of 35 packets of sweets was £9.80. What was the cost of 1 packet ? If 22 packets of these sweets were bought, what would they cost ?

4.   Here is a list of costs for Parcel Post.

   1 A parcel weighs 5.7 kg. How much does it cost to send it by post ?
   2 Two parcels each weighing 1.7 kg are to be sent to the same address. How much would be saved by tying them together to go as one parcel ?

Weight in kg (not over)	£
1	1.85
2	2.30
3	2.85
4	3.10
5	3.30
6	3.60

Note that these rates may not be up-to-date

5.   Where will you be facing if:
   1 you face North and turn 135° clockwise,
   2 you face South-West and turn 90° clockwise ?

6.   **1** Which two of these triangles are congruent to each other ?
     2 Write down the coordinates of the vertices of the triangle which is not congruent to the others.

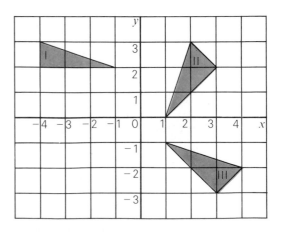

7.   A school has 800 pupils and $\frac{11}{20}$ of them are girls. How many girls are there, and how many boys ?

8.   This is a timetable of the bus service on market days.

Barley Village	dep.	10.40
Thornton Dale	dep.	11.20
Suntown	arr.	12.05
Suntown	dep.	3.55
Thornton Dale	arr.	4.40
Barley Village	arr.	5.15

   1   What is the time taken for the journey from Barley Village to Suntown ?
   2   How much quicker is the return journey ?
   3   Mrs Kenyon uses this service from Barley Village to visit her mother in Thornton Dale. How long can she spend with her mother, if her mother lives 20 minutes walk from the bus stop in Thornton Dale ?

9.   What is the reading on this dial ? If it rises to 9, by how many units has it risen ? It then falls 10 units. What is the new reading ?

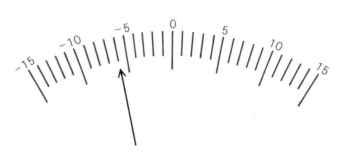

10.   How many axes of symmetry have these shapes ?
   1   An equilateral triangle,   **4**   the capital letter H,
   2   a square,   **5**   the capital letter N.
   3   an isosceles triangle,

11.   A card is drawn from a pack of 52 cards and not replaced. It is queen of hearts. A second card is drawn. What is the probability that it is another heart ?

12.   This pie chart is drawn accurately. Measure the angles in each sector to the nearest 10°. If the whole circle represents a total time of 72 minutes, find the times represented by A, B, C and D.

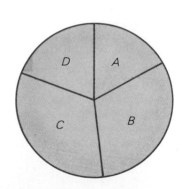

13. Calculate the sizes of angles *a*, *b*, *c*.

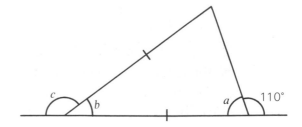

14. From a plank of wood which is 11 ft 4 in long, Alan cuts off 6 lengths of 1 ft 3 in each. He then cuts the remaining piece in half. How long is each half ? (1 foot = 12 inches.)

15. The histogram shows the distances from home to school of a group of children. How many children are there ?
How many live more than 1 mile from the school ?
What is the probability that a child chosen at random from this group lives more than 1 mile from the school ?

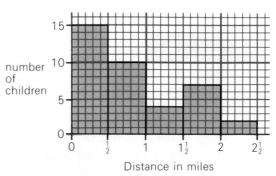

16. A map scale is shown as '1 cm represents 500 m'.
What is the scale shown in ratio form ?
A road is shown on the map as 4 cm long. What is the actual length of road, in km ?

17. A shopkeeper buys an article for £3.60. He then adds onto this price 10% for his profit. How much does he add on ? What would his selling-price be ?

18. This graph converts Dutch guilders into £'s. Use it to find
   1 the number of £'s equivalent to 35 guilders.
   2 the number of guilders equivalent to £6.
   (The rate of exchange may not be up-to-date.)

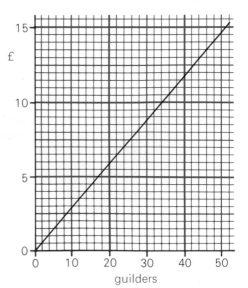

19.   The angles of a triangle are $(x + 5)°$, $(2x + 10)°$, $(3x − 75)°$. Write down an
       equation, and solve it to find the value of x. What are the sizes of the angles ?
       What sort of triangle is it ?

20.   Alan, Bill, Charlie and Derek bought some bottles of wine. Bill bought more
       bottles than Alan, Charlie bought more than Bill, and Derek bought more than
       Charlie. They bought a total of 17 bottles. Each man paid the same number of
       £'s per bottle as the number of bottles he bought. (For example, if a man bought
       4 bottles then he paid £4 each for them.)
       The total cost was £81.
       By a trial method, find how many bottles each man bought.

Exercise C4   Revision

1.   Find the sizes of angles a, b, c.
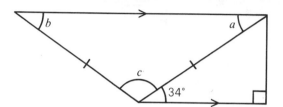

2.   For each of these diagrams, state how many axes of symmetry there are, and
      whether or not there is a point of symmetry.
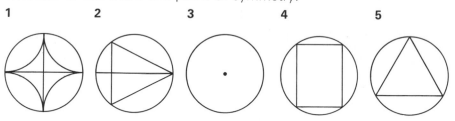

3.   On graph paper, draw x and y axes from $−6$ to 6 using equal scales on both
      axes.
      Plot the points $(4, 3)$, $(−3, 4)$, $(−4, −3)$ and $(3, −4)$.
      Using compasses, draw a circle with centre at $(0, 0)$ and a suitable radius to
      pass through these four points.
      What is the radius of the circle ?

4.   (Try to answer this question without using your calculator.)
      If the length of a man's pace is $80\,cm$, and he takes 100 paces in a minute, how
      far does he walk, in km, in 1 hour ?

5.   A bush is $2.5\,m$ tall. It is estimated that it will increase its height by 8% in an
      average year. How tall is it expected to be in a year's time ?

6.

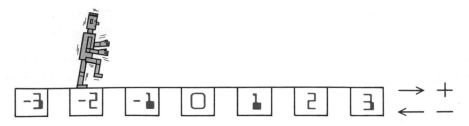

Steve is playing a computer game. To make the robot go to the right he presses
the + key. To make the robot go to the left he presses the − key.
e.g. To get from $\boxed{-2}$ to $\boxed{0}$ he would press +2,
to get from $\boxed{-1}$ to $\boxed{-3}$ he would press −2.

What must he press to move the robot
1   from $\boxed{-2}$ to $\boxed{-3}$,
2   from $\boxed{0}$ to $\boxed{2}$,
3   from $\boxed{3}$ to $\boxed{-2}$,
4   from $\boxed{-1}$ to $\boxed{0}$?

Where does the robot end up if
5   it was at $\boxed{-3}$ and Steve pressed +6,
6   it was at $\boxed{0}$ and Steve pressed −2,
7   it was at $\boxed{2}$ and Steve pressed −5 ?

Where was the robot at first if
8   after Steve pressed −3 it ended up at $\boxed{-1}$,
9   after Steve pressed +3 it ended up at $\boxed{0}$,
10   after Steve pressed −1 it ended up at $\boxed{2}$?

7.   Copy and complete the 1st 9 rows of this pattern.

$$1 = \frac{1 \times 2}{2} = 1$$

$$1 + 2 = \frac{2 \times 3}{2} = 3$$

$$1 + 2 + 3 = \frac{3 \times 4}{2} = 6$$

$$1 + 2 + 3 + 4 = $$

. . .

Now using the method of this pattern, work out the sum of the numbers from
1 to 40.

8.   A piece of wire 75 cm long weighs 10 g. A longer piece of similar wire weighs 2 kg. How long will it be ?

9.   A village hall can seat 160 people. Tickets for a charity concert are to be sold at 75 p for adults and 30 p for children. If 50 tickets are to be sold to children and the rest to adults, what will be the total amount raised ?

10.   An object is made to move along a line. Its distance, S metres, from the starting point after a time t seconds is given by the formula $S = 2t^2 + 3t$.
      1   How far is the object from the starting point after 4 seconds ?
      2   How far is the object from the starting point after 5 seconds ?
      3   Assuming that the object continued to travel in the same direction throughout, how far had it travelled in the 5th second ?

11.   The heights of 94 young men were as follows:

Height	frequency
155 cm but less than 160 cm	3
160 cm but less than 165 cm	13
165 cm but less than 170 cm	37
170 cm but less than 175 cm	29
175 cm but less than 180 cm	10
180 cm but less than 185 cm	2

Six others had heights (in cm), 176, 161, 168, 163, 183, 178.
Re-write the frequency column to include these figures and draw a histogram of the complete list of the 100 men's heights.

12.   Bronze model airplanes weigh 5.5 kg. 0.76 of this weight is copper and the rest is tin. How much copper is needed to make 10 such models ?

13.   The height of Blackpool Tower is $518\frac{3}{4}$ feet. Using 1 foot = 30.48 cm, find this height in metres, to the nearest metre.

14. Use the map of England and Wales to answer these questions.
Find which places are given by these approximate directions and say how far
away they are from the place mentioned. (Measure to the nearest $\frac{1}{2}$ cm and give
the answer correct to the nearest 20 km.)

  1 North of Leeds   **4** South-west of Bristol.
  2 West of Birmingham   **5** North-west of Leeds.
  3 North-east of London.

Give the approximate direction from the 1st place to the 2nd place mentioned
and give the distance between them, to the nearest 20 km.

  6 Birmingham to Norwich.   **9** Birmingham to Hull.
  7 Preston to Manchester.   **10** Dover to Liverpool.
  8 Liverpool to Cardiff.

15. A tank containing liquid is $\frac{3}{5}$ full. When 30 more gallons are put in the tank is
full. How many gallons does the tank hold altogether ?

16. Of the surface of the Earth,
60% is covered by water,
10% by glacial ice and the
remaining 30% by land. Show
this information on a pie chart.

17. There are two discs with numbers on.
One has number 1 on one side and 2
on the other side. The other disc has
number 3 on one side and 4 on the other
side.
The two discs are pulled out of a bag
without looking and placed flat on the
table.

  1 What is the probability that the sum of the two numbers shown is 5 ?
  2 If this procedure was carried out 100 times, approximately how many times
      would you expect the sum to be 5 ?

18.   The table shows the time allowed per unit for local telephone calls.

	seconds
Peak rate	60
Standard rate	85
Cheap rate	330

(These rates may not be up-to-date.)

1   How many minutes will 4 units last on a cheap rate call ?

2   How many units are used on a standard rate call lasting 17 minutes ? If this call had been made at peak rate time, how many extra units would have been used ?

19. O is the centre of the circle.
  1   Explain why $OA = OB$.
  2   Find the sizes of angles a and b.
  3   What sort of triangle is triangle OAB ?

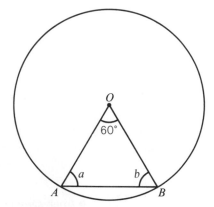

20.   Azara, Bindoo and Carole weighed themselves. Bindoo weighed 5 kg less than Azara and Carole weighed 12 kg more than Bindoo.
      If the weight of Azara is denoted by w kg, what are the expressions for the weights of Bindoo and Carole ?
      Afterwards the girls got on the scales together and the weight shown was 119 kg.
      Write down an equation and solve it to find the weight of each girl.

Exercise C5   Activities

1.   **Random numbers**

     How to collect random numbers was explained on page 284, and you may have got a collection of 100 of them already. For this question you need 200 single-figure random numbers so collect some more, or use some numbers which someone else has collected.

You are going to make a set of random numbers between 1 and 100 by using the single-figure random numbers in pairs.

e.g.   9   2   3   0   1   5   0   4
         92   30   15   4   Count 00 as 100.

Record your new numbers in a grid. You will have 100 of them.

Here are some suggestions for probability experiments.

1   What is the probability of a number chosen at random from the numbers 1 to 100 being divisible by 4 ?
         For the experimental result, count how many numbers on your grid, out of 100, divide exactly by 4.
         You can also calculate the theoretical probability.
         Compare the two answers and comment on them.

2   You can repeat the last question, choosing divisibility by other numbers.

3   You can also find the probability of such a number being a prime number, or a square number.

You can investigate 'runs' of numbers. To do these experiments it would be better if you had more data, so combine someone else's collection of numbers with yours.

4   Runs of odd numbers
         Count from the 1st odd number each time.

e.g. 92   30   15   4   71   38   21   87   39   43   24   15   93   62
                  1   1   4   2

         Put the results on a tally chart and draw a histogram of the distribution. Comment on its shape.
         You can also do runs of even numbers, runs of numbers less than 51, and runs of numbers greater than 50.
         Compare all the histograms and make a comment.

Perhaps you can think of other investigations you could do with your random numbers, or think of other uses for them.

2. **Planning a Day's Outing**

For the next half-term or main holiday, plan a day-out with some of your friends.

First of all, decide what you would like to do and where you would like to go. Perhaps it will be a visit to the seaside, to a country park, a zoo or one of the theme parks where there are numerous amusements. You may like to visit a city to attend a theatre performance, do a sightseeing trip or a shopping trip.

Find the destination on a map. Decide how you are going to get to the place, by train, bus, coach, car or bicycle. Find the route you will take from your home, and find the approximate distance. Draw a sketch map showing the route.

Make a timetable for the day, including the times of the journeys there and back, and the time for lunch.
Decide whether you are going to buy a meal or a snack for lunch, or whether you will take a packed lunch. Will you be home by teatime or will you need another meal out ?

Calculate an approximate cost for the day, including fares, admission charges, food and drinks, and other spending money.

3.   **A geometrical model**

There are many geometrical
models you can make using thin
cardboard. You also need some
suitable glue. Here is an
interesting starry shape. If it had
an inside, it would be called a
solid figure. This one has no
inside so we call it a **nolid**. Its
full name is 'starry nolid
truncated tetrahedron'.

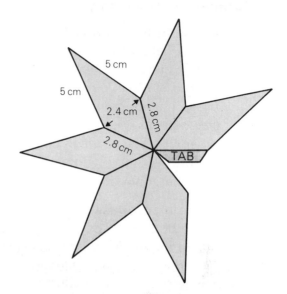

To begin, draw the pattern on tracing paper. Start from the centre point by
drawing a circle of radius 2.8 cm. Then change the radius to 2.4 cm and 'step
off' 7 points round the circumference, and join each point to the centre. Then
change the radius to 5 cm and make the 6 outer points. To transfer the pattern to
cardboard, put the tracing paper on top and prick through the 14 main points
with the point of your compasses. (Put something underneath to protect the
desk.) Then join the points, score the inner lines and add a tab. (The tab can be
drawn freehand. Make it big enough to be easy to glue to the next part.) Cut
the piece out. Bend the scored lines away from the scored side, and glue the tab
onto the next part, leaving the tab showing on the scored side. If you have done
this properly the scored side is the outside of the curved shape. It will later
become the inside of the nolid.
You need 4 similar pieces altogether.

Now glue 2 pieces together along one of the faces.
One face of the 3rd piece will glue to a face of the 1st piece, and the next-but-
one face of the 3rd piece will glue to a face of the 2nd piece, leaving a small
triangular hole in the middle of these 3 pieces.
Then the 4th piece will glue to 3 faces, one from each of the other pieces, and
you have finished the nolid.

If you want to change the measurements to make a larger star, keep the 2.8 cm
and 2.4 cm lines in the same proportion. The 5 cm length can be changed to
make longer or shorter points.

4. **Finding your bearings**

1   **Use a simple compass.** Place
    it on a flat surface so that the
    needle can swing freely, and the
    marked end will point North.
    (Keep it away from metal or
    electricity as these will affect it.)
    When you know which direction
    is North you can work out where
    the other main directions are.

2   **Make a compass.** You need a magnet, a needle, a piece of cork in the
    shape of a disc, and a basin of water.
    Stroke the needle with one end of the magnet, about 20 times, always
    stroking in the same direction. The needle is now magnetised. Put the

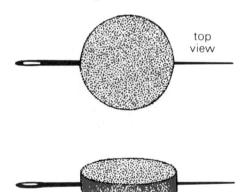

top
view

side view

needle through the cork then
float the cork on the water.
The needle will point in a
North–south direction.
The only problem now is to
decide which end of the needle,
the eye or the point, is pointing
North. It depends on which end
of the magnet you used and
which way you stroked. The next
section may help you to decide.

3   **Make a sun compass.**
    The sun goes round the earth (or at least, it seems to) every 24 hours. At
    6 am it is due East, at 12 noon it is due South, at 6 pm it is due West. If we
    could see it at 12 midnight, where would it be ? At what times is it in the
    north-east, south-west and north-west ?

    Make a circular dial on cardboard. Divide it into 24 equal parts for the
    24 hours and label them, going clockwise. Then put the compass directions
    on in places corresponding to their correct times.

    If at any time, e.g. 7 pm, you line up 7 pm with the sun's direction, your dial
    will show which direction is North, or the other directions.

    You can design the dial differently to use the shadow from the sun instead
    of the sun's direction. Think it out for yourself.

Now, in British Summer Time we put the clocks forward one hour, so you will have to change 6 am to 7 am and put all the times 1 hour more, so perhaps you could write these times in a different colour. There is some discussion about whether we ought to adopt double summer time, and if this happens you will have to put all the times 2 hours forward.

(The compass will not be completely accurate if you are a long way East or West of London, but it is good enough to give a general idea of the directions.)

If you are in the Southern hemisphere you will have to amend these instructions because in your case the sun is due North at 12 noon, and it appears to go in an anticlockwise direction.

4   Go out on a clear, starry night and find the 7 stars of the Plough. (Again, this is not for you if you are in the Southern hemisphere.)

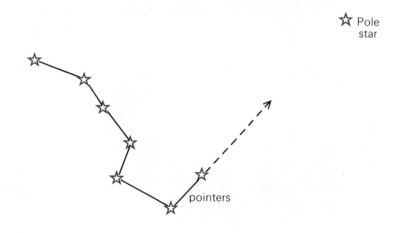

Follow the 2 end stars, which are called the Pointers, for about 5 times the distance between them and you will come to the Pole star, which is in a direction due North of you.

5   Find out how to use a Silva compass.

5. **A mathematical game**

You have probably played games such as snakes and ladders or ludo, where a die is used, or Monopoly or backgammon, where 2 dice are used. There are also games like draughts or chess, played on a board of squares. These do not depend on throws of a die, they are games of skill. You probably know some games you can play with a pack of cards, and there are several games which use cards with instructions on them, such as 'This is your lucky day,—go forward 6 squares'. Noughts and crosses is a quick game, and there are several other pencil and paper games.

Make a list of the games you know, and put them into different categories.

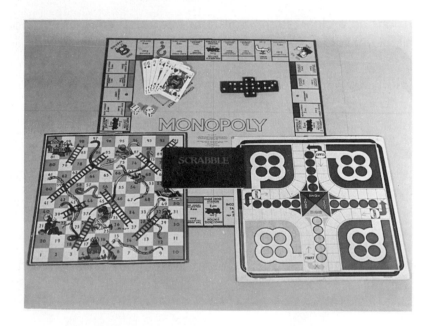

Now design a game yourself, either working alone or with friends. Try to include some Mathematics in it, perhaps negative numbers for going backwards or losing money. It could be based on coordinates. It could include mathematical questions, as in Trivial Pursuit.

Play it several times so that you can make sure that the rules are clear, and improve them where necessary to make the game more fair or more exciting.

When you are satisfied with your game, design attractive equipment for playing it, and lend it to your friends so that they can play it.

6. **A display of weighing and measuring instruments**

If everyone in the class helped by bringing things, you could have a good display of weighing and measuring instruments.
(You will have to discuss this with your teacher. You need to have somewhere to show the display, and if parents are willing to lend equipment you must make sure it is looked after carefully.)

You could begin your planning by making a list of instruments available. To begin with, you have rulers and protractors. The home economics department will have weighing scales and measuring jugs. The science department will have more accurate equipment. The PE staff will have longer tape measures, and stop-watches. Think of what other departments in the school might lend to you. Then a letter to parents suggesting what you are looking for might produce other items. Has anyone a gauge for measuring knitting needles, or one for measuring ring sizes ? Don't forget a type pressure gauge which a motorist might lend. Can you borrow equipment from a surveyor ?

When you know what items you are going to have in your display, you can print out neat labels. Perhaps you will write notes to put with the more unusual items. Decide how best to arrange your display, perhaps putting all the things which measure length together, then weighing instruments, etc. You could divide the display into British and Metric sections.

Take a photograph of the display so you will have a record of it.

7. **A model of a play-house, tree-house or adventure playground**

Decide which of these you would like to design.
A play-house for a small child needs to be large enough for a few children to fit inside. It will also need designs for simple furniture, such as benches and a table. A play-house could also be designed as a log cabin, a fort or perhaps a space ship. A tree-house would be more suitable for older children. You need a tree to build it in, with strong branches at a suitable height. You also need a way to get up into it. If you prefer, plan a children's playground layout with interesting, but safe, equipment. You will probably begin by drawing rough sketches and deciding on the actual measurements. Then make the model, choosing a suitable scale, and using suitable materials. You could paint your model to make it look realistic.

You can extend this activity by deciding what materials, such as wood, would be needed, and in what quantities. Then you could make an approximate estimate of the cost.

Perhaps you will be able to persuade someone to finance the project and help you to make it.

8. **Fourteen**

This is a multiplication square using the numbers
1, 9, 11.
Copy this, but instead of putting the actual answers
in, if the number is 14 or more then divide by 14 and
just write down the remainder. (This is called arithmetic
modulo 14.)
Comment on the pattern.

	1	9	11
1	1	9	11
9	9	81	99
11	11	99	121

Now subtract 1, 9, 11 from 14 and make a pattern with the new numbers.
Can you comment about this one ?
Then combine these numbers to make a table using all the odd numbers under
14, except 7, which is an odd one out.
What about the even numbers ? Begin using 2, 4, 8, and then investigate
further.
(Dividing by other numbers produces patterns like this, so you can continue
your investigations if you have time.)

As an extra discovery, suppose you write 0.07, and then double the number and
move it 2 places downwards, and repeat this several times.

0.07
0.0014
0.000028
0.00000056
0.0000000112
. . .

Do this for yourself, going several places further. Then add up the columns,
except for the smallest columns which you cannot include if there may be
carrying figures from the rows not yet written. What connection has your
answer with 14 ?

9.   **House prices**

Do a survey of house prices, using the advertisements in the local evening newspaper.

You must make a decision about whether to just count houses, or whether to include flats in your survey.

Group your data into suitable classes, for example:

    £0   but under £20 000
£20 000   but under £40 000
£40 000   but under £60 000, etc.

Draw a histogram of the results and comment on them.

If you can get enough data you could do separate surveys, e.g. for semi-detached houses.

If you repeat your survey in a few months' time you could decide whether house prices have risen.

If you have friends in another part of the country, perhaps they could send you their local paper, so that you could compare prices in the two regions.

10. **Conversion program**

Here is a computer program for converting yards
to metres and vice versa.

```
10   REM prog:conv, conversion program
20   CLS
30   PRINT:PRINT
40   PRINT:PRINT
50   PRINT"To convert yards to metres,     press     1"
60   PRINT:PRINT"To convert metres to yards,     press     2"
70   PRINT:PRINT"To finish,                      press     3"
80   X$=INKEY$:IF X$="" THEN 80
90   IF X$="1" THEN 120
100  IF X$="2" THEN 190
110  IF X$="3" THEN 260 ELSE 80
120  CLS:PRINT:PRINT:PRINT
130  INPUT"Enter length in yards or enter -1 to return
     to start";YDS
140  IF YDS=-1 THEN 20
150  LET MTRS=YDS*.9144
160  MTRS=INT(MTRS*100+.5)/100
170  PRINT:PRINT TAB(20);YDS;"yards";TAB(35)"=";MTRS;" metres"
180  PRINT:GOTO 130
190  CLS:PRINT:PRINT:PRINT
200  INPUT"Enter length in metres or enter -1 to return to
     start";MTRS
210  IF MTRS=-1 THEN 20
220  LET YDS=MTRS*1.094
230  YDS=INT(YDS*100+.5)/100
240  PRINT:PRINT TAB(20);MTRS;"metres";TAB(35)"=";  YDS;" yards"
250  PRINT:GOTO 200
260  END
```

You could improve this program so that it would print out a list of conversions
for any pair of units.
You could also write a program which would convert Foreign Currency. Since
the rates change from day to day, you would have to arrange for the up-to-date
rates to be entered at the beginning of the program.

11. **Symmetrical Pattern Drawing**

Here is a computer program which will draw a pattern which will be symmetrical, with a horizontal and a vertical axis of symmetry, and a point of symmetry. It has been written to run on a BBC computer so for other computers you may have to amend it.

```
10   REM PICT : Pattern Drawing Program
20   MODE 1
30   VDU 24, 0; 120; 1279; 1023;
40   VDU 28, 0, 31, 39, 28
50   COLOUR 129:COLOUR 2
60   GCOL 0, 130:CLS:CLG
70   GCOL 0, 0
80   VDU 29, 640; 550;
90   MOVE -640, 0: DRAW +640, 0
100  MOVE 0, 512:DRAW 0, -512
110  FOR L = 1 to 20
120  X1=RND(640):Y1=RND(512)
130  S=RND(3)-1:IF S=2 THEN S=3
140  GCOL 0,S
150  PROCREC(X1,Y1,10,10)
160  PROCREC(-X1,Y1,10,10)
170  PROCREC(-X1,-Y1,10,10)
180  PROCREC(X1,-Y1,10,10)
190  NEXT L
200  CLS: PRINT"To continue Press Y for yes, if not press
     N for no"
210  Y$=GET$
220  IF Y$="Y" OR Y$="y" THEN 110
230  IF Y$<>"N" AND Y$<>"n" THEN 210
240  VDU 28, 0, 31, 39, 0
250  END
260  DEF PROCREC(X,Y,L,W)
270  MOVE X,Y
280  MOVE X+L,Y
290  PLOT 85,X+L,Y+W
300  MOVE X,Y+W
310  PLOT 85,X,Y
320  ENDPROC
```

The programs shown here have just been written to give you some simple ideas. If you are interested in computer programming then you will be able to think of other programs you could write, to link with mathematical ideas.

12. **Using a computer database**

A computer is a machine that is capable of processing information very quickly, but only in accordance with a given set of instructions, and so it is necessary that information is organised in some way.

A **database program** will put the data in order, and can also make selections of various categories from it. You can imagine how useful such a program is for so many kinds of users, from the small market gardener who keeps a database of the seeds he uses, to a Government department which makes vital decisions from the data it collects.

As an example of a datafile, consider the recording of information on pupils in a school. The school requires a **set of information** which relates to each individual pupil. The collection of all the sets of information is called a datafile. The information needed for each pupil will consist of several items. It could be organised in a table as follows:

Surname	Other names	Sex	Date of birth	Address	Form

The entry for any particular pupil is called a **record**.
The headings listed, such as surname, other names, sex, . . . are called **fields**. In some of them, the entry can be a single letter, e.g. for sex, M for male and F for female. It could be numerical, e.g. 17.10.80 for date of birth. For names and addresses the entry would be much longer. The type of field and its length have to be decided when planning the datafile.
There could be further details entered in other fields, for instance, whether the pupil has school dinner.

By giving the relevant instructions the computer could then be made to select certain pupils. For example, the school might need a list of pupils in each form, in alphabetical order of surname; for a medical inspection the names of all 12 year old pupils might be needed in two lists, one of boys and the other of girls. If there were transport problems, so that pupils who lived in a certain district had to be sent home early, a list of the names of all the pupils who lived in that district might be needed, together with the forms they were in so that they could be contacted. The computer program would be able to sort out the data and select what was needed in each case.

Here are the fields an employer might have on a payroll datafile.

Employee number	Name	Dept	Job description	Pay rate	Hours worked

And here are the fields a bookseller might have in the stock datafile.

Book code	Title	Publisher	Author	Category	Price	Copies in stock

A program that will record such data and select from it or sort it into various categories will be quite complicated and so a commercially-produced program will probably be used.

If you have such a program available, then you can make use of it to store some data.

Think of the sort of data you could keep in a database. Maybe it is data from one of your other school subjects. Maybe you have a hobby for which you collect objects or information, and the details could be stored in a database.

There are problems about storing data which include records relating to people. Those who do this must have a licence to do so. If you intend to include people's real names in your database, you should check with your teacher first, to see if you can do this.

If you would like to practise using your database, here is a simple example you can use. If you have not got access to a computer and a database, you could enter this information on small cards and sort them manually, to answer the questions.

A shop sells watches and classifies them in a datafile as follows. (The names and details are fictitious.)

Cat. no	Name	Type	Price £	Digital (D) or with dial (A)	Special features
89/1	Kiddywatch	childs	6	D	animal picture
89/2	Styletime	ladies	7	D	date
89/3	Sparkletime	ladies	26	A	diamante stones
89/4	Bestime	ladies	20	A	gold plated
89/5	Accritime	gents	12	A	second hand, splashproof
89/6	Tradwatch	gents	10	A	Roman numerals
89/7	Scenetime	ladies	8	A	scene on dial
89/8	Telltime	childs	9	A	fully figured
89/9	Oldytime	gents	11	A	pocket watch
89/10	Sportstime	gents	14	D	stopwatch, alarm

Using the datafile, list the watches in order of price, cheapest first.
List the watches suitable for a lady, together with their prices and any special features.
Meg wants to choose a watch as a birthday present for a child. It should not be a digital watch. Which one is suitable, and how much will it cost ?

Index

Answers

Some answers have been given corrected to reasonable degrees of accuracy, depending on the questions.
There may be variations in answers where questions involve drawings or graphs.

Page 3   Exercise 1.1

1.
8	54	49	72	0
30	6	72	4	42
14	0	0	9	132
48	28	2	9	100
25	24	81	63	11
0	45	33	10	24
12	96	84	110	64
88	20	16	12	35
48	77	18	56	70
30	20	144	60	36

2.
11	12	5	9	0
9	6	7	7	9
5	11	5	12	11
12	5	4	8	6
9	6	12	3	9

3. **1** 14   **5** 121   **8** 4
   2 24   **6** 23   **9** 18
   3 13   **7** 7   **10** 18
   4 9

4. **1** 5 r 3   **4** 8 r 0
   2 2 r 4   **5** 8 r 4
   3 5 r 2

5. **1** 5   **2** 6   **3** 7   **4** 2   **5** 4

Page 8   Exercise 1.2

1. **1** 213, 415, 677, 717, 725
   2 415, 725, 1000
   3 102, 213, 528, 717, 828

2. **1** 30, 39, 42, 45, 48
   2 30, 35, 45
   3 35, 42, 49

3. **1** 1, 2, 3, 4, 6, 12
   2 1, 2, 3, 5, 6, 10, 15, 30
   3 1, 2, 4, 5, 8, 10, 20, 40

4. 2, 3, 5, 7, 11, 13, 17, 19, 23, 29

5. **1** 11   **5** 4   **8** 8
   2 9   **6** 12   **9** 2
   3 5   **7** 9   **10** 7
   4 10

6. **1** 21   **5** 30   **8** 6
   2 36   **6** 33   **9** 28
   3 35   **7** 18   **10** 4
   4 24

7. Prime: 71, 73, 79

8. **1** 8, 9, 125, 49, 10 000
   2 5^4, 2^7, 11^2

9. **1** 64, 144, 49, 1, 81
   2 6, 2, 11, 5, 10
   3 64, 1, 1000

10. **1** 23, 31   **4** 27
    2 25, 36   **5** 23, 31
    3 27, 36

12. **1** 15, 18, 21   **6** 70, 64, 58
    2 32, 24, 16   **7** 85, 79, 72
    3 81, 243, 729   **8** 160, 320, 640
    4 26, 37, 50   **9** 16, 4, 1
    5 125, 216, 343   **10** 47, 65, 86

Page 10   Exercise 1.3

1. **1** 4   **2** 2   **3** 3   **4** 1   **5** 3
2. **1** 6   **2** 24   **3** 41   **4** 17   **5** 120
3. **1** 55   **2** 1   **3** 192   **4** 15   **5** 6

9. **1** 12, 14, 16, 18, 20   **4** 11, 13, 17, 19
   2 16   **5** 12, 15, 20
   3 15, 20

Page 24   Exercise 2.1

1. **1** acute   **5** reflex   **8** acute
   2 obtuse   **6** reflex   **9** reflex
   3 obtuse   **7** acute   **10** obtuse
   4 acute

5. **1** acute, 31°   **4** acute, 78°
   2 obtuse, 109°   **5** obtuse, 138°
   3 acute, 89°

Page 31   Exercise 2.2

1. 90°
2. 155°
3. $c = 18°, d = e = 162°$
4. 145°
5. 112°
6. $h = 150°, j = 30°, k = 18°$
7. 72°
8. 48°
9. $a = 134°, b = 226°$
10. $a = 28°, b = 332°$

Page 34   Exercise 2.3

1. **1** $a = b = 125°$
   2 $c = d = 33°$
   3 $e = 45°, f = 135°$

3. **1** 72°   **4** 57°
   2 117°   **5** 102°
   3 48°   **6** 73°

4. $a = b = 54°$

Page 36   Exercise 2.4

1. **1** 36°   **2** 25°
2. $a = b = 62°, c = 118°$
3. $d = e = 48°$
4. $f = 125°, g = 145°, h = 35°$
5. $j = 55°, k = 65°, m = 120°$

6. $n = q = 53°, p = 127°$
7. $r = 72°$
8. $s = 64°, t = 16°$
9. **1** 12 hours   **5** 45°
   2 30°   **6** 6°
   3 135°   **7** 25
   4 120°   **8** 150°

Page 49   Exercise 3.1

1. **1** 470   **6** 450 000
   2 84 000   **7** 160 000
   3 601 000   **8** 300 000
   4 800   **9** 280 000
   5 2 100 000 **10** 24 000

2. **1** 500   **5** 4   **8** 120
   2 7   **6** 3000   **9** 50
   3 90   **7** 20   **10** 350
   4 60

3. 60, 500, 130, 1040, 290, 90, 1430, 580, 100, 210

4. 1300, 2500, 21 000, 500, 1100, 1000, 3100, 9100, 400, 800

5. 4000, 15 000, 3000, 28 000, 3000, 56 000, 9000, 81 000, 4000, 10 000

6. **1** 625, 2704, 11 236, 12 321
   2 26, 31, 45, 88
   3 1331, 148 877

7. **1** 1, 761   **4** 0, 35 620
   2 4, 1584   **5** 6, 396
   3 6, 28 836

8. **1** 805   **5** 23   **8** 9
   2 13   **6** 360   **9** 29
   3 180   **7** 11   **10** 7
   4 360

9. **1** 13   **5** 4   **8** 16
   2 24   **6** 14   **9** 30
   3 5   **7** 5   **10** 25
   4 36

10. **1** 33 r 3   **4** 13 r 25
    2 480 r 4   **5** 59
    3 64 r 8

Page 50   Exercise 3.2

1. 3091

2. **1** 600   **2** 16

3. 6400

4. 20

5. 0

6. 28

7. **1** 160   **2** 81

8. 2400

9. **1** 2000, 4300, 5300, 6800, 11 800
   2 2000, 4000, 5000, 7000, 12 000

10. **1** 38   **5** 240   **8** 10
    2 78   **6** 7   **9** 39
    3 46   **7** 100   **10** 9
    4 88

11. 1st one, 6

12. **1** Thursday   **2** £400

13. 180, 190, 190, 200, 210; 970

14. 3600, 3600

Page 61   Exercise 4.1

1. **1** 9   4. **1** 0.295
   2 80.2   **2** 0.076
   3 341.2   **3** 0.005
   4 0.61   **4** 0.0358
   5 4.5   **5** 0.019

2. **1** 379   5. **1** 7.17
   2 15   **2** 15.9
   3 1250   **3** 8.22
   4 3.6   **4** 1.03
   5 70   **5** 32.03

3. **1** 1.492   6. **1** 2.08
   2 4.76   **2** 1.07
   3 0.208   **3** 7.21
   4 0.03   **4** 1.63
   5 0.004   **5** 3.48

7. **1** 56.14   13. **1** 0.0451
   2 12   **2** 4.27
   3 2.88   **3** 18.1
   4 30.1   **4** 9270
   5 0.18   **5** 716 000
                          6 321
8. **1** 3.14   **7** 49 600
   2 1.92   **8** 0.0303
   3 0.63   **9** 6.05
   4 0.15   **10** 5.90
   5 0.008
                     14. **1** 340.866
10. **1** 5.3   **2** 78.71
    2 5.5   **3** 0.10875
    3 0.4   **4** 1.134
    4 1.1   **5** 0.1666
    5 2.1
                     15. **1** 0.16
11. **1** 3.58   **2** 7.33
    2 5.81   **3** 7.40
    3 0.70   **4** 2.87
    4 6.59   **5** 67.04
    5 0.01
                     16. **A** 0.7
12. **1** 37   **B** 3.3
    2 24   **C** 6.0
    3 4.8   **D** 10.5
    4 4.5   **E** 13.9
    5 0.30
    6 0.30   17. **A** 0.2
    7 0.59   **B** 2.0
    8 0.29   **C** 3.6
    9 0.051   **D** 7.5
    10 0.73   **E** 9.9

                     19. **A** 0.10
                         B 0.27
                         C 0.40
                         D 0.69
                         E 0.94

Page 64   Exercise 4.2

1. 10

2. **1** 3208   **2** 3207.93   **3** 3200

3. **1** 9.274   **4** 40.83554
   2 6.76   **5** 79.12
   3 199

4. **1** 16.82   **5** 0.3   **8** 7
    2 2.03   **6** 2.6452   **9** 3.84
    3 3.14   **7** 100   **10** 1.03
    4 0.67

Page 69   Exercise 5.1

1. $(8 - b)$ years

2. $5w$ kg

3. $(c + 40)$ pence

4. $\dfrac{d}{20}$ metres or $5d$ cm

5. £$(m - 2)$

6. $(2l + 2b)$ cm or $2(l + b)$ cm

7. $\dfrac{3000}{f}$ (m^2)

8. $(5g + 2h)$ pence

9. pq pence, $(100 - pq)$ pence

10. $(6 + m)$ minutes

Page 72   Exercise 5.2

1. **1** a **5** $2fg$ **8** 0
    2 0   **6** h^3 **9** $3mn$
    3 cd **7** $3j^2$ **10** $4p^2$
    4 e^2

2. **1** $2a$ **5** e **8** 0
    2 $2b$ **6** $12f$ **9** $3j$
    3 0   **7** $6g$ **10** k
    4 $5d$

3. **1** a
    2 1
    3 0   **7** $\dfrac{5g}{3}$ or $\tfrac{5}{3}g$
    4 $\dfrac{d}{2}$ or $\tfrac{1}{2}d$ **8** $\dfrac{3}{j}$
    5 $\dfrac{e}{3}$ or $\tfrac{1}{3}e$ **9** $\dfrac{m}{n}$
    6 $\dfrac{2f}{5}$ or $\tfrac{2}{5}f$ **10** 0

4. **1** 6   **5** 24   **8** 26
    2 2   **6** 5   **9** 27
    3 15   **7** 49   **10** 17
    4 18

5. **1** $2a + 4b$ **6** $7\ell + 10$
    2 $4c - 4d$ **7** $8m - 6$
    3 $3e - 6f + 9g$ **8** $7p$
    4 $5h + 40$ **9** $10s + 4t$
    5 $2j - 8k$ **10** $8x - 7y + z$

6. **1** 36   **4** 592
    2 52   **5** 56 pence
    3 180

Page 73   Exercise 5.3

1. **1** $2a$ **2** 0   **3** a^2 **4** 1   **5** a

2. **1** $8b$ **2** $4b$ **3** $12b^2$ **4** 3   **5** 0

3. $(6p - 2)$ kg

4. 140 (minutes), $(20 + 40m)$ minutes

5. £140, $A = 50 + 30n$, £350

6. £87, $H = 18n + 3m$

7. 280 km

8. 5 litres

9. 144°

10. 720, 1980

Page 82   Exercise 6.1

1. **1** 80   **6** 5000
    2 4000   **7** 10 000
    3 50   **8** 1500
    4 2000   **9** 6
    5 3000   **10** 2

2. **1** 2.56 kg   **6** 3500 g
    2 0.25 m   **7** 3.6 cm
    3 4000 ml   **8** 8ℓ
    4 80 mm   **9** 3.56 m
    5 230 cm   **10** 750 g

3. **1** 10.46 kg   **2** 2.15 kg   **3** 650 ml

4. AB = 7.7 cm EF = 6.8 cm
    CD = 10.1 cm GH = 8.5 cm

5. **1** 4.8 cm   **2** 10.6 cm   **3** 5.8 cm

Page 84   Exercise 6.2

1. 7 kg

2. 50

3. 48, 49 or 50, depending on the pattern

4. 6   12. 6 g

5. 550   13. 50

6. 15ℓ   14. 301.5 m

7. 54.4 cm   15. 4.8 m

8. 28.6 m, 85.8 m   16. 540 g

9. 0.9 m   17. 75 cm

10. 450   18. 18, 62

11. 800 g

Page 91

Example 2.   40, 37

Page 92

Example 3.   frequencies 8, 19, 10, 7, 4, 2

Page 95   Exercise 7.1

4. frequencies:- red 22, white 18, pale blue 13, grey 12, beige 9, dark blue 7, black 7, brown 5, green 5, yellow 2; total 100

5. frequencies:- car 17, plane 9, car and ferry 5, coach 2, train 2, canal barge 1, cruise ship 1; total 37

6. frequencies:- prawn 11, onion 5, vinegar 5, plain 4, cheese 4, tomato sauce 2, beef 2, bacon 1, chicken 1; total 35

7. frequencies:- (1) 32, (2) 28, (3) 23, (4) 12, (5) 5; total 100

8. frequencies:- (3) 2, (4) 4, (5) 5, (6) 4, (7) 14, (8) 22, (9) 23, (10) 17, (11) 23, (12) 26, (13) 22, (14) 16, (15) 10, (16) 5, (17) 3, (18) 4; total 200; most, 12; least, 3

10. frequencies in order:- 26, 17, 12, 6, 5, 1, 2

Page 98   Exercise 7.2

1. totals for goals by home team:- (0) 16, (1) 11, (2) 8, (3) 4, (4) 4, (5) 1. totals for goals by away team:- (0) 16, (1) 15, (2) 5, (3) 7, (4) 1.

2. frequencies:- (0) 7, (1) 10, (2) 9, (3) 6, (4) 4, (5) 4, (6) 2, (7) 1, (8) 0, (9) 1

3. totals for girls:- (1) 13, (2) 18, (3) 4, (4) 1, (5) 1. totals for boys:- (0) 10, (1) 23, (2) 4 totals for children:- (1) 2, (2) 17, (3) 12, (4) 3, (5) 1, (6) 2

Page 106   Exercise 8.1

1. **1** £3   **2** £42

2. **1** £7.92   **2** £20.93

3. 58p, 83p, 47p, 34p, 19p

4. £4.52, £1.39, 89p, £2.70, £3.27

5. 4, (50p, 10p, 5p, 2p); 4, (20p, 10p, 2p, 1p)

6. **1** 5p, 5p, 2p, 2p, 2p or 8 of 2p
   2 5p, 5p, 5p, 2p, 2p or 5p and 7 of 2p

7. £10.20, £9.80   14. £251

8. £2.68   15. 5p

9. £28.95   16. £41.67

10. £43.60   17. £1.89

11. £7.68   18. 58, 14p

12. £3.75, £1.95   19. 32

13. £3.60   20. 37

Page 111   Exercise 8.2

1. 02.10, 19.00, 14.15, 16.05, 23.50 3.50 am, 7.30 am, 12.05 pm, 6.18 pm, 10.10 pm

2. **1** 2.35 pm   **2** 14.35

3. **1** 8 min 27 sec   **4** 11 yr 7 mth
   2 6 hr 35 min   **5** 67 hr 10 min
   3 43 yr 8 mth

4. 2 hr 43 min

5. £56

6. 3.10 pm

7. 3 hr 30 min, 01.50

8. 40 min

9. 2000

10. **1** Tuesday **3** Monday
    2 Thursday **4** 6th May

11. **1** 29 **2** 29 **3** 28 **4** 29 **5** 28

12. **2** 13 **4** 73

Page 112   Exercise 8.3

1. 1100, £71.10

2. £99.99

3. Larger packet

4. **1** £150 **2** £149.97

5. 85p

6. **1** 80p **2** 75p

7. **1** £151.20 **2** 45 hrs

8. **1** 2 hr 15 min **2** 4 hr 55 min

9. **1** 15.54 (3.54 pm), 25 min, 8 min
   2 16.22 (4.22 pm), 32 min

10. 5 hr 30 min

Page 116   Exercise A1

1. 121

2. 60p

3. 45

4. 4.38

5. 2 m

6. 1998

7. 6b

8. 3

9. 4, 8

10. 50°

11. 36 years

12. 10

13. 140 cm

14. 20th June

15. 63°

Page 117   Exercise A2

1. 84

2. 30 056

3. £2.01

4. obtuse

5. 17, 20

6. 54

7. 3

8. £1.40

9. 30 ml

10. 15.30

11. 800

12. £15y

13. 7

14. 42.7

15. £9

Page 118   Exercise A3

1. **1** 32 **2** 64 **3** 9 **4** 5 **5** 1 000 000

2. 75°

3. **1** 10 400 **2** 7500 **3** 43 300 **4** 3600 **5** 5000

4. $(5x + 3y)$ pence, $c = 5x + 3y$

5. 300 g

6. **1** 16 **2** 21

7. 1 hr 35 min

8. 31, 37

9. 75°

10. **1** 6a **2** a **3** $2a^2$ **4** a^3 **5** 1

11. **1** 7.18 **2** 6.28 **3** 2029.16 **4** 46.79 **5** 0.04

12. **1** 60 **2** 2000 **3** 3000 **4** 5000 **5** 400

13. 48

14. 640

15. 12

16. B £135, C £75

17. 10

18. $a = 146°, b = 134°, c = 46°$

19. **1** 253   **4** 0.0351
    2 56 800   **5** 291
    3 7.08

20. £180

Page 140   Exercise 9.1

1. **1** $\frac{3}{8}$ **2** $\frac{1}{3}$ **3** $\frac{1}{3}$ **4** $\frac{1}{2}$ **5** $\frac{1}{3}$

3. **1** $\frac{1}{3}$ **5** $\frac{2}{5}$ **8** $\frac{3}{8}$
   2 $\frac{2}{3}$ **6** $\frac{1}{4}$ **9** $\frac{3}{4}$
   3 $\frac{3}{4}$ **7** $\frac{7}{10}$ **10** $\frac{7}{9}$
   4 $\frac{1}{2}$

4. **1** $\frac{9}{24}$ **5** $\frac{15}{50}$ **8** $\frac{42}{48}$
   2 $\frac{10}{12}$ **6** $\frac{3}{6}$ **9** $\frac{6}{27}$
   3 $\frac{10}{15}$ **7** $\frac{8}{20}$ **10** $\frac{8}{32}$
   4 $\frac{27}{36}$

5. **1** $\frac{22}{6}$ **5** $\frac{20}{3}$ **8** $\frac{25}{3}$
   2 $\frac{17}{6}$ **6** $\frac{13}{5}$ **9** $\frac{22}{7}$
   3 $\frac{21}{10}$ **7** $\frac{17}{4}$ **10** $\frac{19}{10}$
   4 $\frac{15}{4}$

6. **1** $1\frac{3}{4}$ **5** $4\frac{5}{6}$ **8** $3\frac{1}{8}$
   2 $2\frac{1}{3}$ **6** $11\frac{1}{9}$ **9** $5\frac{1}{2}$
   3 $1\frac{5}{12}$ **7** $8\frac{2}{5}$ **10** $6\frac{2}{3}$
   4 $3\frac{7}{10}$

7. **1** 30, 10, 22, 5, 40, 8, 17, 35, 28, 100
   2 2, 5, 8, 22, 11, 16, 6, 30, 3, 12
   3 22, 4, 2, 6, 21, 12, 8, 13, 30, 50
   4 2, 14, 50, 12, 66, 40, 8, 30, 18, 20
   5 3, 15, 120, 27, 9, 21, 60, 75, 33, 45

8. **1** £2.85   **6** 97p
   2 2.5 km   **7** 3.6 ℓ
   3 135°   **8** 500 g
   4 40 cm   **9** $1\frac{1}{2}$ hr
   5 140 g   **10** £100

9. **1** £4.17   **4** £1.92
   2 £2.94   **5** £17.89
   3 39p

10. **1** 8.75 m   **4** £47.70
    2 500 g   **5** 18 ℓ
    3 40 min

Page 144   Exercise 9.2

1. **1** $\frac{3}{10}$ **4** $\frac{6}{25}$
   2 $\frac{3}{4}$ **5** $\frac{2}{5}$
   3 $\frac{3}{20}$

2. **1** 0.18   **4** 0.11
   2 0.95   **5** 0.6
   3 0.06

3. **1** £2.64   **4** £11.40
   2 60p   **5** £18.72
   3 £3.30

4. **1** 12 cm   **4** 4.5 cm
   2 300 g   **5** 1.05 ℓ
   3 18 min

5. **1** £2.65   **4** £116.60
   2 £90   **5** £276
   3 £6.24

Page 144   Exercise 9.3

1. £4.50

2. 63

3. $\frac{1}{10}$

4. 25 200

5. Mr A 630, Mr B 1400,
   Mr C 1120, Mr B won,
   280 votes more

6. $\frac{3}{10}$

7. 63, $\frac{9}{40}$

8. £180

9. 120 ℓ

10. 2 hr 30 min, 10.30 am

11. 198

12. 225

13. £118.80

14. 18 (kg)

15. £15; 4 get £11.25 each

16. £102

17. 308 kg

18. £96, £8

19. £283.40 (£283)

20. £25 200 (£25 000)

Page 152   Exercise 10.1

1. 36, 10°, Science, 5, 4, 7

2. 156°, 12°, bus 11, car 4, cycle 2, walk 13

4. blue 10, pink 8, black 6, red 5, yellow 4, green 2, white 1

6. fizzy drinks 187°, squash 119°, fruit juice 54°

7. £1800, £5

8. Weekly income £180, food $\frac{1}{3}$, mortgage $\frac{1}{4}$, clothing $\frac{1}{18}$, fuel $\frac{1}{12}$, car expenses $\frac{1}{9}$, other expenses $\frac{1}{6}$

10. South Africa 288°, USSR 47°, Canada 14°, Other countries 11°

Page 155   Exercise 10.2

1. **1** A 90°, B 105°, C 165°
    2 120   **3** 3°   **4** B 35, C 55

3. $a = 360$, $b = 120$, $c = 80$, $d = 300$, $e = 500$, $f = 100$

Page 161   Exercise 11.1

1. **1** 0   **5** -5 **8** 0
    2 -2 **6** -1 **9** -2
    3 -11 **7** -1 **10** -4
    4 3

2. **1** down 3   **6** down 6
    2 up 7   **7** up 3
    3 down 5   **8** up 1
    4 down 3   **9** up 4
    5 up 4   **10** down 8

3. **1** 9   **2** 3   **3** -5 **4** -1 **5** -4

4. **1** $+11°$ **6** $-14°$
    2 $-3°$ **7** $+2°$
    3 $+2°$ **8** 0°
    4 $-7°$ **9** $+1°$
    5 $-6°$ **10** $-4°$

5. **1** risen 4°   **6** fallen 5°
    2 fallen 2°   **7** fallen 4°
    3 risen 3°   **8** fallen 5°
    4 risen 1°   **9** risen 5°
    5 risen 2°   **10** risen 8°

Page 163   Exercise 11.2

1. **1** $+6$ **6** step 1
    2 -2 **7** step 3
    3 -5 **8** step -4
    4 $+7$ **9** step -1
    5 $+2$ **10** step -3

2. **1** 8 min past 1   **4** 5 min to 4
    2 10 min to 2   **5** 10 min past 5
    3 2 min past 3

3. **1** 17   **4** 9
    2 20   **5** 20
    3 15

4. **1** £250   **4** £180
    2 £120   **5** overdrawn £70
    3 £60

5. **1** 0   **4** -2
    2 4   **5** 4
    3 -9

6. **1** $-5°$ **4** $-7°$
    2 11°   **5** $-3°$
    3 15°

7. **1** 0, -5, -10 **4** -2, 3, 8
    2 -2, 0, 2   **5** 2, -2, -6
    3 9, 12, 15

8. 0, -35, -10, 0, 30

Page 173   Exercise 12.1

1. **1** $\angle A = 85°$, $\angle B = 52°$, $\angle C = 43°$
    2 $\angle D = 37°$, $\angle E = 112°$, $\angle F = 31°$

2. **1** $AB = AC = 6.5$ cm, $(BC = 4.0$ cm$)$, $\angle A = 36°$, $\angle B = \angle C = 72°$
    2 $AB = BC = 6.4$ cm, $(AC = 11.5$ cm$)$, $\angle A = \angle C = 25°$, $\angle B = 130°$

3. **1** 59°   **4** 25°
    2 17°   **5** 92°
    3 44°

4. **1** $a = 139°$ **4** $d = 41°$
    2 $b = 33°$ **5** $e = 57°, f = 63°$
    3 $c = 51°$

5. **1** 18°, obtuse-angled
    2 90°, right-angled
    3 60°, equilateral (acute-angled)
    4 120°, obtuse-angled
    5 74°, isosceles (acute-angled)

6. $a = 24°$

7. $a = 34°, b = 73°$, isosceles (acute-angled)

8. $a = 28°, d = 44°$

9. **1** a
    2 g
    3 e
    4 $\angle ACD\ (\angle DCA)$
    5 $\angle BDC\ (\angle CDB)$
    6 $\angle ABC, \angle DBC, \angle CBA, \angle CBD$

10. **1** 45°   **2** 60°   **3** 105°

Page 176   Exercise 12.2

1. $a = b = 70°, c = 40°$

2. $d = f = 36°, e = 108°, g = h = 72°$

3. $j = 65°, k = 40°$

4. $m = 36°, n = 77°, p = 41°$

5. $a = 60°, b = 45°, c = 15°$

6. $a = b = 30°, c = 80°$

7. $\angle B = \angle ACB, \angle ABC = \angle BCA = 66°,$
    $\angle ACD = 42°, \angle CDB = 90°, \angle BCD = 24°$

Page 192

Example 1.   rectangle
Example 2.   square

Page 193   Exercise 14.1

1. right-angled

2. isosceles (acute-angled)

3. isosceles (obtuse-angled)

4. equal and parallel

5. equal and perpendicular

Page 193   Exercise 14.2

1. (2, 0)

3. **2** lines are parallel

4. (1, 3)

5. $y = x^2$, 30.3 $(30\frac{1}{4})$, 6.3

Page 199   Exercise 15.1

1. **1** 23 772   **5** 22 638   **8** 21 054
    2 14 911   **6** 11 880   **9** 82 355
    3 33 354   **7** 44 462   **10** 9882
    4 4602

3. 3816   7. 3000

4. £7056   8. 80.6 m

5. 6912   9. 3775 kg

6. 13.04 km   10. 116.8 m

Page 200   Exercise 15.2

1. **1** 4515   4. **1** 52 272
    2 9216   **2** 47 619
    3 22 876   **3** 36 630
    4 24 840   **4** 23 661
    5 23 100   **5** 11 088

2. **1** 6100   5. **1** 27 540
    2 3200   **2** 24 381
    3 11 275   **3** 11 970
    4 16 750   **4** 20 274
    5 13 225   **5** 15 624

3. **1** 2010   6. 55 m²
    2 4875
    3 12 150   7. 10.7 kg
    4 7635
    5 9270   8. £2128

Page 211   Exercise 16.1

1. **1** $x = 5$ **6** $x = 12$
    2 $x = 12$ **7** $x = 11$
    3 $x = 8$ **8** $x = 2$
    4 $x = 15$ **9** $x = 3$
    5 $x = 6$ **10** $x = 7$

2. **1** $x = 10$ **6** $x = 3$
   2 $x = 7$ **7** $x = 8$
   3 $x = 3$ **8** $x = 1$
   4 $x = 0$ **9** $x = 9$
   5 $x = 1$ **10** $x = 1$

3. **1** $x = 6$ **6** $x = 11$
   2 $x = 3$ **7** $x = 7$
   3 $x = 6$ **8** $x = 2$
   4 $x = 4$ **9** $x = 12$
   5 $x = 9$ **10** $x = 8$

4. **1** $x = 2$ **6** $x = 4$
   2 $x = 9$ **7** $x = 4$
   3 $x = 6$ **8** $x = 4$
   4 $x = 3$ **9** $x = 1$
   5 $x = 0$ **10** $x = 2$

5. **1** 9   **2** 10   **3** 5
   4 car 75p, tractor £1.25
   5 26 (5p), 78 (2p)

Page 212   Exercise 16.2

1. $k = 9$, $y = 45$
2. 5
3. 30 m and 42 m
4. **1** 72   **2** 35   **3** 18
   4 10   **5** 50
5. £1.60
6. 6 workers
7. $x = 12$, $y = 24$, $z = 12$
8. $x = 26$; 90°, 45°, 45°; right-angled isosceles

Page 214   Exercise B1

1. £9
2. 7
3. 7
4. equilateral
5. 7°
6. 100
7. 0
8. 3.9
9. $\frac{1}{4}$
10. 120°
11. 110°
12. $100 - b$
13. £12
14. 22 years
15. 80p

Page 215   Exercise B2

1. 1200
2. 45
3. 0.03
4. 30
5. 3
6. −3°C
7. 2.89
8. 44%
9. $\frac{1}{8}$
10. £1.25
11. 12
12. 48p
13. x^3
14. 0.7
15. 50°

Page 215   Exercise B3

1. 72
2. 62
3. **1** $\frac{2}{3}$ **4** $\frac{7}{11}$
   2 $\frac{5}{7}$ **5** $\frac{5}{9}$
   3 $\frac{3}{5}$
4. 110°
5. 9
6. 50
7. £13.50
8. **1** 7.6   **4** 1.2
   2 3.2   **5** 200
   3 0.2
9. £60
10. **1** $a = 30$ **4** $d = 5$
    2 $b = 3$ **5** $e = 3$
    3 $c = 7$
11. 2.56
12. 29°
13. 19, 29, 59
14. 0.4
15. $8x$ pence, $(500 - 8x)$ pence
16. D (4, 2), $\angle ODB = 90°$,
    E (−4, 8), rectangle

17. $a = 62°$, $b = 56°$, $c = 124°$, $d = 28°$

18. 234 m

19. 480 kg

20. $-7°C$

Page 238   Exercise 17.1

1. **1** 75 inches   **6** 8 feet
    2 115 lb   **7** 3 lb
    3 17 pints   **8** $2\frac{1}{2}$ gallons
    4 36 oz   **9** 3 miles
    5 440 yards   **10** 30 yards

2. **1** 5°C   **4** 59°F
    2 25°C   **5** 104°F
    3 95°C   **6** 176°F

3. **1** 7 st 9 lb   **3** $3\frac{3}{4}$ inches
    2 $\frac{3}{8}$ pint

4. **1** 38 km   **4** 9 ℓ
    2 3 kg (or 2.7 kg)   **5** 3 tonnes
    3 2 m

5. **1** 8 inches
    2 21 pints or 2.6 gall
    3 22 lb
    4 160 to 180 lb
    5 2 lb

6. **1** 38.6 km
    2 2.72 kg
    3 2.03 m
    4 9.09 ℓ
    5 3.05 tonnes
    6 7.88 inches
    7 21.1 pints or 2.64 gall
    8 22.1 lb
    9 176 lb
    10 1.98 lb

7. **1** $\frac{1}{4}$ **2** $\frac{1}{5}$ **3** $\frac{3}{8}$ **4** $\frac{1}{2}$ **5** $\frac{3}{8}$

8. **1** 1 ft 4 in   **4** 6 inches
    2 9 oz   **5** 7 lb
    3 10 pints

9. **1** 9 lb 1 oz   **4** 1 lb 7 oz
    2 7 inches   **5** 1 ft 8 in
    3 9 gall 4 pints

Page 239   Exercise 17.2

1. 33 lb

2. £1.82

3. 7350 km

4. 6.2 miles

5. 22.9 cm by 11.4 cm by 7.0 cm

6. **1** 4.4 cm or 4.5 cm   **2** $3\frac{1}{2}$ in

7. 16 inches

8. 155 lb

9. $7\frac{1}{2}$ inches

10. $1\frac{1}{4}$ yards

11. 126 miles

12. 1 st 10 lb, 11 st 2 lb

13. 8

14. 6 lb 15 oz

15. 2.9°, 1.5°

16. **1** 68°F, 20°C,   **2** 32°C   **3** 61°F
     4 75°F, 81°F, 88°F, 88°F, 84°F

17. **1** 8 oz, 4 oz, 2 oz
     2 2 lb, 4 oz, 2 oz
     3 2 lb, 1 lb, 8 oz, 1 oz

21. **1** 6s 11d   **2** 467   **3** £7354
     4 £2 – 17s – 3d   **5** 18s 4d

Page 248   Exercise 18.1

(Frequencies in order)

1. 1, 4, 8, 6, 5

2. 11, 10, 8, 7 (+1), 1, 3, 1

3. 3, 9, 10, 13, 5; 40 boys

4. 2, 4, 5, 8, 3, 2

5. 800, 8

6. **1** 75
    2 11 kg (11 to under 12 kg)
    3 20
    4 $\frac{1}{3}$

8. 4, 8, 14, 8, 11, 6, 3, 4, 2

Page 250   Exercise 18.2

Frequencies in order:

1. 1, 7, 14, 7, 10, 9, 2

3. 5, 6, 12, 5, 5, 3, 4, 2, 4, 2, 1, 1
    2nd table:- 5, 18, 10, 7, 6, 3, 1

4. 38, 22, 25, 26, 20, 14, 18, 9, 10, 10, 6, 2
    2nd table:- 60, 51, 34, 27, 20, 8

Page 259   Exercise 19.1

4. **1** 3   **2** 2   **3** 5

5. **1** 3   **2** 4   **3** 4

9. rectangle, rhombus, square

10. **1** 4   **2** 1   **3** 0   **4** 2   **5** 0
    point of symmetry:- **1**, **4**

11. **1** 4   **3** 3   **4** 2   **5** 5

13. **6** 4

Page 264   Exercise 19.2

1. A and H, B and F, C and D, E and G

2. A and F, B and E, C and D

3. $\triangle ABX$ and $\triangle ADX$, $\triangle CBX$ and $\triangle CDX$,
    $\triangle ABC$ and $\triangle ADC$

4. $\triangle ABC$ and $\triangle EDC$, $\triangle ADC$ and $\triangle EBC$,
    $\triangle ABE$ and $\triangle EDA$, $\triangle ABD$ and $\triangle EDB$

Page 268   Exercise 19.3

1. $BC = 6.9\,\text{cm}$, $\angle B = 44°$, $\angle C = 82°$

2. $\angle A = 55°$, $\angle B = 45°$, $\angle C = 80°$

3. $AC = 7.3\,\text{cm}$, $\angle B = 44°$, $\angle C = 46°$

4. $AB = 5.6\,\text{cm}$, $AC = 7.5\,\text{cm}$, $\angle A = 74°$

Page 270   Exercise 19.4

3. **1** 54°   **3** $c = 52°$, $d = e = 38°$
    2 50°

4. A and F, B and D, C and E

5. EF

6. $\angle B = \angle C = 56°$, $\angle D = 68°$, $\angle H = 56°$,
    $DF = GH = 6\,\text{cm}$, all triangles are congruent

7. **1** $\triangle ABE$ and $\triangle ACE$, $\triangle ADE$ and $\triangle AFE$,
    $\triangle ADB$ and $\triangle AFC$
    2 BC, BA, AC, CF
    3 120°
    4 9 cm

8. $AE = 4.3\,\text{cm}$, $EC = 4.3\,\text{cm}$

9. $\angle A = 68°$, $BD = 2.5\,\text{cm}$, $DC = 5.0\,\text{cm}$

10. $\angle A = 47°$, $\angle C = 38°$, $AC = 9.6\,\text{cm}$

11. $\angle ABD = 27°$, $\angle BDE = 27°$

12. $AC = 8.0\,\text{cm}$, perimeter 24 cm

Page 280   Exercise 20.1

1. **1** $\frac{1}{6}$ **2** $\frac{1}{2}$ **3** 50

2. **1** $\frac{1}{3}$ **2** $\frac{1}{4}$ **3** $\frac{1}{4}$ **4** $\frac{1}{3}$

3. $\frac{1}{10}$

4. **1** $\frac{1}{8}$ **2** $\frac{1}{4}$ **3** $\frac{1}{2}$ **4** 125

5. $\frac{1}{10}$

6. **1** $\frac{1}{13}$ **2** $\frac{1}{4}$ **3** $\frac{1}{52}$

7. **1** $\frac{1}{11}$ **2** $\frac{2}{11}$ **3** $\frac{4}{11}$ **4** $\frac{6}{11}$

8. $\frac{2}{5}$

9. **1** $\frac{3}{10}$ **2** $\frac{4}{5}$

10. **1** $\frac{5}{9}$ **2** $\frac{4}{9}$ **3** $\frac{1}{3}$ **4** $\frac{2}{9}$

Page 282   Exercise 20.2

1. **1** $\frac{1}{4}$ **2** $\frac{1}{3}$ **3** $\frac{5}{12}$ **4** $\frac{8}{11}$

2. **1** $\frac{1}{16}$ **2** $\frac{1}{9}$

3. **1** $\frac{3}{7}$ **2** $\frac{3}{10}$ **3** $\frac{8}{35}$ **4** $\frac{1}{4}$

4. $\frac{1}{7}$, 14

5. $\frac{1}{3}$, $\frac{4}{7}$

6. **1** 6   **3** 5   **5** 56
    2 $\frac{1}{6}$ **4** $\frac{1}{18}$

8. $\frac{1}{10}$, 20

Page 288

Width 3.4 cm, 3.4 m

Page 290

Example

1	NE	**5**	NW	**8**	*B*
2	S	**6**	*F*	**9**	*E*
3	SW	**7**	*G*	**10**	*H*
4	E				

Page 290   Exercise 21.1

1. 7 m, 6.2 cm

2. 360 m; 4 cm, 2.4 cm

3. **1** 2.7 km   **2** 4.2 km

4. 11.7 cm, 2340 m

5. 67.5 cm by 7.5 cm

6. Chalet 12.8 m by 8.0 m,
    bedrooms 6.3 m by 3.4 m and
    4.6 m by 3.8 m

7. 1 : 120

8. **1** 10.0 m   **3** 10.2 m
    2 7.0 m   **4** 6.0 m

Page 294   Exercise 21.2

1. shop, *A, B, C, F, G, D,* shop; 2300 yards

2. **1** 2   **2** 1   **3** 3   **4** 5   **5** 3

Page 295   Exercise 21.3

1. 16.0 cm, 8.0 km

2. 1 : 8; 52 cm

3. **1** 28 km   **5** NE
    2 40 km   **6** SE
    3 Yorston   **7** N
    4 Wayton   **8** SW

4. **1** N   **4** SW
    2 NW to SE   **5** E
    3 NW

6. NW, 21 km; NE, 49 km; 52 km

Page 307   Exercise 22.1

1. **1** 39   **5** 53   **8** 13
    2 58   **6** 21   **9** 22
    3 32   **7** 18   **10** 62
    4 72

2. **1** 13 r 5   **4** 33 r 9
    2 14 r 3   **5** 35 r 7
    3 29 r 2

3. **1** 34.5   **4** 30.8
    2 37.5   **5** 25.1
    3 12.8

4. 13   8. 14

5. 62   9. 32

6. 28 cm   10. 38, 6 ℓ over

7. 54

Page 308   Exercise 22.2

2. **1** 26   **4** 18
    2 19   **5** 17
    3 23

3. **1** 21   **4** 33.44
    2 15   **5** 36.48
    3 16.44

4. 14 get £55.80, 1 gets £61.80

5. 32

6. £35

7. 66

8. 14, 19, 210 mm by 12 mm

Page 315

Example

1 135 fr or 140 fr   **2** £8.00

Page 315   Exercise 23.1

1. **1** 56 km   **2** 62 miles

2. **1** 55 g   **2** 3.6 oz

3. **1** 3750 esc   **2** £6.40

Page 316   Exercise 23.2

1. **1** 68°F   **2** 37°C

Page 323   Exercise 24.1

1. 31, 32, 33

2. 22, 31

3. Tony's 63, Karen's 83

4. 12

Page 323   Exercise 24.2

1. 3.1 sec

2. 458 m

3. 28 m and 40 m

4. 29.4 m

5. 163 kg

Page 326   Exercise C1

1. £8.80   9.   4 cm

2. isosceles   10. 18.9

3. 350   11. 70°

4. $\frac{1}{6}$ 12. 18ℓ

5. 3 miles South   13. $\frac{1}{2}$

6. 0.8   14. 1 m

7. x 15. £3

8. 4

Page 327   Exercise C2

1. 3   9.   17.35

2. 416   10. 1 : 100

3. 5   11. 26

4. 7°   12. $\frac{1}{13}$

5. 5   13. 80

6. 45 m   14. £50

7. 3.5   15. 64 km

8. $\dfrac{100}{q}$ cm

Page 328   Exercise C3

1. **1** 0.31   **4** 0.44
    2 0.71   **5** 0.89
    3 0.55

2. $\frac{7}{25}$

3. 28p, £6.16

4. **1** £3.60   **2** £1.50

5. **1** SE   **2** NW

6. **1** II and III
    2 (−4, 2), (−4, 3), (−1, 2)

7. 440 girls, 360 boys

8. **1** 1 hr 25 min
    2 5 min
    3 4 hr 40 min

9. −6, 15, −1

10. **1** 3   **2** 4   **3** 1   **4** 2   **5** 0

11. $\frac{4}{17}$

12. A 60°, 12 min; B 110°, 22 min;
    C 120°, 24 min; D 70°, 14 min

13. $a = 70°, b = 40°, c = 140°$

14. 1 ft 11 in

15. 37, 12, $\frac{12}{37}$

16. 1 : 50 000, 2 km

17. 36p, £3.96

18. **1** £10.30   **2** 20 guilders

19. $x = 40$; 45°, 90°, 45°;
    right-angled isosceles

20. Alan 2, Bill 4, Charlie 5, Derek 6

Page 331   Exercise C4

1. $a = b = 34°, c = 112°$

2. **1** 4, yes
    2 1, no
    3 an infinite number, yes
    4 2, yes
    5 3, no

3. 5 units

4. 4.8 km

5. 2.7 m

6. **1** −1   **6** −2
    2 +2   **7** −3
    3 −5   **8** 2
    4 +1   **9** −3
    5 3   **10** 3

7. 820

8. 150 m

9. £97.50

10. **1** 44 m   **2** 65 m   **3** 21 m

11. frequencies in order:- 3, 15, 38, 29, 12, 3

12. 41.8 kg

13. 158 m

14. **1** Newcastle, 140 km
    2 Aberystwyth, 140 km
    3 Norwich, 160 km
    4 Plymouth, 160 km
    5 Carlisle, 160 km
    6 E, 220 km
    7 SE, 40 km
    8 S, 220 km
    9 NE, 180 km
    10 NW, 380 km

15. 75 gallons

17. **1** $\frac{1}{2}$ **2** 50

18. **1** 22 min   **2** 12, 5

19. **2** $a = b = 60°$ **3** equilateral

20. Bindoo $(w − 5)$ kg, Carole $(w + 7)$ kg;
    Azara 39 kg, Bindoo 34 kg, Carole 46 kg